THE FIRST GENESIS

THE SAGA OF CREATION vs EVOLUTION

WILLIAM F. DANKENBRING

Triumph Publishing
Box 292
Altadena, Calif. 91001

Library of Congress Catalog Card Number 75-10841

Dedicated to

Nathan, Natalie, and Nancy

Table of Contents

Table of Contents (Cont.)

Table of Contents (Cont.)

List of Illustrations

Page

Foreword

Every year millions of human beings are born into this unhappy world without their own knowledge or consent. Surrounded by poverty and corruption in society—or living in islets of prosperity—we humans all share the common tragedies and frustrations and sorrows of life.

Does this world have to be like it is?

Creationists assure us there is a God. But if there is a God who created the universe and brought life into being, then that God in some way is responsible for allowing the world to be in its present state of crisis. We cannot claim a happy God as the Creator and suddenly absolve Him of all responsibility when crises beset His universe.

But if there is no God and we live instead in an evolving universe whose origins we cannot yet understand, where shall the responsibility for the present state of crisis be placed? And where shall we turn for a solution to correct what clearly has gone wrong? Is there something fundamentally defective in the physical universe? Is an evolving universe, as proposed by cosmologists, unable by its very nature to resolve the problems of the mind, the emotions, and the body?

Here is indeed a dilemma. A Creator God, once active and speaking the universe into existence, now apparently strangely silent. Or an evolving universe that begets its own seeds of sorrow and self-destruction.

Author William Dankenbring proposes a disarmingly simple answer in his examination of broad areas of scientific evidence. An a long-time editor, educator and researcher, I find *The First Genesis:A New Case for Creation* is more than an explanation of origins and an uprooting of theological and scientific superstitions and hypotheses. It is a reasonable explanation of the *purpose* of the universe.

April 1975 Herman L. Hoeh

Preface

For a person living in the Middle Ages the world, for all its mysteries and beauties, was simple: The Earth was the center of the Universe. Up in Heaven, above the clouds, resided God, while man, made to His image, was the epitome of His creation. As long as man lived a pious life and obeyed the rules laid down by the Church, he had nothing to fear and would ultimately join the Lord and his angels in their heavenly abode.

Modern science has devastated this beautiful but simplistic view of the world in which we live. Soon after Nicolaus Copernicus had demoted the Earth from its central position in the Universe to that of a minor planet of our sun, Giordano Bruno declared that the entire firmament of stars was not formed by tiny holes in a huge celestial crystal dome, but that each of these billions of stars was a sun just like our own. God clearly reigned over a much larger kingdom than medieval man had thought.

Three hundred years of scientific onslaught have badly battered the ramparts of the churches, those fortresses of man's faith in God. But with all the new scientific knowledge we have acquired, we now have really even more reason to admire God and His handiwork than medieval man in his little self-centered world. Science and religion may use different methods to seek revelations about the ultimate truth: The purpose of science is to understand the creation and its laws, while the purpose of religion is to understand the Creator and His divine intentions. As there can be no creation without a creator, a will and purpose that brought it all about, they both really seek the same.

Wernher von Braun
Germantown, Maryland

Chapter One

Science Versus Religion?

Is there a God? A Creator of the Universe? Or did all things evolve by blind, dumb luck—what evolutionists call "chance"?

This is the central question—the main issue. But the answer involves much more than mere theoretical and abstract knowledge. The answer to this question overflows into every arena and aspect of life—public education, politics, philosophy, and even morality.

Two hundred years ago the faculty of any large university in the Western world would have had a high regard for the Bible. Some of the greatest men of science and literature were devout believers in Holy Writ. But if you visited a modern American university today, you would find out that more than ninety percent are materialistically inclined, with little or no regard for the Scriptures. They have become passe. Modern university professors, by and large, are not religiously inclined, but rather are naturalistic in their approach toward life.

Why the dramatic change? What happened? Why is the Bible so little regarded today? Says Bernard Ramm, "The battle to keep the Bible as a respected book among the learned scholars and the academic world was fought and lost in the nineteenth century" (*The Christian View of Science and Scripture,* p.15). Supplanting the Bible view of history, geology, and life, came the theory of evolution delineated by Charles Darwin and evangelized by Thomas Huxley. The reason for the complete reversal in modern thinking is complex, and is largely due to the folly and absurdity of ancient religions arguments, and embellishments on the Scriptures. The theologians more or less lost the academic battle by default. They did seldom confront evolutionary theory on its own terms, and the world cried out for freedom from religious hierarchy and bondage to medieval superstition.

Says Bernard Ramm, "The result of losing the battle of the Bible and science in the nineteenth century is simply and tragically this: Physics, astronomy, chemistry, zoology, botany, geology, psychology, medicine and the rest of the sciences are taught in disregard of Biblical statements and Christian perspectives, and with no interest in the Biblical data on the sciences, and no confidence in what the Bible might even say about the same" (*ibid.,* p.19).

Unfortunately, today we see the academic world divided into not two or three, but many hostile camps—scientists argue over how evolution occurred and are divided into several conflicting schools of thought, and theologians argue heatedly over the proper interpretation of Genesis and the correct understanding and exegesis of the Biblical origin of life and Creation. We believe it is time for both sides, and all the armed camps, to cease hostilities, and to "come, let us reason together, saith the Lord." In the bitter, sentient atmosphere which has traditionally prevailed, logic is thrown out the window; neither side is willing to admit the other has *any* valid objections or demonstrable proofs. The fight has degenerated into name-calling, cat calls, and rhetoric.

In this book, I pay respect to *both* science and Scripture. I see no contradiction between the two. I abhor the spirit of bitter condemnation and bigoted acrimony which has prevailed in the past. Let's not automatically shut each other out. Let's pay attention to the facts, the arguments, the solid and substantial reasons other people may disagree with us on this or that point. Let's be generous in our attitudes. Let the theologian not be anti-scientific or blindly dogmatic in his self assurance. Let not the academician or scientist scoff at the theologian, accusing him of being gullible, credulous or superstitious.

We believe that a positive relationship must, and indeed, does, exist between science and true Christianity. The theologian must always be on guard against reading his own private opinions or interpretation into the Bible, claiming it is "revelation" when in fact, he may succumb to human error—his interpretation of a particular passage relating to creation *could be wrong.* There may be other equally or more compelling views. As John Pye Smith observed, "It is not the Word of God, but the expositions and deductions of men, from which I dissent."

The great trap for the theologian is to dogmatize—and later to be proved wrong by science as it amasses stroke by stroke weighty evidence to the contrary. The theologian too often "represents his own interpretations of Scripture as unquestionable; and so confident is he in the infallibility of his own deductions as to identify them with the Divine Veracity, and to think himself entitled to take it for an analogy to his own reasoning" (Smith, *On the Relation Between the Holy Scriptures and some parts of Geological Science,* 1840, pp.70, 157).

Both theologians, and scientists, we must all admit, are fallible human beings, prone to errors. Both have arguments with their wives, have difficulties getting along with superiors or supervisors, must work in order to make a living and support their families. Both make mistakes.

Evolutionists often lump all Creationists in the same bag, not realizing there are broad and vast differences of thought among Creationists about Creation itself. For example, not all Creationists believe Archbishop Ussher was right when he suggested creation occurred 4004 B.C. Not all believe the Scriptures teach the universe and everything within it were created by divine fiat in six working days. Scientists then must be doubly careful when they attempt to define modern neo-Creationist beliefs.

Likewise, theologians must be careful not to pronounce some scientific theory as final, or presume some hypothesis to be a fact. We must not judge matters prematurely; we must have patience. The theologian, for example, may be unaware that there are more than then theories as to the origin of the solar system. All of us must, as Bernard Ramm says, "be keenly aware of the imperfections of human knowledge in both science and theology. Scientific theory is somewhat fluid under our feet. The history of atomic theory from 1885 to 1950 is so rapid it is almost breath-taking. Each removal of a past imperfection is a prophecy of a future imperfection. The same is the case with exegesis. Archaeology, philology, and history are constantly enriching our knowledge of the Old and New Testaments. With this enriched knowledge attends a more careful and accurate exegesis. Thus exegesis, to a certain extent, is in a state of flux" (*op cit.*, p.36).

William F. Allbright, the dean of modern archaeology, declared: "The account of Creation is unique in ancient literature. It undoubtedly reflects an advanced monotheistic point of view, with a sequence of creative phases so rational that modern science cannot improve on it, given the same language and the same range of ideas in which to state its conclusions. In fact, modern scientific cosmogonies show a disconcerting tendency to be short-lived and it may be seriously doubted whether science has yet caught up with the Biblical story" ("The Old Testament and Archaeology," *Old Testament Commentary,* edited by Alleman and Flack, p.135).

The Biblical account is one thing. But for Lightfoot of Cambridge in the seventeenth century to postulate that creation took place the week of October 18-24, 4004 B.C., with Adam created on October 23 at 9:00 A.M., is altogether a different bolt of cloth.

But when untrained theologians, with very limited professional experience in geology, set forth to re-interpret the geological record, the result is staggering. Such a one was George McCready Price, a Seventh-Day Adventist who became the leading fundamentalist exponent on flood geology. He ascribed the entire geology column to Noah's flood which lasted one short year. A vigorous writer, Price's work for years formed the backbone of most orthodox fundamentalist interpretation of the geologic record. In his mind, dinosaurs and man were contemporary. Trilobites and porpoises lived side by side. And all physical life on earth has only existed a few thousands of years, at best.

With theologians adopting such rigourous and ungainly views, basing them on a particular interpretation of Scripture, in spite of literally all the evidence in the geologic record demanding TIME—on the order of millions, and billions of years—is it any wonder that many scientists become impatient with their theological brethren, and simply dismiss them with a wave of the hand as cantankerous mossbacks and feather-brained lightweights?

In this book, we will deal with flood geology, and the Genesis record. We will show that one flood was by no means capable of creating the massive geological column; not even several floods, although, in fact, the geologic column is pierced by numerous catastrophes.

Let us, then attempt to set the record straight:

1. Not all Christians believe the world was created 4004 B.C.

2. Not all evangelical Christians believe the earth is flat, and the center of the solar system. Although the medieval Church pronounced Copernicus' theory as heresy which contradicted the Bible, much water has passed under the bridge since that time.

3. Not all Christians subscribe to Flood geology, which runs contrary to evidences in Nature, although most Christians believe there was a deluge of massive proportions in the days of Noah. But the geologic record is the result of far more than one short-lived flood.

On the other hand, not all scientists agree with Simpson who said: "... those who do not believe in it (evolution) are, almost to a man, obviously ignorant of the scientific evidence."

Not all scientists agree with Huxley who insisted: "It will soon be as impossible for an intelligent, educated man or woman to believe in a god as it is now to believe that the earth is flat." On the contrary, many scientists agree with Mayr, who said of Simpson's evolutionary theory: "The basic theory is in many instances hardly more than a postulate."

Huxley himself, at times, did not appear so sure of himself. He admitted at one point when discussing evolution and the problem of originating new types, "... evolution is thus seen as a series of blind alleys" (1942, p.562).

Although evolution has been embraced by the academic world with nary a backward glance, Norman Macbeth in *Darwin Retried* puts it plainly: "Unfortunately, in the field of evolution most explanations are not good. As a matter of fact, they hardly qualify as explanations at all; they are suggestions, hunches, pipe dreams, hardly worthy of being called hypotheses" (p.147).

As a layman, or scientist, or theologian, then, what are you to believe? Julian Huxley tells a television audience: "The first point to make about Darwin's theory is that it is no longer a theory, but a fact." At the same time, other leading scientists tell us that Darwin's theory is on very shakey ground. Whom are we to believe? What is the truth?

Is the idea or concept of a Creator God merely myth? Has God, as Huxley declares, been forced to abdicate, "evacuating section after section of His kingdom?" Huxley added: "Operationally, God is beginning to resemble not a Ruler, but the last fading smile of a cosmic Cheshire cat." Are evolutionists about to drive God from His own Universe?

Professor Fleischmann, zoologist of Erlangen, took issue with Huxley. He averred: "The Darwinian theory of descent has not a single fact to confirm it in the realm of nature. It is not the result of scientific research, but purely the product of imagination."

Likewise, Sir William Dawson, highly respected Canadian geologist, said of evolution: "It is one of the strangest phenomena of humanity; it is utterly destitute of proof."

Despite these voices raised in opposition to evolutionary dogmas of modern academia, the world after Darwin has embraced his theory, and evolutionary philosophy is the cornerstone of modern education, both as to its purpose and methodology. The consequences have been dire indeed, as the violent history of the 20th century reveals. The concept of the "survival of the fittest" and the "struggle for survival" have become rooted in modern politics, and was used by Mussolini and Hitler to justify their attempts to conquer the world and rid it of "inferior species" of mankind, in particular lashing out in virulent hatred against the Jews, Poles and Russians. Darwinism became applied to physiology, economics, politics, medicine, sociology.

Hailed as one of the greatest discoveries of all time, it cast a long shadow over the world. The principles of natural selection were applied to politics. Herbert Spencer saw the application of evolutionary ideas to every sphere of life. Evolution fostered extreme competition among business, and cut-throat entrepreneurs had their heyday. Any and all evil-doing could now be justified as natural selection and the "survival of the fittest." Robert E. D. Clark wrote: "Evolution, in short, gave the doer of evil a respite from his conscience. The most unscrupulous behaviour toward a competitor could now be rationalized: evil could be called good" (*Darwin: Before and After*, p.106).

There have been wars down through all ages, but only after Darwinism did the world begin to look upon war as desirable—a way to eliminate the unfit and for the strong to achieve their "rightful" ascendency in world politics. The theory of evolution did away with the existence of hell. God no longer would be the final Arbiter. Men would no longer have to fear the final Assize. Mankind, society at large, was now *free*—free from the chains of restraint. Now, anything went! "The new evolutionary doctrines at once provided the worst of mankind with an escape from their own remaining restraint. Darwin had shown how science could be used as an escape from theology and he showed how every worker of evil could justify his ways.

"Nor was the world at all slow to learn the lesson. If, in the under-developed American continent, Darwinism encouraged the unscrupulous practices of big business, in countries where a strong militaristic clique existed, it encouraged war. Its influence, was, indeed, enormous and worldwide. Darwin's books were translated into all the main languages on earth—including Spanish, Czech, Polish, Russian, Hebrew and even Japanese" (*ibid.*, p.109).

The effect was incalculable. The effect of Darwinism on the German mind was incredible. Darwinism fostered and encouraged a rising tide of unbelief in the Bible. Nietzsche was much influenced by Darwin. The German evolutionist Haeckel wanted to found a new religion based on evolution. It was to be taught in schools instead of Christianity. Karl Marx read the *Origin of Species* in 1860 and said, "Darwin's book is very important and serves me as a basis in natural science for the struggle in history." Thus Communism and Marxism owe much to Darwinian thought.

Mussolini was dominated by evolutionary thinking from boyhood. *Mein Kampf* epitomizes evolutionary ideas derived from Darwin. Hitler argued that a higher race would always conquer a lower, "a right which, as we see it in Nature, can be regarded as the sole conceivable right, because it is founded on reason." Said Hitler, ". . . the whole world of Nature is a mighty struggle between strength and weakness—an eternal victory of the strong over the weak. There would be nothing but decay in the whole of nature if this were not so. States which should offend against this elementary law would fall into decay."

Evolution was drilled into the German public. Darwin's materialistic doctrine of the struggle of species was expounded repeatedly. Since all history was a struggle for the survival of the fittest, any trick or ruse was permissible in order to "win at all costs." Immorality, ruthlessness, savagery and brutality came to dominate the human mind, cut off from further contact with God, or the Bible. The restraints were now loosened; Pandora's box was now open wide, and every evil imaginable was free to escape prison and fly away, bringing curses upon the earth. The enormous harm that evolutionary thinking has done still has not been fully appreciated.

Professor Sedgwick, the Cambridge geologist, saw Darwin's book for what it really was immediately. It was, he declared soon after it was published, "a dish of rank materialism cleverly cooked and served up merely to make us independent of a Creator."

Sedgwick ventured to prophesy that if Darwin's teachings were accepted humanity "would suffer a damage that might brutalize it, and sink the human race into a lower grade of degradation than any into which it has fallen since its written records tell us of its history."

He was right.

At the same time, Darwinian theory has been an impediment to science. The narrowness of mind engendered by Darwinism hindered early attempts to grasp morphology, genetics, the paleontological record, anatomy, embryology, heredity, and ecology. Nevertheless, the devotees to evolution are astonishingly blind to the real issues involved in evolutionism. They fail to see that the fundamental problem to evolution is "*how* chemical molecules of gigantic complexity came into existence and have been able to arrange themselves in increasingly complicated ways" (Clark, *op. cit.*, p.127).

Robert E. D. Clark discusses the various mechanisms suggested for bringing about evolution and discards them one by one. Finally he says, "Thus every theory of evolution has failed in the light of modern discovery and, not merely failed, but failed so dismally that it seems almost impossible to go on believing in evolution!" (*ibid.*, p.145).

Evolutionists apparently are like the Scottish preacher who was expounding a difficult passage of Scripture. He said to his congregation, "And now my friends we come to a difficulty. Let us look it straight in the face—and pass on!"

Where then does this leave us? Evolution has become to the world a substitute god—a surrogate god. It encourages men to think highly of themselves, to become proud, to believe that human salvation lies within ourselves. This false hope leads to depression, and disillusionment when men and women find out that they cannot accomplish the impossible. Evolution has led mankind away from God, the Creator, and into a blind, dark and dangerous alley.

Evolution has loosed the bonds of moral restraint and opened the floodgates of a permissive, "anything goes" society. It fosters a fiendish selfish approach toward life, the "law of the jungle." It contravenes and contradicts the very heart of the message of Jesus Christ who said, "It is more blessed to give than to receive." It repudiates and scoffs at the Golden Rule Jesus taught: "Do unto others *as* you would have them do unto you." It scorns love for neighbor and teaches love for self. It puts Self on a pedestal and makes an idol out of "Number 1."

Even though there is no proof for evolutionary theory, which some evolutionists admit in their more candid moments, Julian Huxley said, "Our *faith* in the idea of evolution depends on our reluctance to accept the antagonistic doctrine of special creation" (Huxley, *Dogma of Evolution,* p.304).

This same Huxley, in a less candid moment, claimed, "In the evolutionary pattern of thought there is no longer either need or room for the supernatural. The earth was not created; it evolved. So did the animals and plants that inhabit it, including our human selves, mind and soul as well as brain and body. . . . Evolutionary man can no longer take refuge from his loneliness in the arms of a divinized father-figure whom he has himself created" (Julian Huxley, *Issues in Evolution,* Vol. III, pp.252, 253).

A similar challenging statement was hurled by Oscar Riddle in *The Unleashing of Evolutionary Thought:* "Never again," he intoned, "can a majority of the best-informed minds of any advanced culture give support or countenance to a belief in the supernatural."

Huxley, one of the outspoken proponents of organic evolution, has expressed himself repeatedly on the matter. He has done so with an almost religious zeal, like his ancestor Thomas Huxley. Why is he so enchanted with evolution? Why is he putting on the sacerdotal robes of the high priest of Evolution, as it were? He himself explains: "For my own part, the sense of spiritual *relief* which comes from rejecting the idea of God as a supernatural being is enormous" (Julian Huxley, *Religion Without Revelation,* p.24).

A close relative of Julian Huxley, Aldous Huxley, went even further. About thirty years ago this noted writer, philosopher and evolutionist discussed in one of his books the question of whether or not the world has purpose and meaning. Speaking of an earlier period of his life, he confessed: "I had motives for not wanting the world to have a meaning; consequently assumed that it had none, and was able without any difficulty to find satisfying reasons for this assumption.

"Most ignorance is vincible ignorance. *We don't know because we don't want to know.* It is our will that decides how and upon what subjects we shall use our intelligence. Those who detect no meaning in the world generally do so because, for one reason or another, it suits their books that the world should be meaningless."

Later, Huxley added: "The philosopher who finds no meaning in the world is not concerned exclusively with a problem in pure metaphysics. He is also concerned to prove that there is no valid reason why he personally should not do as he wants to do. . . .

"For myself, as, no doubt, for most of my contemporaries, *the philosophy of meaninglessness was essentially an instrument of liberation* from a certain political and economic system and liberation *from a certain system of morality.* We objected to the morality because it *interfered with our sexual freedom;* we objected to the political and economic system because it was unjust.

"The supporters of these systems claimed that in some way they embodied the meaning (a Christian meaning, they insisted) of the world. There was one admirably simple method of confuting these people and at the same time *justifying ourselves in our political and erotic revolt:* we could deny that the world had any meaning whatsoever."

Aldous Huxley added: "Similar tactics had been adopted during the eighteenth century and for the same reasons. From the popular novelists of the period . . . we learn that the chief reason for being 'philosophical' was that one might be free from prejudices—*above all prejudices of a sexual nature*" (Huxley, *Ends and Means,* 1937, pp.312, 315, 316).

And so there we have it—a peculiar insight into the minds of the modern philosophers and theoreticians who claim the world is meaningless, the result of a pure chance, and happanstance, without any need for a supernatural Being, Architect, Master-builder, Designer, or Creator.

Undoubtedly, the most ardent and passionate priests of evolutionary theory also have their own personal reasons for their involvement in the ongoing debates, controversy, and spiritual warfare.

Nevertheless, I think it would be prudent for us to remember what the apostle Paul wrote about the world's leading philosophers of his own time and their subtle and devious bend of mind. Whether philosophers from one generation change much from those of another generation, I don't know. But Paul wrote: "For we see divine retribution revealed from heaven and falling upon all the godless wickedness of men. In their wickedness they are *stifling the truth.* For all that may be known of God by men lies plain before their eyes; indeed God himself has disclosed it to them. His invisible attributes, that is to say his everlasting power and deity, have been visible, ever since the world began, to the eye of reason, in the things he has made. There is therefore no possible defence for their conduct; knowing God, they have refused to honour him as God, or to render him thanks. Hence all their thinking has ended in futility, and their *misguided minds are plunged in darkness.* They boast of their wisdom, but they have made fools of themselves . . .

"For this reason God has given them up to the vileness of their own desires, and the consequent degradation of their bodies, because they have bartered away the true God for a false one, and have offered reverence and worship to created things instead of to the Creator, who is blessed for ever; amen.

"In consequence, I say, God has given them up to shameful passions. Their women have exchanged natural intercourse for unnatural, and their men in turn, giving up natural relations with women, burn with lust for one another; males behave indecently with males, and are paid in their own persons the fitting wage of such perversion.

"Thus, because they have not seen fit to acknowledge God, he has given them up to their own depraved reason. This leads them to break all rules of conduct. They are filled with every kind of injustice, mischief, rapacity, and malice; they are one mass of envy, murder, rivalry, treachery, and malevolence; whisperers and scandal-mongers, hateful to God, insolent, arrogant, and boastful; they invent new kinds of mischief, they show no loyalty to parents, no conscience, no fidelity to their plighted word; they are without natural affection and without pity. They know well enough the just decree of God, that those who behave like this deserve to die, and yet they do it; not only so, they actually applaud such practices" (Romans 1:18-32, *The New English Bible*).

Those words are very strong—plain. The parallels between the ancient philosophers who denied God, and modern evolutionists who likewise deny God—are considerable. Let each person, whether theologian, scientists, layman or evolutionist judge himself, and evaluate his own attitudes, conduct, reasonings and rationalizations, in the light of the Holy Word of God, which cuts right to the quick. "For the word of God is alive and active. It cuts more keenly than any two-edged sword, piercing as far as the place where life and spirit, joints and marrow, divide. It sifts the purposes and thoughts of the heart. There is nothing in creation that can hide from him; everything lies naked and exposed to the eyes of the One with whom we have to reckon" (Hebrews 4:12-13).

In the following pages, you will read the story—indeed, the amazing saga—of creation versus evolutionary theory. You will read about THE FIRST GENESIS—that is, the original, or primeval, "genesis"—or, "beginning." You will see the errors of both evolutionists, and dogmatic theologians. You will observe and experience the pain of new proved truth taking its rightful place in the world in spite of the opposition of superstitious orthodoxy. You will behold many of the fathomless "proofs" for the existence of a Creator. And you will learn that there is harmony between the facts of science and a proper and cautious interpretation of the Scriptural record. You will also be thrilled, baffled and astounded, by the magnificent panoply of life and "miraculous" living creatures.

But in truth this book is merely an Introduction—an Introduction to the Great God, the Magnificent Creator, the One who gave us this world, and rulership over its animal and plant kingdoms, and our own lives, our fantastic bodies, and our mysterious minds with which we can grapple with reality and contemplate the question of "origins."

I trust you will find the *saga* of creation versus evolution inspiring, stimulating and a spiritual experience—a prod and a spur to get to know your personal Creator, the Great God, better, more intimately, and His son Jesus Christ.

Let this book be, for you, truly a FIRST GENESIS—a new *beginning* in life!

Mind has mountains;
cliffs of fall
Frightful, sheer, no-man-fathomed.
—Gerard Manley Hopkins

Chapter Two

Creation, Evolution and Superstition

In the sweltering summer of 1925, in the small town of Dayton, Tennessee, an unusual trial occurred in which John Scopes, high school biology teacher and football coach, was prosecuted by the state for allegedly using a book containing the theory of evolution to instruct a biology class.

Interest in the trial grew phenomenally. The public was captivated by the controversy between fundamentalist religion, on the one hand, and evolutionary theory, on the other. Famed criminal lawyer Clarence Darrow led the defense; well known political figure William Jennings Bryan led the prosecution. The trial itself sometimes bordered on a three ring circus, and over one hundred correspondents converged on Dayton to telegraph detailed stories to the entire world.

The trial settled nothing. The smoldering issue of creation versus evolution has always lurked beneath the seemingly calm facade of science, ready to burst into prominence when conditions are right.

The whole issue, on the surface, seems to be a confrontation between fundamentalist religion and academic science—not merely creation versus evolution, but faith versus fact, science versus theology. However, the real issues go much deeper. They involve the whole purpose and being of human life and human potential.

Confusion abounds. Most of the creationists—those who believe that a supreme being created the earth and life upon it—are divided among themselves as to when creation supposedly occurred, how it occurred, and how to interpret the creation account in the biblical book of Genesis.

On the other hand, evolutionists, too, are divided; they are in disagreement as to the how's and why's of evolution. Some see a divine hand behind the process of evolution, whereas others claim that evolution is a natural, biological process requiring no outside or divine guidance. Furthermore, there are a host of modern theories about evolution, each suggesting a different method of evolutionary progress.

Illustrating the divergence of opinion on the creation-evolution issue, Jean-Francois Revel, well-known editorialist of *L'Express*, wrote an article called "The Science of the Magicians." He asserted: "We now learn that the theory of evolution rests strictly on no proof at all. In a word, we are dealing with a religion."

Conversely, the Englishman Julian Huxley has charged: "No serious scientist would deny the fact that evolution has occurred, just as he would not deny the fact that the earth goes around the sun."[1] He unequivocally asserted, "The earth was not created; it evolved."[2]

In his book *Religion Without Revelation*, Huxley claimed: "It will soon be as impossible for an intelligent, educated man or woman to believe in a god as it is now to believe that the earth is flat."[3]

Others, however, favor a spirit of compromise. Pierre Teilhard de Chardin, French philosopher-scientist, sought to reconcile biology with creation through theistic evolution—the belief that a supreme being guided and directed evolution.

But what do the facts reveal? Who—if anyone—is right? And why are scientists as well as theologians in disagreement among themselves?

Science Versus Theology?

Down through the lengthening shadows of the ages of time, there has been an incessant conflict between logical, empirical thinkers, and the "religious establishment."

The conflict between superstition and science goes back into the earliest roots of human history and prehistory—back to the ancient hunters and the shamans or medicine men of their tribe.

From earliest ages men have squabbled over whether one should live according to the way of human reason, or after the guidelines of a religious "authority." It was the classic confrontation between ironclad dogma on the one hand or human conscience on the other. Perhaps there would never have been a conflict in the first place if the religious authority had not erred, and interposed itself in fields where it was an unreliable guide.

Science wants to investigate and learn new facts. But all too often religious authority demands absolute acceptance of a particular interpretation of ancient dogma.

True, we may look at the incredible, awesome universe around us, and the marvelous intricacies of life, and infer that there must have been a Creator God. Our logic might impel us to this conclusion. But for the evolutionist, it is not so simple. His frame of mind impels him to the belief that it all gradually, randomly, accidentally evolved. There is no room for a Creator in his system of thinking. This is sometimes due to the errors of religion.

Throughout history, as biologist George Simpson wrote, "As a matter of fact, most of the dogmatic religions have exhibited a perverse talent for taking the wrong side on the most important concepts of the material universe . . ."[4]

This has often been ludicrously true. When Medieval religion insisted the earth is flat and the sun and planets and stars all revolve around it, it took a dogmatic stance which was proved to have been in serious error.

Robert Gorney writes in *The Human Agenda:* "The emotionally precious view of earth's centrality in a fixed, unchanging universe was crystallized by Ptolemy in the second century A.D., and then taken over by the Christian Church. What had been ancient pagan punishments for contradicting pagan theology became orthodox Christian punishments for questioning orthodox Christian dogma. Despite man's continued secret probing, fourteen centuries brought no serious challenge."[5]

It was not until 1543 that Copernicus, who was, interestingly enough, a Catholic priest, near the end of his life published his theory of the heliocentric solar system. His theory met with stiff opposition from the church, and in 1600 Giordano Bruno, who subscribed to the Copernican theory, was burned alive as a heretic in Rome for his obduracy.

In 1604 Galileo Galilei noted that the universe is not changeless; the appearance of a new star demonstrated that fact. His telescopes confirmed that Copernicus was right; the earth and other planets do revolve around the sun!

Martin Luther ridiculed the idea of a heliocentric solar system by quoting Scripture. Since Joshua commanded the sun to stand still, he reasoned, that must prove the sun revolves around the earth!

One archbishop of the Catholic Church admonished Galileo, "Ye men of Galilee, why stand ye gazing up into the heavens?" This pun upon the name of Galileo, an astronomer, was used to ridicule his gazing at the stars through his telescope, quoting Biblical "authority" to do so.

Not until 1835 did Popes cease to dignify their dogma that the earth is the center of the solar system with their claim to infallibility. Protestants in general accepted the centrality of the earth until the days of Isaac Newton.

During the Inquisition, religious orthodoxy felt extremely pressured and threatened. Consequently, the inquisitors declared: "If earth is a planet, and only one among several planets, it cannot be that any such great things have been done specially for it as Christian doctrine teaches. If there are other planets, since God makes nothing in vain, they must be inhabited; but how can their inhabitants be descended from Adam? How can they trace their origin to Noah's ark? How can they have been redeemed by the Saviour?"[6]

Somehow, these questions made sense to them. Thus churchmen claimed that the astronomers "pretended discovery vitiates the whole Christian plan of salvation" and "upsets the whole basis of theology."

The idea that the sun is at the center of the solar system was branded as "of all heresies the most abominable, the most pernicious, the most scandalous."

Also, during the Middle Ages, geology was suspect. As evidence accumulated that the earth was much, much older than Archbishop Ussher's date of creation of 4004 B.C. churchmen attacked the science as "a dark art," "infernal artillery," as "calculated to tear up in the public mind every remaining attachment to Christianity."[7] Scientists, particularly geologists, were assailed as "infidels," "atheists," "heretics," etc. When evidence was amassed that the earth is far older than October 23, 4004 B.C., the fossil evidence was dismissed by certain religious leaders as deliberate deceptions of the devil![8]

Was the Bible itself in error? Did churchmen stumble and founder because they were trusting in an error-riddled Book?

Or had they misinterpreted the ancient Book itself, and read their own dogma into its pages?

This is a distinct possibility which we should be willing to acknowledge. Christian, atheist, agnostic, or whatever, all should be willing to check the evidence and not assume falsely.

Geological Knowledge

During the last few hundred years, man began to discard preconceived dogma and opinion. They began to study the earth in a systematic manner. As geologists studied the changing landscapes, fossils, retreat of glaciers, and the cutting of river channels, many concluded that the earth must be much older than the 6,000 years which the theologians had told them.

Not all theologians, however, believed that the 6,000-year figure was correct. Some thought that the "days" of creation mentioned were really long periods of time, perhaps thousands of years in length—not literal "days" as such. Thus, early attempts were made to harmonize the Bible with science.

Early scientists still tended to view the earth in terms of the Bible record. And when geologists saw evidences on the earth's surface that seemed to bespeak tremendous cataclysm and destruction, they immediately assigned such evidence to the Noachian deluge.

A modern geology textbook admits:

> The greatest of all past catastrophes described in the Bible with any detail is Noah's Flood, or the Deluge. Controversy over the Flood still exists, but there was a time not many decades past when the debate was even more heated and serious. When geology was still in its infancy, it was customary to explain practically everything in terms of the Deluge. The effects of erosion were attributed to the currents and storms that accompanied the Flood, and mountains and hills were formed by the violent stirrings and mixings of the waters. The Flood offered a convenient explanation, too, for the existence of fossil remains, not only on the earth's surface but also in caves or deep in the earth. . . . Early generations of scientists, as well as theologians, turned to the Flood to explain practically all evidences of geologic change.[9]

But continuing study and scientific progress showed that the early scientists and theologians who ascribed all geological evidences to the Flood were wrong! Geologists know better. Careful observation shows that changes in the geology of the earth, as recorded in the strata, necessitate long periods of time. This evidence set the stage for Darwin's theory of organic evolution.

Charles Lyell's theory that the present is the key to the past, and that naturally operating laws of nature today best explain what occurred in the geologic record, paved the way for Darwin's theory of evolution. Although geologists recognized that catastrophes have indeed occurred in thc earth's history, they concluded almost to a man that it was folly to ascribe most of the earth's geological strata to one event, such as Noah's Flood.

Impact of Darwin

In 1859 Charles Darwin published *Origin of Species* in which he put forth his theory of organic evolution. The hue and cry from religious people was enormous. But Darwin's theory of evolution found a champion in Thomas Huxley who propounded it with missionary zeal.

Since Darwin's time, the theory of organic evolution has become the basic philosophy of all education in the western world—all the social sciences, the humanities, history, law, political economy, and even religion itself.

Asserted C.L. Prosser in the *American Scientist: "The Origin of Species* has had more influence on Western culture than any other book of modern times. It was not only a great biological treatise, closely reasoned and revolutionary, but it carried significant implications for philosophy, religion, sociology and history. *Evolution is the greatest single unifying principle in all biology."*[10] (Emphasis mine throughout book except where otherwise noted.)

The impact of Darwin's theory was tremendous—even where Darwin did not intend it. Karl Marx wanted to dedicate his book *Das Kapital* to Darwin. Mussolini's attitude was completely dominated by evolution. In public utterances, he repeatedly used the Darwinian catchwords while he mocked at peace. In Germany, Adolf Hitler was captivated by evolutionary teaching. Evolutionary ideas—quite undisguised—lie at the root of the "bible" of Nazism—*Mein Kampf.*

Renowned world geopolitical expert Hans J. Morgenthau, in his textbook *Politics Among Nations*, points out the vast impact of Darwin's theory of evolution on world leaders in the 20th century. Says he: "In modern times, especially under the influence of the social philosophies of Darwin and Spencer, the ideologies of imperialism have preferred biological (evolutionary) arguments. Transferred to international politics, the philosophy of the survival of the fittest sees in the military superiority of a strong nation over a weak one a natural phenomenon that makes the latter the preordained object of the former's power. According to this philosophy, it would be contrary to nature if the strong did not dominate the weak and if the weak tried to be the equal of the strong."[11]

Morgenthau points out that Communism, Fascism, and Nazism, as well as Japanese imperialism, used the concept of evolution to justify and support political ambitions and desires for conquest.

Declared one evolutionist: "Here is a theory that released thinking men from the spell of a superstition, one of the most overpowering that has ever enslaved mankind." He added, "We owe to the *Origin of Species* the overthrow of the myth of creation. . . ."[12]

What happened? Where did the world go wrong?

Superstition Revisited

Unfortunately, most scientists and philosophers who believe in the evolutionary theory, as opposed to creation by an act of God, made several fallacious assumptions.

First, they assumed that medieval "Christianity" received its ideas about creation, the solar system, and the age of the earth, from the Bible. Nothing could be further from the truth. Most of the cosmological concepts of the Middle Ages came from ancient Babylon—not from the Bible!

Dreyer states in "Medieval Cosmology": "When we turn over the pages of some of these Fathers, we might imagine that we were reading the opinions of some Babylonian priest written down some thousands of years before the Christian era; the ideas are exactly the same, the only difference being that the old Babylonian priest had no way of knowing better."[13]

The superstition of the Middle Ages, which professed to teach and explain the Bible, was based on ancient pagan concepts and obstructed scientific progress.

Today, evolutionary theory has replaced medieval cosmology and superstition. But, as Dr. G.A. Kerkut, professor of physiology and biochemistry at the University of Southampton, England states, the world appears to have passed from one dogma to another. He points out that throughout the Dark Ages and the Middle Ages, learning was under the aegis of the Church, and that this hold was but slowly relinquished. Until 1871, it was the custom for the majority of the dons at Cambridge to be ordained before they could carry out any of the duties of the college.

Dr. Kerkut charges that many of the Church's "worst features are still left embedded in present-day studies." He observes that the serious student of the previous centuries was brought up on a theological diet from which he would learn to have faith and to quote authorities when he was in doubt.

Declares Dr. Kerkut: "Intelligent understanding was the last thing required. The undergraduate of today is just as bad; he is still the same opinion-swallowing grub. . . . In this he differs not one bit from the irrational theology student of the bygone age who would mumble his dogma and hurry through his studies in order to reach the peace and plenty of the comfortable living in the world outside. But what is worse, the present-day student *claims* to be different from his predecessor in that he thinks scientifically and despises dogma. . . ."[14]

Said Dr. Kerkut, the modern student accepts evolutionary theory as a fact, yet probably hasn't even read Darwin's *Origin of Species.* He unquestionably accepts evolution and "repeats parrot fashion the views of the current Archbishop of Evolution. In fact he would be behaving like certain of those religious students he affects to despise. He would be taking on faith what he could not intellectually understand. . . ."[15]

Has the modern world indeed passed from one superstition to another?

Consider: The definition of dogma is "something held as an established opinion." It is "a point of view or tenet put forth as authoritative *without adequate grounds.*"

Is evolution a modern "dogma"?

The Human Factor

Perhaps the best explanation why most scientists accept evolution was given by the renowned American naturalist Joseph Wood Krutch. He wrote: "Many biologists have moments when they acknowledge the ultimate mystery and wonder of life but often they are too irrevocably committed to mechanistic dogmas and *too afraid of the sneers of their fellows* not to hedge even when their own logic compels them to admit that the accepted premises are by no means wholly satisfactory."[16]

This famed scientist saw the fallible, human side of science—the side where currents of prejudice, opinion, and bias run strong and deep. He discerned that many scientists probably are committed to evolution, not because of its own strong logical arguments and proof, but because they are afraid to question a theory which has been generally endorsed by the scientific community. They don't want to face the sneers, ridicule, or jokes of contemporaries who regard belief in a Creator God as mere superstition and myth.

An Alternative to Evolutionary Theory

In this book we will look at the Biblical record, as well as the theories of theologians, and the theories of evolutionists. It will become crystal clear that there is an alternative to both the errors and dogmas of theology, and the assumptions of materialistic evolutionists.

The Biblical alternative, we will see, fits the facts of science. It doesn't contradict any established scientific fact regarding biology, geology or physics.

The Bible, we will discover, does not say what millions have assumed. Although it is not a science text, as such, nevertheless it is amazingly accurate scientifically. Its statements are completely in accord with the empirical knowledge amassed by scientists, astronomers, biologists.

Most have not understood that the real conflict never was between true science and the Biblical record. The real historic battle has been between sincere but misguided theologians who did not understand the Bible and misinterpreted the Bible, and rational scientists who could see that the theologians were wrong, but who leaped into the opposite ditch.

Consequently, many scientists rejected all theology, and invented a "new" theology–belief in evolutionism.

The world has traded in one superstition for another one. Religious dogmatism has given way before the onslaught of evolutionary dogmatism. Today in intellectual circles the iron hand of the theologians has been replaced by the iron fist of the evolutionists.

Chapter Three

The Miracle of Life

Where did life come from?

If you are married, and have children, think back to the birth of your first baby. Remember that crying, squalling little bundle of flesh? Remember the delight you felt as you watched that little bundle of joy first smile, and crawl, learn to take his or her first few faltering steps? Remember your joy when your child first broke into an infectious grin, smiling at you with pure joy?

But consider for a moment: Was that little bundle of flesh an accident of evolution?

But let's go back in time. What about the first human baby ever born? Was it the product of something not quite human?

Can all life on earth—all the estimated three million species of plants and animals, ranging from insects to elephants and from fungi to the giant California redwoods—be traced back to two amoeba or some such creature that itself evolved from a few scattered chemicals and a dose of sunlight or radiation?

Let's notice what evolutionary scientists postulate as to the origin of life. What tangible evidence exists that life evolved from nonliving matter aeons ago?

Origin of Life a Mystery

What does science *know for certain* about the origin of life? Has science demonstrated that life arose from nonliving matter through evolutionary processes?

Writes John Pfeiffer: "The origin of life, like the origin of the earth, *is a mystery*. Man's approach to this mystery has been a mixture of thoughtful *conjecture* and continuing *awe*."[1]

Says this same writer, " . . the essential scientific question of how life began *remains unsolved*. Cell research on the molecular level has revealed many of the processes by which living matter reproduces itself, develops in complexity . . . But the great gulf between life and nonlife remains an enigma. Science can only conjecture about the basic steps of the process."[2]

Does that sound like evolution is amply demonstrated, that it is now impossible for an intelligent, thinking man to believe in a God? Is there now no longer any need or room for the supernatural? Is belief in a God really as unscientific as belief that the earth is flat?

A Key Experiment

In 1952 an American graduate student in Chemistry, Stanley L. Miller, made an apparatus including glass tubing and a globelike flask and circulated through it a mixture of water vapor, hydrogen, ammonia and methane. Miller created a 60,000-volt spark inside his apparatus, simulating lightning.

After letting the mixture circulate about a week, Miller studied the resultant solution at the bottom of the flask. He found that several simple carbon compounds had been formed, including amino acids which are the building blocks of proteins. Miller had synthesized four different types of amino acids, besides another half dozen compounds.

Other investigators performed experiments similar to Miller's and found that not only electricity but also ultraviolet light would produce amino acids and other compounds.

What was the real significance of these experiments? Many evolutionists have believed that long, long ago the earth had an atmosphere filled with ammonia, methane, water vapor and hydrogen. Since these experiments revealed that ultraviolet light and electricity can produce amino acids and similar compounds, evolutionists concluded that this is how life probably evolved on earth. Ultraviolet light from the sun and lightning, they concluded, synthesized amino acids and these gradually combined into proteins, enzymes, and evolved eventually into living cells!

Picture the vast primordial ocean. In it simple compounds are converted into more complicated compounds. The lash of ultraviolet light and of lightning causes amino-acids, purines, pyrimidines, pentoses and many other types of compounds to be formed. As time crawls on, they gradually thicken the ocean into a soup. More and more compounds are formed, they collide with one another more frequently, and frequently stick together.

Purine and pyrimidine compounds combine with pentoses and phosphates and form "nucleotides." Then two of these combine to form double molecules. One of these may collide and combine with another nucleotide or amino-acid to form a triple molecule—and so forth.

As this process goes on, great numbers of compounds are formed. The multiple amino-acids evolve into protein and the multiple nucleotides becomes nucleic acid. Finally, the historic day comes when a nucleic acid molecule and a protein molecule collide, stick together, and form a nucleoprotein—a nucleoprotein sufficiently complex and properly constructed to be able to self-reproduce.

Life has thus evolved from the not-living!

This *is* a fascinating, spell-binding melodrama.

But now let's see just how probable, or improbable it is.

The Spontaneous Generation of Life

Evolutionists themselves sometimes have difficulty believing this incredible theory of the chemical origin of life. One such evolutionist is George Wald, Harvard University, Professor of Biology, writing in the *Scientific American*.

In an article entitled "The Origin of Life," Wald admits that Louis Pasteur firmly proved that today it is *impossible* for life to arise from nonliving matter. This was the common belief among the ancient Egyptians, Greeks, and among most scientists during the Middle Ages. Pasteur, however, performed rigorous experiments which thoroughly demolished this theory. In 1860 Louis Pasteur used a flask containing boiled broth and exposed it to free air from which all microorganisms had been removed. The broth remained clear and sterile indefinitely.

Pasteur's experiments, rigorously performed, demolished the belief in spontaneous generation of life. He proved conclusively that life does not arise from inanimate matter—life comes only from life!

But if life can come only from the living, where does this leave evolution? It is a difficult problem. In fact, writes Wald: "Most modern biologists, having reviewed with satisfaction the downfall of the spontaneous generation hypothesis, yet unwilling to accept the alternative belief in special creation, are left with nothing."[3]

What a remarkable statement! Wald admitted that most biologists are unwilling to accept the belief in special creation—belief in a Creator God. Yet, unless they can somehow rescue the spontaneous-generation hypothesis, they are left with nothing to account for life's existence.

So what is the solution? Says Wald: "I think a scientist has no choice but to approach the origin of life through a hypothesis of spontaneous generation." Thus, despite the impressive evidence offered by Pasteur, most biologists today conclude life *must* have arisen by spontaneous generation!

Clearly, evolutionists are men of great faith.

Wald admits, "The most complex machine man has devised—say an electronic brain—is child's play compared with the simplest of living organisms."[4] He confesses: "One has only to contemplate the magnitude of this task to concede that the spontaneous generation of a living organism is *impossible. Yet here we are—as a result, I believe, of spontaneous generation.*"

Obviously, here is an example of great *faith*—faith in the theory of evolution!

But how can intelligent men "believe" a theory which they admit is proven "impossible"?

Here is the answer:

Says Wald: "*Time is in fact the hero of the plot.* The time with which we have to deal is of the order of two billion years. . . . Given so much time, the 'impossible' becomes possible, the possible probable, and the probable virtually certain. One has only to wait: *time itself performs the miracles*."[5]

But is this necessarily true? Can time alone work miracles? Can time create life out of the nonliving? Can you derive a mathematical formula that will explain the origin of life by the use of time?

Just what is this thing we call "life," anyway?

It is very difficult to define life, scientifically. However, we all know that to live an organism must be able to eat, respire, grow, move, reproduce, and expel wastes. We also know that every living creature on earth contains protein.

But what is protein?

Protein molecules always contain atoms of carbon, hydrogen, oxygen and nitrogen, and usually contain sulfur, and perhaps other elements. Protein molecules are very large and complex.

A protein that occurs in milk contains 5,941 atoms and has a molecular weight of 42,020–it is 120 times as large as a molecule of table sugar! But even this is a *small* molecule. Writes Isaac Asimov: "The average protein has a molecular weight of 60,000. Many go much higher. Some of the proteins in clam blood, for instance, have a molecular weight of 4,000,000. And some of the viruses consist of protein molecules with molecular weights in the tens of millions and even the hundreds of millions."[6]

Could Hemoglobin Have Evolved?

Let's examine a particular protein molecule–the hemoglobin protein, which is common to many life forms.

Hemoglobin is the chief protein of the red blood cells. It captures oxygen in the lungs and carries it to all the cells of the body where it releases the oxygen and returns to the lungs.

Hemoglobin is a protein of only average size–comprised of 539 amino acids of twenty different kinds. Scientists have identified the particular amino-acids in hemoglobin and the number of each. What are the "chances" that the hemoglobin molecule just accidentally evolved?

Let's assume that we are Las Vegas gamblers. We have a "good hand"—a group of 539 amino acids—just the right ones to make hemoglobin. But to win the game each one of these 539 cards must turn up in precisely the right order!

In order for the hemoglobin protein to be formed, these 539 amino acids must go together in just the right sequence, with no mistakes. What are the chances of that happening?

If we had one each of two kinds of amino acids, they could be arranged in only 4 different ways—aa, ab, bb, and ba. If we had a molecule consisting of three amino acids, any one of the three could be in the first position, the second position, and the third position. Thus the total number of possible combinations would be 3 x 3 x 3 or 27.

How many possible combinations would there be to a hemoglobin molecule containing 539 amino acids with 20 possible amino acids at each position? The correct answer is obtained by multiplying 20 by itself 539 times. The total number of combinations possible would be 20^{539}.

The answer is a fantastic, totally incomprehensible number which far exceeds all the estimated stars in the universe (which has been estimated at 10^{22} or 10,000,000,000,000,000,000,000 stars)! The total number of possibilities turns out to be 1.8×10^{701}. In other words, that's 18 followed by 700 zeroes. Here's what that number would look like:

180,000,000,000,000,000,000,000,000,000,000,000,000,000,
000,000,000,000,000,000,000,000,000,000,000,000,000,000,
000,000,000,000,000,000,000,000,000,000,000,000,000,000,
000,000,000,000,000,000,000,000,000,000,000,000,000,000,
000,000,000,000,000,000,000,000,000,000,000,000,000,000,
000,000,000,000,000,000,000,000,000,000,000,000,000,000,
000,000,000,000,000,000,000,000,000,000,000,000,000,000,
000,000,000,000,000,000,000,000,000,000,000,000,000,000,
000,000,000,000,000,000,000,000,000,000,000,000,000,000,
000,000,000,000,000,000,000,000,000,000,000,000,000,000,
000,000,000,000,000,000,000,000,000,000,000,000,000,000,
000,000,000,000,000,000,000,000,000,000,000,000,000,000,

000,000,000,000,000,000,000,000,000,000,000,000,000,000,
000,000,000,000,000,000,000,000,000,000,000,000,000,000,
000,000,000,000,000,000,000,000,000,000,000,000,000,000,
000,000,000,000,000,000,000,000,000,000,000,000,000,000,
000,000,000,000,000,000,000,000,000,000.

The human mind cannot possibly comprehend the size of such a number, but let's try to put it into perspective. Scientists estimate the age of the universe as about six billion years—or 6×10^9 years. The human population of the earth, today, is 3.5 billion—or 3.5×10^9.

If we had a universe containing a trillion (10^{12}) galaxies, each galaxy composed of a trillion stars like our sun, and each sun orbited by 10 planets like our earth (obviously preposterous), and if on each of these planets you had ten billion inhabitants, and if each of these inhabitants had the same amount of blood as the average human being (and so the total amount of red blood cells on just one planet would be 2×10^{23}), and if each blood cell contained 3×10^8 hemoglobin molecules—then the total number of hemoglobin molecules in the whole universe would be 6×10^{56}. Compared to the possible combinations of the 539 amino acids in hemoglobin (1.8×10^{701}), this number is infinitesimally small—virtually *zero*!

But let's make the game even more interesting. Let's say you have a billion new hemoglobin molecules for each original one every second for the 6 billion years some scientists guess that the universe has been around. During that span of time, almost 2×10^{17} seconds would have elapsed. Therefore, with a billion new hemoglobin molecules replacing each original one every second, the total number you'd have had after 6 billion years would be 1.2×10^{83} hemoglobin molecules—and this number would still be totally insignificant compared to the total possible combinations of the amino acids in just one hemoglobin molecule!!!

Even given all these things, the chances of evolving just one hemoglobin molecule would be roughly one in 1.5×10^{618} (or one chance in 15 followed by 617 zeroes)!

Are you beginning to get the picture? Are you beginning to see the point?

By indulging in this little mathematical game, we should be able to see with greater clarity than ever why even the evolution of ONE average-size molecule such as hemoglobin—even if we are given the amino acids to work with—is as IMPOSSIBLE as anything could ever be!

No Las Vegas gambler would ever place a bet on such an occurrence. The chances of winning would be ridiculously minute.

"But," evolutionists might argue, "there is still a chance—one chance. It *could* happen."

Technically, they have a point. But that whimsical occurrence—as breathtaking as it might be—still would only be one tiny hemoglobin molecule!

The Probability of Life

In his book *Human Destiny,* Lecompte du Nuoy, a French biochemist, computed the probability that a random sequence of amino acids would duplicate any given protein. If the protein were 100 amino acids long and each amino acid slot may be filled by any one of 20 amino acids, the chances of random assembly of a given protein would be one in 20^{100}, or 10^{130}. This figure is vastly greater than the number of elementary particles in the universe, 10^{80}. Lecompte du Nuoy concluded that life could not have arisen by mere chance!

Incredibly smaller than the chance of assembling even the above protein would be randomly assembling a DNA molecule from nucleotide phosphates. I.S. Shklovskil and Carl Sagan in *Intelligent Life in the Universe* showed that one could perform the exercise of reassembling the DNA molecules one a second for the lifetime of the Galaxy and not come close to assembling one of his own or anyone else's chromosomes. They suggest, however improbable by chance, such might have come about by natural selection which serves as a sort of probability sieve, extracting those structures and functions which better adapt the organism to its environment.[7]

This suggestion, however, has been refuted by L.E. Orgel. He points out the rather obvious fact that natural selection cannot operate until nucleic acid replication is underway. A self replicating molecule arising by mere chance would, therefore, still seem to be an awesomely improbable event![8]

Peter T. Mora put his finger judiciously on the core of the problem. He questions the assumption that "given enough time" anything can happen. Says Mora: "A further aspect I should like to discuss is what I call the practice of *infinite escape clauses*. I believe we developed this practice to avoid facing the conclusion that the probability of a self-reproducing state is *zero*."[9]

Zero!

Mora clarifies what he is discussing: "These escape clauses postulate an almost infinite amount of time and an almost infinite amount of material (monomers), so that even the most unlikely event could have happened. This is to invoke probability and statistical considerations when such considerations are *meaningless*. When for practical purposes the condition of infinite time and matter has to be invoked, the concept of probability is *annulled. By such logic we can prove anything, such as that no matter how complex, everything will repeat itself, exactly and innumerable.*"[10]

Something is seriously wrong with a theory that forces scientists to resort to such mathematical charades.

Nevertheless, skeptics of creation refuse to face the obvious. It is not very fashionable among active scientists to postulate a divine Creator, in this age of materialism.

Declares J.D. Bernal in *The Origin of Life*: "It is difficult to imagine a god of any kind occupying himself creating, by some spiritual micro-chemistry, a molecule of deoxyribonucleic acid which enabled the primitive organism to grow and multiply. The whole hypothesis has now come to its natural end in absurdity."[11]

But such imagery and assumptions prove nothing at all about the creation process. Evolutionists are still faced with critical and unsolved problems in the origin of life.

Chapter Four

Inside a Cell

Biologists used to believe that cells were very simple little blobs of protoplasm, or "living stuff." Until a relatively few years ago, man's concept of the cell was greatly limited. Evolution of a cell, evolutionists believed, did not seem to present much of a problem.

But with the invention of the electron microscope about 30 years ago, a whole new microscopic world of startling complexity was revealed! The electron microscope has revealed much more detail of the interior of the cell. Biologists were astonished to discover that the cell, far from being a "simple" little entity, was incredibly complex!

The electron microscope revealed that the interior of cells contain a network of microtunnels, known as the *endoplasmic reticulum*, which extends throughout the cell much like blood vessels. Also, it showed the existence of tiny cellular "factories," called *ribosomes*, which manufacture the protein compounds that compose a large part of living organisms. A cell may have *thousands* of such ribosome "factories." Also discovered were mysterious areas called *Golgi complexes*, named after Camillo Golgi, the Italian physician who discovered them. The Golgi complexes are hollow, saucer-like discs stacked on top of each other. They appear to function as a protein packaging warehouse for the cell.

Another electrifying discovery was objects within the cell which appeared to be cells within the cell. Called *mitochondria*, they turned out to be the chief power plants of the cell. An

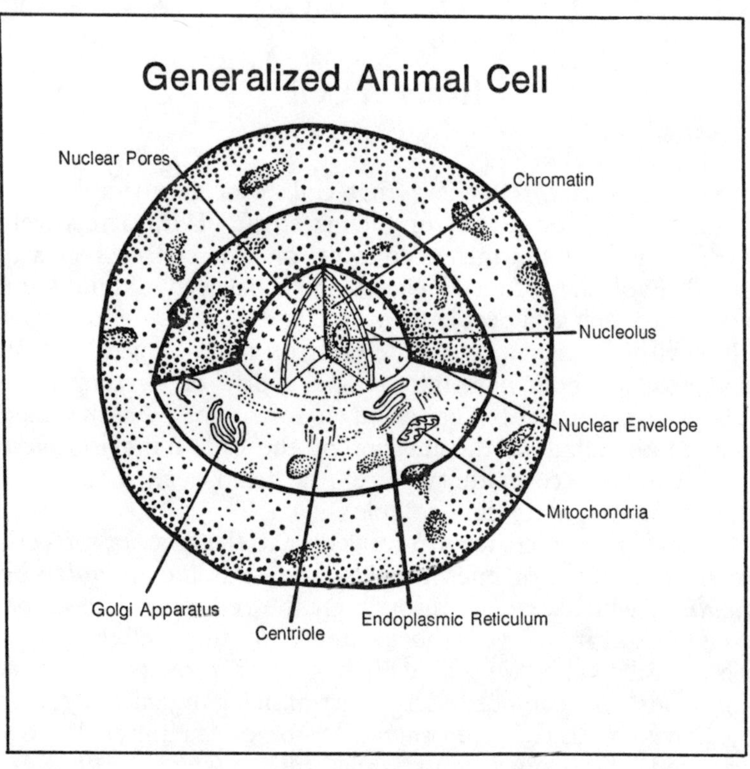

The simple little cell is not so simple after all, but is really a tiny microscopic teeming and bustling metropolis of highly integrated functions and directional activity. A miniature living "universe."—*Illustration by Andy Voth.*

estimated 90 percent of the chemical energy required by the cell comes from reactions which occur in the chambers and compartments of the mitochondria. An average cell contains about 1,000 mitochondria. The interior of mitochondria has been described as resembling a cutaway model of an ocean liner. In some cells, the mitochondria move, twist, and slither about, constantly splitting and fusing and forming intricate systems in the cytoplasm.

Inner Cell Mysteries

The membrane which surrounds a cell is not merely a "bag" that holds it together. Rather, it is dynamically active and utilizes complex mechanisms to admit or exclude various molecules. Just how it does this is one of the head-scratching problems facing modern cytologists.

Another subcellular mystery involves *lysosomes*. These objects apparently consist of a single outer membrane which houses a powerful fluid that is rich in destructive hydrolase and acidic phosphatase enzymes. Lysosomes appear to serve as tiny policemen or scavengers in the cell. Their functions may include the self-digestion of dead cells, the consumption of mitochondria which are no longer needed or useful, the liberation of food within a cell, and cell defense—the destruction of invading bacteria or dangerous foreign proteins that may enter the cell.

Lysosomes have been found in cells of the kidney, spleen, thyroid and in certain protozoa. Their internal enzymes are capable of hastening the breakdown of proteins, carbohydrates, nucleic acids and organic compounds of sulfur and phosphorus.

Biologists are still puzzled about what makes the lysosome membrane able to withstand its vitriolic, destructive contents!

The "Capital" of the Cell

Almost everything the cell does is supervised by the nucleus—the control center or "brains" of the cell. The nucleus carries the hereditary traits of the cell and is responsible for reproduction, as well as supervision of the cell's manifold activities. The nucleus is highly complex—unbelievably so!

The nucleus of a human cell, for example, contains 46 threadlike *chromosomes*. These are composed of smaller segments called *genes*. There may be as many as 1,250 genes on a single human chromosome.

What are genes composed of?

In several important experiments performed between 1941 and 1944, Dr. Oswald T. Avery and two colleagues at the Rockefeller Institute discovered that genes are composed of protein coatings and *nucleic acid*—actually, deoxyribonucleic acid, called DNA.* This discovery was corroborated by succeeding experiments, and scientists now know that DNA contains the basic "code of life." The DNA structure determines the cell's hereditary traits; it is like a master blueprint.

Analysis of the DNA molecule itself showed it is a giant molecule composed of simple sugars known as deoxyribose, phosphates, and four nitrogen compounds. These compounds or bases are called adenine, thymine, cytosine and guanine (A, T, C, and G for short).

How are these ingredients put together to form the DNA molecule? In 1953 James D. Watson and Francis H.C. Crick attempted to make a model of DNA. They described it as a twisting ladder, with the sugars and phosphates forming the frame and the bases forming the rungs. According to their theory, each rung is composed of two bases joining at the middle.

---

*Nucleic acids are composed of building blocks known as nucleotides. A nucleotide is a molecule made up of phosphate groups, five-carbon sugars, and nitrogen bases. There are two different series of nucleotides. One is characterized by ribose sugar, and the other deoxyribose sugar. "Deoxy" merely means "minus one oxygen." The only difference between these two types of sugar is one lacks an oxygen atom.

The nucleotides containing deoxyribose sugar are linked together in long chains to form deoxyribonucleic acid (DNA). The nucleotides containing ribose sugar make up ribonucleic acid (RNA). The function of RNA is to build the proteins specified by the nucleotide sequences of the DNA molecules.

How much DNA does a living cell contain? The coiled DNA in a simple virus may be a "ladder" 1/2,000 of an inch long, containing 170,000 "rungs." By comparison, the DNA in a single human cell, if it were unravelled and stretched out, would extend for three feet and contain about six billion "rungs." Thus, the DNA molecule in a human being is incredibly complex—yet it is all contained in the tiny nucleus of each living cell.

Writes John Pfeiffer: "All the DNA instruction for a human being, if spelled out in English, would require several sets of a 24-volume encyclopedia."[1] He adds that if the DNA in every human cell were put end to end, it would stretch for about *10 billion miles!*

Scientists believe that heredity is determined by the particular structure and form of the DNA molecule. The structure of the DNA molecule spells out a "sentence" making up a long coded message or blueprint. This message or blueprint can transmit a tremendous amount of genetic data. "Statistically," says John Pfeiffer, "this means that the number of ways to spell the complete message of life is greater than the number of subatomic particles in the solar system."[2]

DNA does more than mastermind reproduction, however. It also directs the manufacture of thousands of proteins by dispatching precise "blueprints"—in the form of "messenger-RNA" molecules—which direct protein construction in conjunction with the ribosomes and transfer RNA's of the cell.

Does all this sound complex? It is! Microchemists are just beginning to unravel the mysteries of DNA and RNA.

But the question facing evolutionary theory is—how such an intricate, complex, perfectly functioning system "just evolved" at *random* from atoms and simple molecules found in nature?

Can your mind really accept the theory that all the complex DNA molecules—the nuclei of living cells, carrying the "code of life" and containing millions of vital "instructions" which dictate heredity and cell metabolism—slowly, effortlessly, and gradually evolved from random atoms?

Can you believe the seemingly miraculous properties of DNA are merely due to lucky happenstance—that these incredible molecules somehow were designed and built by an "accident" of nature and that there was no Creator?

The Complex Cell City

The living cell is not a "simple blob of protoplasm." Rather, it has been compared to a bustling metropolis, a complex society comparable to New York City—but with no pollution problem, no garbage strikes, an efficient police department, an effective fire department, smooth-running (and non-polluting) factories, manufacturing plants, industrial complexes and power plants.

Compared to the smooth-functioning of a living cell, man's huge metropolises such as London, Tokyo, or New York City are monstrous examples of inefficiency, waste, confusion, and chaos!

If a cell were as chaotic and inefficient as a man-made city, it would not survive! Says one college level text:

> Complex molecules are being broken down, other equally complex ones built up; each is synthesized according to a specific formula and for a specific function. *Exactness is all important*, even to the final placement of the final atom in each molecule; *one atom out of place, one reaction misfiring, may mean death to the cell.* In the course of these activities, meanwhile, powerful chemicals that might destroy life are neatly avoided or bypassed, the temperatures that might destroy life are precisely controlled. What man needs fabulous machinery or extreme temperatures to accomplish, the cell performs every living second, smoothly, quietly, efficiently within its own delicate walls, with its own watery physiochemical magic.[3]

Truly, the living cell is an awesome thing—making the greatest works of men look sickly and insignificant in comparison!

Could all cells have accidentally evolved?

When I tour a factory, a steel mill, a nuclear electric generating plant, I *know* that they had to be designed and built by highly intelligent men. I know without even questioning that such plants or factories were man-*made*. All the compartments, pipes, valves, redundant safety devices, turbines, wires, dials, control room gadgets, computers, fuel rods, cranes, tanks, etc., that make up the San Onofre nuclear generating facility near San Clemente, California, did not accidentally fall together over a period of time, or evolve mindlessly. That plant was carefully, cautiously *designed* by human creators.

When I drive through a bustling city such as London, Rome, Zurich, Los Angeles, Boston, or New York, I know those cities were built. Generations of men built the highways, streets, roads, put up the telephone lines, constructed the sewers, erected the factories, markets, houses, offices, government buildings. I know cities did not gradually evolve from the random action of molecules or atoms.

Yet the staggering efficiency and complexity of the cell puts man's cities to shame. Since I *know* even man's cities reveal that they had to have a designer and maker, I am even more convinced that the construction of a living cell reveals the existence of a Master-Designer, and a Master-Craftsman.

The Designer Revealed

The sheer unbelievable complexity of a living cell attests to the existence of a Divine Designer—a Supreme Organizer—God.

As biochemist Duane T. Gish, who helped elucidate the chemical structure of the protein of tobacco mosaic virus, wrote:

> The physical and chemical laws operating today, which must have been operative since the days of creation, are completely incapable of giving rise to the unique, specific, and purposeful structures and organization that we find in the living cell. . . .
>
> Life is more than just a master chemical, more than a vast collection of molecules endowed with special properties, more than the many hundreds of thousands of chemical reactions that occur in protoplasm. Life, as represented by the living cell, is *a vast master plan*, unique in this universe, incomprehensibly complex, awesomely constructed. Life was the climatic event in the creation of the universe by a *Supreme Intelligence* . . .[4]

Cytologist and zoologist L.F. Gardiner said:

> The knowledge that man has gained about cellular structure and

> function bears witness to a *Designer* who is responsible for such incredible complexity. . . . If man, with his highly sophisticated instruments, his skill in experimentation, and his great capacity for solving complex problems, has been able to gain understanding of the cell only at such a slow and wearisome pace—and gain a decidedly imperfect understanding at that—how masterly and superhumanly brilliant a *Designer* must be to be responsible for its existence![5]

How could mere atoms organize themselves in such a manner that would *perpetuate* the resulting organized system? It is inconceivable. Assuming that nucleotide phosphates spontaneously assembled into polynucleotides that were capable of self-replication, eventually all the nucleotides in the ocean would have been tied up in polynucleotides, "and the entire synthetic process would then have ground to a halt."[12] Since polynucleotides have no catalytic properties, and proteins have no reproductive properties, both are necessary to make life possible. But how did they come together in partnership aeons ago? How did the genetic code originate?

It is a bit puzzling to all scientists.

Says Carl Sagan: "The molecular apparatus ancillary to the *operation of the code*—the activating enzymes, adapter RNA's, messenger RNA's, ribosomes, and so on—are *themselves* each the product of a long evolutionary history and are produced according to *instructions contained within the code. At the time of the origin of the code such an elaborate molecular apparatus was of course absent.*"[13]

Absent? But then how was the genetic code developed? How did it first begin operation? And how did these vital substances necessary for life themselves evolve?

How did such an incredible thing as the living cell evolve?

Could Cells Have Evolved?

Consider the dilemma of an evolutionist. He is a learned man. He knows that only living cells can create proteins and enzymes.

He knows that *living* organisms can build up complex compounds and molecules from simple ones. But can natural

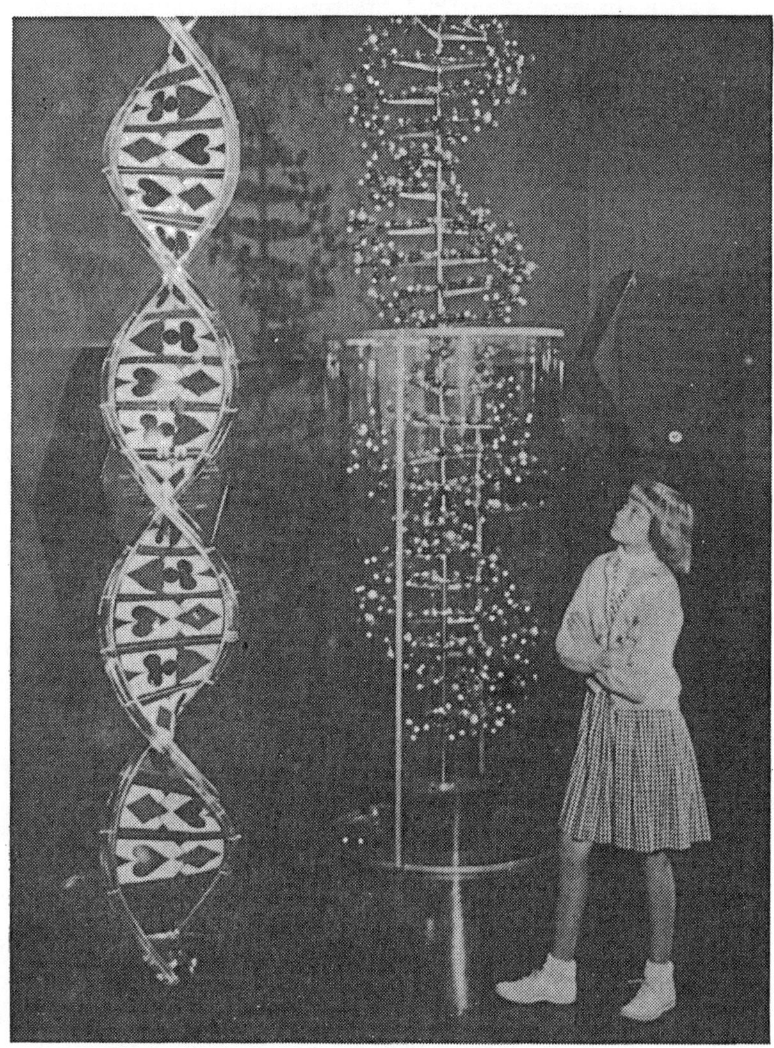

The DNA molecule—the most complex molecule known to man—carries the "blueprint" of heredity within its genes and chromosomes which are arranged, according to Watson and Crick, in a twisting "ladder" or helix.—*Courtesy of Pacific Science Central Foundation.*

forces—the lifeless elements of the world—build up such incredibly complex molecules? His theory requires it.

Says William Stokes after discussing such problems: "This leads us to what may be the *most basic riddle of all. How, when no life existed, did substances appear that today are absolutely essential to living systems, yet can only be formed by these systems?*"[6]

That's quite a question!

"Indeed," the author concludes, " *the problem verges on the absurd*. How can anything begin that needs for its beginning something that it must create *before* it can begin?"[7]

That is the mind-paralyzing paradox evolutionists still have not been able to answer. How could they? The whole problem seems illogical—insane.

However, evolutionists are unwilling to admit defeat. They will never give up. Says this same writer: ". . . we cannot admit defeat as long as any avenue for research remains unexplored."[8]

Declares Stokes: "We must, therefore try to understand what distinguishes living from nonliving matter, what chemical elements life requires, and how living matter operates to stay alive. *If investigations along these lines fail, we may then have to admit that life is still an incomprehensible mystery*"![9]

Incomprehensible? Indeed yes, for evolutionary theory which seems to stumble endlessly and repeatedly upon its own shoelaces. Life is incomprehensible from an evolutionary point of view. Probability theory digs evolution's grave and then the living cell buries it.

The Creationist, however, can look at the marvels of life, and its complexity, and worship the Creator, the author of life and its mysteries.

I shall never believe that God plays dice with the world.

—Albert Einstein

Chapter Five

Sex, Courtship and Mating Rituals

Evolution, we are told, was a long, slow process until some remote ancestor of life happened upon the blissful, exciting discovery of sex.

What is the truth about sex? Where, how did it originate? How do living things, from lowly insects to giant Sequoias, reproduce and carry on their kind of life?

The story of sex and reproduction is one of the most singularly fascinating and marvelous aspects of the entire study of life's varied organisms.

Did Sex Evolve?

Nature's showcase of reproduction includes myriad ways and methods of producing successors to each generation. Among lower animals and plants, reproduction may be accomplished without eggs and sperm.

Ferns shed millions of microscopic spores which grow into new plants when they settle into a suitable environment. Flower bulbs bud off new bulbs on the side, giving rise to a new generation of flowers. Jellyfish, sea anemones, marine worms, and other creatures of the sea bud off parts of the body giving rise to populations of new, identical individuals.

Single celled plants and animals, such as the paramecium, reproduce by the single process of cell division, giving rise to enormous populations of mostly identical descendants.

However, nonsexual forms of reproduction result in offspring which are genetically identical with the parent. The descendants possess the identical traits for better or worse. Evolutionists claim that such methods of reproduction, if universal, would greatly slow down the process of natural selection and evolution.

Enter sex.

Sexual reproduction not only provides for offspring, but gives rise to populations which are, we are told, more adaptable, because the offspring are more varied in their genetic make up. Offspring resulting from sexual reproduction have two parents and thus are seldom exact replicas of either. Thus increased variability is introduced into the species by means of sexual reproduction.

Sex, and sexuality, then, provides a greater base upon which evolution through natural selection can take place. If every generation of living things were identical to the parent, then it can easily be seen how this fact would effectively halt evolution in its tracks before it even got started! Sexual reproduction, then, provides for greater variety in offspring, depending upon the genetic traits of the parents. Variation and individual inherited differences, however, are still obviously a long, long way from evolutionary progress in the real sense of the term.

The Origin of Sex

The origin of sex has mystified and baffled men for many generations. Just what is this thing we call sex? As any happily married couple knows, whatever it is, it is certainly one of the most intimate, romantic, enjoyable aspects of life! One of the highlights of life is when a man and woman become married and set out upon their "honeymoon." The honeymoon, with all its promise of romance, intimacy, sexual fulfillment, union, and love, is the beginning of a new life for a couple. Sex helps bind a man and woman together in mutual attraction, affection, and love.

But why sex?

How did it all come about? Is there a significant difference between human sexuality and that of other forms of life on the earth?

Sex is vital for evolutionary theory. Says the *Encyclopedia Britannica:*

> The first business of reproduction is to produce perfect copies of the parental organism, without any mistakes. The second is to introduce novelties; i.e., new models that make possible other life styles. Extreme conservatism, in either sexual or nonsexual reproduction, may be disastrous to the species in the long run. Extreme variability may also be detrimental, resulting in the production of too high a percentage of misfits. A delicate balance has to be struck. Variability is necessary but must be kept within bounds. *Sex is responsible for controlled diversity, without which adaptation and evolution could not take place.*[1]

How is sexual reproduction important to evolutionary theory? First, it permits the process of natural selection to work upon a population. As an environment changes, some of the offspring may become more adaptable and suitable for the new environment than others with different characteristics or strengths.

Secondly, variability also serves to correct abnormalities which may sooner or later appear. During nonsexual reproduction of single-celled organisms, as virtually identical individuals are built up over the generations, sooner or later more abnormalities appear and a general waning of vigour ensues. But when such organisms subsequently fuse in pairs, similar to sexual reproduction, a rejuvenation and revival of healthy strains follows.

Sexually reproducing populations, George Gaylord Simpson points out, are the commonest recent organisms, and almost universal among fossil representatives. "When change to asexual reproduction has occurred," he adds, "which is common only among plants, this has usually led into an evolutionary blind alley . . ."[2]

How does natural selection work upon sexual reproduction? The basic idea is simple: Some organisms have more offspring than others, which in turn grow up and produce still greater numbers of offspring. If these individuals differ genetically from less successful individuals, their genetic characteristics will become more frequent in the genetic pool. "Evolution will therefore occur, and it will be nonrandom, antichance, oriented in the direction of more successful reproduction,"[3] says Simpson.

Obviously, one cannot argue with this point. He is right. But this type of "evolution" or change is not, strictly speaking, evolution in the full-blown sense of the word. No one maintains that such relatively small changes or evolution cannot take place. There are differences between the horses extant in the world today and their ancient forebears. But the point is, of course, they are still horses, not some entirely novel creature!

But now let's get to the root of the problem. Individuals produced by the union of male and female gametes, or sex cells, display characteristics from both parents, and the combinations in a large population provide new variations in great numbers. Asexual reproduction provides no such variety. But nevertheless, the new variations are still discrete members of the same type of plant or animal population!

But let's get to the real issue: Sex. If sexuality is really such a key to evolutionary progress, then evolutionists should be able to explain all about how and when sexuality arose in geologic time. What can they tell us about it?

Strangely, evolutionists must admit ignorance on this question. William Stokes hazards a guess: "Sexual reproduction . . . probably appeared rather early in the history of life," he suggests, but then goes on to other matters.[4]

The *Britannica* tells us: "When did it all begin? The generally accepted answer is that the fundamental, or molecular, basis of sexuality is an ancient evolutionary development that goes back almost to the beginning of life on earth, several billion years ago, for it is evident among the vast world of single-celled organisms, including bacteria."[5]

Under certain conditions, says this authority, even single-celled bacteria which normally reproduce by cell division will come together and fuse in pairs, a form of sexual behavior comparable to the fusion of an egg and a sperm. In such cases, a combined cell is produced in which nuclear exchange or recombination of nuclear material has occurred.

Paramecium, for example, may reproduce almost indefinitely by ordinary cell division. But when two populations of paramecium are mixed together, mating usually occurs immediately between individuals from the two different populations.

The *Britannica* points out that all degrees of difference between male and female sex cells can be found in nature and says, "It is probable that the basic and characteristic distinction between the sex cells of both animal and plant life in general was established very early in the course of evolution, during the immense period of time when virtually all living organisms consisted of single cells."[6]

Thus evolution pushes the emergence of sex cells in all their diversity and glory back to the primordial world when supposedly only single cells existed on the earth–geologically back in the Pre-Cambrian world of which virtually nothing is really known biologically. Pushing the origin of sexuality back into the dimmest recesses of the past, of course, means that evolutionary scientists do not feel so obligated to explain how such sexual differentiation occurred–or even why early single celled plants and animals began to reproduce by sexual means! The question of how and why sexual reproduction arose is thus neatly sidestepped.

Joe, The Discoverer of Sex

But the enigmatic questions remain. If single celled organisms were capable of reproducing indefinitely by asexual behavior, then why did they "learn" to reproduce by sexual methods? If they were successful with asexual reproduction, what was the purpose of "learning to reproduce sexually?"

The question, of course, goes unanswered.

Let's speculate for a moment, and think back to that ancient seashore when a lonely Paramecium, whom we will call Joe, was swaying with the tide in a small pool. Joe, a rather intelligent Paramecium for his kind, knew that for millions of years, perhaps, his kind had always reproduced by cell division. But somehow Joe couldn't manage to split. He had groaned and grunted and struggled and squirmed, but he couldn't split. Maybe it was his mental attitude, or perhaps he was impotent. As far as Joe was concerned, if that was all there was to life, then he would just as soon end it all. Joe, the paramecium, was frustrated. What to do? In his deepest misery, he didn't notice when Jimmy, his friend, sashayed by.

"Hello, Joe," Jimmy said, "What's bothering you? You look down in the dumps."

"I'm impotent," Joe sighed with great overwhelming grief. "It's no use, Jimmy. I can't reproduce. Life is worthless to me."

"Is there anything I can do to help?" Jimmy emoted.

"No. I've tried everything—from positive thinking to aerobics. Nothing seems to help."

"How about a change of pace, then? There's a new paramecium colony that just moved into the neighborhood. Maybe if you met one of them, it would take your mind off your troubles."

Joe had nothing better to do, so he went along with the idea. The two paramecium swam a short ways, and then Joe was suddenly astonished. Before his very eyes was the cutest, most voluptuous paramecium he had ever seen!

Breathless, Joe asked: "What's your name?"

The cute little paramecium fluttered her flagella, and cooed, "Shari. I'm from across the pond. We've lived there for generations and generations, but the last storm blew us over here to your neighborhood." She fluttered her long flagella again, and Joe was entranced. Never had he seen such a sensual, pulchritudinous paramecium. Joe felt suddenly dizzy, and swooned. He had a strong case of lovesick blues, but since he had never been in love before, he didn't know what the malady was. Nor did he know what to do about it.

Shari was attracted to the new friend, and when he swooned, she became alarmed. "Are you all right?" she asked, reaching out to help him.

Accidentally, they touched.

"Do that again," Joe whispered.

"What?"

"What you just did. Touch me." Shari touched him. Before he knew what he was doing, Joe and Shari were in a deep embrace. Several minutes later, about twenty to be accurate, Shari gave birth to a new little paramecium baby. Joe was ecstatic with joy. He was a father! He had discovered a new way to reproduce!

Naturally, Joe taught his newly discovered knowledge about sex to Joseph, Junior, and that's how sex education began, back in the warm sunlit ponds of the primeval world.

This story, of course, is pure fabrication—fanciful and without any foundation in fact. It does not explain how "Shari" became female and Joe became male in the first place. The truth of the matter is that evolutionists cannot explain how sexuality came into existence, or why asexual creatures suddenly developed a curiosity about sexuality.

Nor can evolutionists explain how or why sexual apparatus evolved from such primitive beginnings. The little paramecium didn't need sexual organs—they were only one-celled creatures, anyway.

But once multicellular creatures come on the scene, how did they know they needed sexual apparatus if they had never seen any? How did they evolve sexual organs when they had never even been aware that such things were missing?

And how did these early creatures ever decide who was going to be the male, and who would be the female?

How did the first so-called females learn to create egg cells that needed to be fertilized by the male sperm cells? And how did the early males invent sperm cells?

Was it all accidental? Like two cars colliding in the night? Was it sheer blind luck?

Reproductive Anatomy

Consider for a moment the impasse at which evolution has arrived: The first multicelled creature that intended to reproduce sexually, instead of asexually, had an enormously complicated problem to work out. First, he had to find a willing "female" partner. Then he had to combine the elements of wizardry, genius, chemistry, engineering, physics together and produce a *perfect* sperm cell, or millions of them—otherwise the exploratory sexual reproduction attempts would have ended in failure, and he would have perished from the earth! Likewise, that first female had to be a brilliant chemist, gynecologist and obstetrician all in one. She had to create the world's first perfect egg, complete with all its parts, the perfect complement for the first male sperm cell.

But that is not all. Both male and female had to invent and install within themselves a reproductory system—the male needed testes and gonads and accessory structures built within his body, and the female needed ovaries, tubes, and whatever was necessary for shedding the eggs and nurturing the developing young.

It was all very complicated, to be sure, and not even the best human biologists can fully explain the sexual function of plants and animals, today.

But if the most brilliant scientists, trained representatives of earth's highest form of life, cannot fully understand it, then how did that primitive first male and female not only fathom the mystery, but also successfully create the world's first sexual apparatus in themselves?

How indeed!

The origin of sex is a mystery that I suggest can never be adequately explained in purely evolutionary terms!

The Fascinating Mystery of Sex

Mating is vital for reproduction of many creatures. How is it achieved? Mating and fertilization must take place at the right time for spawning.

Fish eggs are fertilized as, or shortly after, they are shed by the female. Mating generally involved no more than a coming together of the male and female, side by side, so that simultaneous shedding of sperm and eggs can be accomplished.

Consider the male stickleback. At mating time the sides of the male stickleback turn transparent with glowing red, its back becomes an iridescent blue-green, and its eyes glow a brilliant emerald green.

There then follows a passionate dance of life or death, leading to mating or a battle. Fighting stickleback recognize the sex of a member of their species by seeing how it responds to the ritualized movements of the dance.

After the dance, in which every luminous color of the fins is brought into play, the female folds her fins and the love ceremony begins. The male has dug a nest in the bottom, and escorts his new "bride" toward the nest. The male always exhibits his broadside to his partner, but the female remains at right angles to him. Keeping her head always turned toward him, she follows him, and he swims around and around her, in ever narrowing circles until their bodies touch.

Then quickly the male slings his body around the female, gently turning her on her back, and quivering, both fulfill the drama of sexual reproduction, discharging into the water ova and semen simultaneously.

Releasing the female, the male glides downward and gathers the transparent eggs in his mouth, and blows them into the nest he has prepared. There the eggs float, coated with his spittle.

Consider this ritual of courtship and mating and sexual reproduction. Evolutionists will blandly say that it is a marvel of nature's ability of adaptation. But such tautalogical reasoning explains nothing. Here we see a glorious pattern of courtship and romance, most of it totally unnecessary if the sole purpose of the ritual was merely the need to reproduce. Why go into the whole elaborate ceremony? The specifics of the courtship and mating ceremony of the stickleback defy evolutionary explanation.

Helix pomatia is a species of snail, about three inches in length. This interesting creature falls in love twice a year, in spring and fall.

At that time his antennae reach out, probe the air, and then he moves out at high speed to find the object of his amour. During the courtship, which may last for hours, the two snails first bite each other, and then prod around the side of the neck where the genital opening is located. The two snails—each of them actually hermaphrodites, possessing male and female organs—then unite at the neck and one becomes pregnant.

About twelve days after mating, the pregnant snail digs a hole about three inches deep at the base of a tree or near grass roots to insure food supply for the young. During the next 12 hours it drops perhaps 26 tiny eggs, one at a time, into the nest, and then covers up the hole and leaves the eggs.

Another sexual adventurer is the squid. This extraordinary creature sometimes "courts" the female or fights with other males for her favor. Sometimes, however, he merely seizes her abruptly in a multiple-armed embrace. Ludicrous as it sounds, sometimes he absent-mindedly forgets what he is up to, and has his companion for dinner!

The sex organs of male and female squids are hidden down inside the cavity of the mantle. During the sex act, the male squid reaches into his mantle cavity with one of his tentacles, takes a few packets of sperm and places them in the mantle cavity of the female. The packets unravel and the sperm are released and fertilize the eggs of the female as they pass to the outside.

The female then blows the fertilized eggs through her siphon, catches them in her arms, presses them against underwater objects in 12 inch strings and leaves them. About a month later the rainbow hued babies are hatched, anywhere from a few hundred to 30,000 at one time.

Angler fish have a system all their own to reproduce themselves. These small creatures cruise around at great depths and are most unlikely to meet a member of the opposite sex when the female happens to be ready to shed her eggs. How does the male angler solve this perplexing problem?

This unique creature has a solution to the dilemma. Whenever any small, young male happens to meet a large female, he immediately fastens on to her head or sides by his jaws and from that moment he lives a totally parasitic existence, sustained by the juices of the female's body. Thus whenever the female is ready to spawn, sperm become available to fertilize the eggs.

The angler fish—with built in fishing pole and flesh "bait"—waits for unsuspecting prey to come along. The female angler also waits for a male angler, who, once he finds her, literally will "never let her go" as he attaches himself to her side for the rest of his life.

Mating of Birds

Birds are another fascinating study. Often a female may not be ready to mate, and stimulation in the form of dance or song may be required to create the appropriate mood. Bird wings are a poor substitute for arms in a sexual embrace, and therefore the fullest cooperation between males and females is necessary for success.

Most birds form a long-lasting bond between a male and female, which often lasts an entire lifetime. The bond is reinforced by ritual behavior during the onset of each breeding season and other occasions when they have been separated for a period of time.

This presents a problem in various gull colonies, where one bird looks pretty much identical to another, at least to us humans. But gull partners in mating are able to tell each other from the hordes of other gulls by various posturings, and many small idiosyncrasies of action that add up to individuality, distinguishing each bird's mate from all the others in the colony.

Penguins, however, seem to have trouble even distinguishing between the sexes. How to tell a boy from a girl penguin! They cannot dance or sing, so male penguins use this trick: They offer a pebble to a prospective female. If she accepts it as a contribution to building her nest, the courtship is on.

The paradise widow bird, tangerine breast aglow, embarks on his courtship ritual by the craziest stunt. Black tail dangling like a fan, he stamps a ring into a patch of grass by bouncing up and down in gigantic 50 or 60 foot leaps into the air. In the center of this ring, sitting demurely, is his beloved, goading her swain on to more herculean efforts.

The courtship dances and songs of male birds lead to the production of an egg by the female of the species. Each egg, a complex and intricate object, with layers of yolk, albumen, membrane and shell, is generally triggered and falls into the oviduct when the male begins his courtship. The pheasant jabs at the earth and fans his tail; the blue bird of paradise hangs upside down and shakes his iridescent feathers; the *Loddigesia* hummingbird male spins his long twin tails like an eggbeater, drumming the tails and wings in rhythm in his courting dance; a common nuthatch selects choice sunflower seeds and presents them to his female, and if she is still unwon, he shucks them for her; the lapwing waves his wings; cranes dance, and the woodcock spirals into the sky, air whistles through his outer primary feathers creating his love call, before fluttering to the ground. Whatever the means, these rituals of courtship lead to romance and offspring. How can blind evolution explain these dazzling, humorous, bizzare antics of courtship?

Insects and Other Creatures

Consider the courtship of the firefly. On any warm, humid evening, from June through August, as evening approaches, the male wakes up from his daytime nap, spreads his gossamer wings, and whirs off to find a female, his body tilted at a 45 degree angle.

The common eastern United States firefly flips on his light toward the end of a steep dip and keeps it burning while he pulls out of the dive and climbs upward.

The earthbound female, watching this fiery pyrotechnical display, can tell a firefly of her own species by the length of his flashes of light. When she spots the flash she is waiting for, she sends out a reciprocal blink. The male's recognition of the signal of a female depends on how long after his own flash the answering blink comes.

Curiously, the pattern of flashing of fireflies is as fixed and definite as is the song of different birds. This unique creature turns 92 to 100 percent of his lantern energy into visible light, whereas an ordinary lightbulb burns with about 10 percent efficiency.

How can evolution explain this marvelous sexual adaptation? How in the world did two ancient flies dissatisfied with their previous mode of courtship, decide to evolve the ability to light up at night, and incorporate two chemicals, luciferin, and luciferase, into their body? How did they develop the ability to utilize ATP—adenosine triphosphate—in order to renew their light again and again? How did they learn to switch the light on and off and on and off again? Many mysteries remain to be answered about the courtship ritual of the typical firefly!

But perhaps one of the most peculiar courtship rituals involves that of the spider called the tarantula. Every advance toward a female spider is fraught with peril. Therefore male spiders make love alone, to a web, before handing their cells of life to a female.

The male tarantula spins a sheet in which there are two holes, a large and small one. A narrow band of strong silk is left between the holes. As he steps through the large hole, hanging below, strengthening its edges, he releases a drop of sperm fluid. Crawling back to the top, he draws the fluid into bulbs near his head to be handed to his mate. Then he destroys the web and enters the perilous portion of his journey.

The female is almost always larger and not ready to receive the gift of the sperm fluid. She charges at him, threatens him, and sometimes eats him! Cautiously, the male tarantula approaches his mate, leaping sideways to avoid her hostile thrust. Jumping aside, he pets her, and when she opens her fangs to bite and poison him, he quickly grabs her fangs with hooks on his front legs, hangs onto them, and deposits the sperm in a pocket in her abdomen. Having finished the dangerous task, he can now leave safely.*

Other male spiders use different techniques to subdue the females. The crab spider ties his mate down with strong threads, crisscrosses her body with threads, and virtually stakes her body to the ground.

The Amazing Moose

When breeding season comes, the male moose is quite a spectacle. As the almost two month rutting season starts, the

---

*Another incredible example of reproduction in nature is the praying mantis. The male cannot copulate unless the female first bites off his head to disinhibit him.

bull moose, with swollen neck, bloodshot eyes, short temper, becomes a brute with one purpose in mind. Bellowing, grunting, mooing his lovesick desires, his voice rising and ending in a cacaphonous siren, the roused bull moose is no beast to tangle with.

When an interested cow moose responds in shrill moos and bawling, the courtship begins and lasts for ten days. Usually a male moose will mate with four cows before the end of October. By the end of the rutting season, he is gaunt from lack of food, and worn out from his strenuous sexual activity. The moose's antlers, which begin growth in April, are bone hard by August and smooth and powerful by the time rutting season begins, now become a useless appendage and are discarded in December.

The bull moose's love call isn't likely to be attractive to anything except a cow moose! But here again we have a spectacle of sexual ritualism that defies evolutionary explanation. But the sexual saga of the bull moose does shed light on the fascinating nature of the Creator God who, with a tremendous sense of humor, created the moose's sexual antics.

The Giant Sequoia

The largest of all living things is the giant sequoia which grows in the Sierra Nevada's western slopes in northern California. The largest living sequoia is the General Sherman tree, 272 feet high, with a base circumference of 102 feet. Sixteen feet above the ground it is still 24 feet in diameter.

These huge trees sometimes live for 30 centuries. A giant sequoia does not put out its first flowers for about 200 years after it sprouts up. A single tree, however, will bear when in full vigor millions of male and female conelets from November to late February.

The seed that grows into this giant living thing is so small that 3000 of them would equal one ounce. There may be as many as 300 seeds to one conelet, and the cone itself is only about the size of a large leathery button.

The seeds are food for squirrels and blue jays, and perhaps

only about 15 percent of them have the vitality to sprout. Of a million seeds cast off in autumn, perhaps only one will eventually sprout and take root when late spring snow waters and sun quicken its dormant vital forces.

The huge sequoia, with its unique life span, and its tiny seeds—can evolutionary theory explain how it stumbled upon its particular method of reproduction? The mystery of the big trees remains unsolved.

The Flowers and the Bees

Nature's miracles and mysteries are far from being solved by evolutionary science. No evolutionist, in studying the reproduction of flowers, has been able to explain how primordial flowers learned to lure insects with the promise of nectar, a sugary sap that is irresistible to them. Nor can the evolutionist explain why or how nature saw to it that the insects will tread precisely the right places in each flower to reach the pollinating stamen.

Many flower petals have nectar guides—white or yellow streaks, or bright dots—that come together at the entrance to the nectar repository. The tiger lily, for example, has red glands that merge as nectar guides and which glisten deceptively, as though coated with drops of nectar.

Insects, to impregnate the stigma with pollen from another flower, must slide their proboscis in at precisely the right angle; the curve of the insect's stomach or back must be just right to pick up or leave pollen. Yet everything is accomplished with precision.

How did red clover, the lady's slipper, the great blue lobelia, and hosts of other flowers, ever learn to attract bees and insects of various kinds to serve as vehicles for cross-pollination? How did the insects learn how to recognize all the flowers' signals and signs? Why are the insects just the right size to accomplish this feat of legerdemain?

How can this be explained except by the marvelous ingenuity of the Creator God?

The Incredible Bee

We've seen the flower's side of the pollination story. But what about the bee's side? The study of a beehive brings us to some of the most remarkable evidence for a Creator God.

Honeybees belong to the order Hymenoptera. They are social insects noted for providing their nests with large amounts of honey. A colony of honeybees is now recognized by scientists to be a highly complex cluster of individuals which function as a single organism.

The queen bee is a fertilized female capable of laying a thousand or more eggs per day. Besides the queen, a beehive consists from a few to 30,000 sexually undeveloped females, the worker bees; and up to 1,000 male bees, or drones.

When a bee colony becomes too crowded and there are not enough cells where the queen can lay large numbers of eggs, worker bees select a dozen or so tiny larvae which would normally become worker bees, and feed them copiously with royal jelly, something like mayonnaise, produced in the heads of the worker bees. At that point, the mother queen, and a portion of the workers, depart from the colony in a swarm, searching for a new homesite. The first of the new virgin queens to emerge immediately attempts to kill the others. If two or more emerge at the same time, they fight to the death.

A week later, the surviving queen soars off on her mating flight, and frequently mates with more than one drone. After two or three such days, the repetitions of the mating flight, the queen settles down to laying eggs and rarely ever leaves the hive again. Enough sperm from the mating flights are stored in her sperm pouch to fertilize all the eggs she will lay for the rest of her life. In the act of mating, by the way, the drones give their lives. The only duty of the drones is to mate with the queen.

The ovary of the queen bee is composed of several hundred ovarioles, each of which contains about 60 eggs and nutrition cells. The sperm which enter the queen's sperm pouch, called the spermatheca, can remain alive there for several years. When an egg passes down the oviduct, emerging sperm may or may not fertilize it, depending on the discretion of the queen. If the female relaxes a muscular ring around the sperm duct, allowing sperm to pass through, then the eggs become fertilized and result in females. Unfertilized eggs result in males or drones.

Honeybee reproduction is also remarkable because of pronounced differences that exist between male and female members of the colony. Female bees are sensitive to yellow, blue-green, blue and ultraviolet light, important in locating flowers. Drones are blind to yellow, and the yellow color of many flowers is of no significance to them since they cannot feed themselves. But they are sensitive to ultraviolet light; sunlight, which contains much ultraviolet light, is vital in orienting the drones during the mating flight.

The members of a bee colony are completely dependent on each other. The colony is a family community of which each insect is an integral part. Away from the community, or cut off from it, a bee cannot function properly or survive for long.

Perhaps the most remarkable demonstration of communication in insects is the so-called dance of the honeybee. After a worker bee discovers a new source of food, she returns to the colony and notifies the other bees about the new source by means of various dancelike bodily movements. The liveliness and duration of the dance movements of the bee tell about the quality and quantity of the food source, and its location is indicated by the rhythm of the dance and the orientation of the axis of the bee's tail in respect to gravity. A "round" dance indicates the food source is near, whereas a "tail-wagging" dance means it is more than 260 feet away.

Many entomologists now consider the beehive as a single organism composed of many parts. When it is mature, it gives birth to new swarms, or infants, and can repair itself when plundered or wounded.

In a beehive, when necessary, the sterile can lay eggs; the senile can rejuvenate glands that have atrophied. In Russia, Mrs. L.I. Perepelova removed the queen bee, larvae and eggs from the hive, and watched. She observed that after several hours one of the attendant bees lifted her antennae and began to circle, exchanged food with a nearby wax maker, and the wax maker drummed her wings. The whole cluster seemed to moan and suffer, and the entire group of bees began to throb as if stricken by a fever. Then, several weeks later, the "impossible" happened—a few "sterile" worker bees began to lay eggs! Nurses gathered around and fed them bee milk, and slowly, laboriously, the workers produced eggs, six to eight a day, compared to a queen's usual 2000 to 3000.

In Yugoslavia, Mrs. Vasilja Moskovljevic put 503 old forager bees, with dried up bee milk glands, on an isolated brood comb with the queen. Would the hatched larvae die, since they had no nursing bees to provide bee milk? Days passed and nothing happened. And then Mrs. Moskovljevic spotted a forager leaning into a cell, and saw a drop of bee milk. Where did it come from? She placed the forager's glands under a microscope and looked, and the old dried glands were swollen and filled with bee milk! A miracle had occurred!

The remarkable bee is another proof of the existence of a great Creator God who fashioned the first bee hive, and provided the unique instructions for bee reproduction. Evolutionary theory cannot explain or account for the peculiar ritual of bee reproduction, or the ability of worker bees to provide milk or lay eggs.

What intelligence tells bees that a hive is in danger? What intelligence informs them that more bee milk is needed? Or that a new queen is needed? Or that worker bees must begin to lay eggs? What intelligence informs a queen bee which eggs should be fertilized to become worker bees, nurses, guards, foragers, receivers?

The humming, buzzing bee hive swarms all over the immobile, helpless theory of evolution, and visits sting after sting upon its angry, flushed countenance. But evolutionists, unlike the brown bear or grizzly, don't seem to know when to leave the scene of the conflict, before being stung into ignominy!

Human Sexuality

The marvels and mysteries of reproduction in the plant and animal worlds astound the human imagination. They cannot be adequately explained except in terms of creation and teleological design. The gratuitous attempts of evolutionary theory to explain sexuality among living organisms amounts to nothing more than pure speculation and guess work.

But what about human sexuality? In comparison with the sexual activity of other primates, the human being is unquestionably unique. Consider: Hardly any of the monkeys and apes develop a prolonged pair-bond relationship, which characterizes human marriage. In the primates, pre-copulatory sex play is brief or nonexistent. In baboons, the time taken from mounting to ejaculation is seven or eight seconds, no more. Furthermore, in the females there is nothing which could be called an orgasm.

The female monkey or ape is sexually receptive to the male only a week or so in a monthly cycle. In lower animals, sexual receptivity is even more limited.

Mankind, however, is unique. Men and women in good health are sexually capable at many times. Once a female monkey or ape becomes pregnant, or is nursing a baby, she is not sexually active. But among men and women sex is possible during most of pregnancy, and throughout the nursing period, within six weeks or so of childbirth itself. Why does this difference exist?

Evolution, frankly, cannot explain it satisfactorily. But the answer is revealed in the Scriptures. It is simple. Sex, between man and wife, is a holy, wonderful, God-ordained activity which is meant to bind a marriage together in intimate love. Its purpose is far more than mere procreation and reproduction, as in animals. Its purpose is to cement the family relationship, and unite a husband and wife in continuing, steadily increasing love and devotion to each other.

For the animal and plant world, sex is merely a means to an end—and the end is survival of the species.

But for mankind, sex has a definite and noble purpose. It was meant by the Creator to be thoroughly enjoyed. It was designed to be fun! God intended for a husband and wife to love each other deeply and passionately, and to cling to each other, and sexuality is the most intimate form this love can take in physical expression.

In the beginning of man's creation, we read in the Biblical record: "Therefore a man leaves his father and his mother and cleaves to his wife, and they become one flesh" (Genesis 2:24). This is the purpose God had in creating human sexuality, and this is why he made us significantly different from lower animals and primates. God intends us to use this gift, and to use it rightly, wisely, in the way that will increase matrimonial love and unity.

When we look at the history of sex, and the striking examples of sexuality in nature, and then look at the wonderful pinnacle of human sexuality in marriage, how can we not see the loving hand of the Creator behind it all?

God created sex. And everything he created was good! He who cannot see the omnipotent hand of God in the design and articulation of sexual patterns of all living things should check his eyeglasses and see if some fallacious assumptions haven't come between him and reality.

Which came first—the honey bee or the flower with its pollen? Evolutionists are hard pressed to answer *that* one! Because both are absolutely vital for the existence of the other.

Chapter Six

Master Architects of the Animal World

There are many instances in the world of nature when the marvels of animal instinct and the inventiveness among insects, birds and mammals actually make human beings look relatively inept, and behind-the-times.

Long before human technicians ever dreamed of such things, creatures of the animal world perfected fishing nets, underwater diving bells, overhanging roofs, built-in air conditioning systems, highways, central cities with satellite suburbs, hinged doors, cells with waterproof lining, and temperature-controlled dwellings.

The precision of the architectural and building skill of animals makes biologists and human engineers pause with admiration. Animal architectural ability frequently surpasses that of human architects, when size and utility are taken into consideration.

Who are some of these avian architects and master carpenters and craftsmen of the animal world? How did they develop their specialized abilities? Can animal architecture's surprising feats be adequately explained in terms of evolutionary theory?

The Mysterious Animal World

The most massive structures built by either animal or man are not the Great Pyramids of Egypt, or the skyscrapers of New York City.

They are the limestone edifices constructed over millions of years by coral polyps of the warm oceans. The coral polyp secretes a calcareous substance from its bottom surface in a delicately ribbed pattern. Forming large colonies of tightly compacted individuals, corals may grow several centimeters in a year and develop into huge constructions with millions of individuals, though the individual animals usually measure less than one centimeter in diameter.

Growing, multiplying constantly, living in the shallow depths of warm seas, requiring a water temperature of at least 20 degrees Centigrade (68 degrees F.), reef-forming species of coral may follow the coastline of a major continent, such as the Great Barrier Reef of Australia, extending for thousands of miles.

Such reefs sometimes extend to depths of 4–6,000 meters into the frigid depths, although growth only occurs to depths of forty to fifty meters as coral polyps need light to nourish algae that live inside their cells.

Coral reefs near the Bahamas have been growing since Cretaceous times, for an estimated 80 million years. These massive reefs are monuments to the architectural skill of tiny creatures hardly bigger than a pinhead which cannot see, hear, or move about!

These little creatures, building on top of previous generations, have contributed to the creation of a beautiful submerged world, providing a habitat for thousands of fish and other assorted marine creatures.

Coral polyps, of course, build their homes–lofty mansions of the seas–without benefit of architectural blueprints, plans, or "building codes." Somehow they just seem to know how to do their job, through innate drives and instinct.

The Spider's Web–Sheer Gossamer Delight

Spiders are the strangest creatures. Each one carries about its own private silk factory fitting inside its abdomen, consisting of six pairs of silken thread producing glands, each gland connected to structures called "spinnerets" at the rear of the abdomen.

Though all six glands secrete silk, a protein substance, the threads produced by each gland have a different consistency and purpose.

To catch flies and other insects, the spider's web must be sticky, but the spider itself must not get caught in the web. This problem is solved through the use of more than one kind of thread to build the web—dry threads, which the spider herself moves on, gripping them firmly by her legs which have little claws and bristles, and the sticky spiral threads covered by a substance secreted by her glue glands.

When a fly strikes her web, the spider can quickly tell where the victim hit by means of the vibrations of the thread. Vibrations betray the location of the prey as well as its presence. The tension of the spokes of the net inform the spider of the size of the prey.

How does a spider fashion her gossamer web? To do so she becomes an aerial rope artist, much akin to a mountain climber scaling sheer granite walls of towering crags. But she carries all her mountain climbing gear, and "ropes," within her own body! With considerable agility and skill, she forms a bridge composed of silken thread from one solid object to another. She quickly adds fresh threads, creating an outer frame, the future hub of the orb, and spokes. Finally the sticky insect-trapping threads are laid down.

Amazingly, the twenty thousand known species of spider each construct different kinds of web. One, the water spider *Argyroneta aquatica*, found in ponds over Europe and Asia, lives its entire life underwater but is actually an air-breathing animal. It carries its own supply of air about underneath the water by creating an underwater air-filled balloon, or "diving bell." The balloon is attached to aquatic plants and submerged branches by a network of threads. Once the net is in place, the water spider traps air bubbles at the surface by crossing her hind legs over her abdomen, and carries each bubble down to her nest, releasing it under the web, eventually filling a hemispherical diving bell of about two centimeters in diameter.

Thus *Argyroneta aquatica* discovered the secret of the "diving bell" aeons before mankind developed the same type of engineering ability in order to explore the depths of the seas and to search for sunken treasure.

The Incredible Termites—
Masters at Civil Engineering

The examples of master builders in nature are everywhere, from the lowly ant to the bee colony, but perhaps the most awesome creature of all is the little termite.

More than two thousand species of termites live in tropical and subtropical regions, belonging to the order of Isoptera, considered to be one of the oldest and most primitive groups of insects.

The building achievements of termites are unique. Termite colonies may have over ten million individual inhabitants, larger than the largest ant colonies. Yet termites have tender skin and can thrive only with warmth and high humidity. They are blind or have very rudimentary eyes and dwell in darkness.

The colony begins when a male and female, after a whirlwind courtship of 20 minutes to two days, construct a hidden chamber, reach sexual maturity, and enter their new abode as king and queen. At first they tend their new brood, but soon the royal pair is waited on hand and foot by their progeny and devote themselves entirely to the job of reproduction.

In some species the queen's abdomen becomes enormously enlarged, perhaps fourteen centimeters long and three and a half centimeters wide. She lays 30,000 eggs in a day.

As the colony grows, so must the termites' living quarters. Termite nests may be gigantic structures rising over twenty two feet in the air with numerous subterranean passages leading into the surrounding area where workers collect seeds, leaves and other food. Because they require humid and warm living conditions, termite hills are covered with a compact layer of building material which serves as a shell of reinforced concrete and helps regulate the interior climate. The interior of the colony reveals the central royal cell and surrounding nursery chambers, a group of storage chambers containing leaf particles, and other chambers where the mycelium of a mushroom is cultivated on a leaf compost or wood particles.

One species living in tropical rain forests even puts a series of roofs with overhanging eaves on their towering temple-like mounds, making them look like escaped denizens of Walt Disney's *Fantasia*.

How do termites achieve their spectacular results? How does each termite know the proper orientation of the colony, or a new "street" or chamber? Scientists believe that they are guided in some mysterious way by the lines of the magnetic field. How they respond to this field is not known, however.

One of the most astounding marvels of a termite dwelling, even more than the evidence of a definite building plan with systematic layout of chambers, the fungus gardens, and the network of communications, is their unparallelled air conditioning system.

When a termite mound reaches a height of 12 feet, containing over two million termites, it is like a miniscule New York. All inhabitants must eat, live, work, rest, breathe. Their oxygen consumption is considerable, and without adequate ventilation they would all suffocate within twelve hours! How is their metropolis ventilated?

There are no windows. No oxygen tanks. But according to Professor Martin Luscher, between the nest proper and the hard outer wall, there are narrow air spaces, and below it there is a "cellar." Another air space above the central nest reaches down into the nest proper, like a chimney. "Channels as thick as an arm radiate from the upper air space into the ridges, where they divide into many small ducts. These come together again to form channels as wide as the first leading into the cellar. . . . The ventilation system of the termitary is completely automatic," says Dr. Karl von Frisch.[1]

Another problem termites face is water. As any human city needs an adequate water supply, so do termite mounds. Relative humidity is 89 to 99 percent, and much water is needed to keep it that high. Also, water is needed for consumption, mortar and other purposes. Some desert termites have been found that drive bore holes down to water at a depth of forty meters, or 130 feet! Says von Frisch: "The construction of such deep shafts through loose soil is a truly prodigious feat of civil engineering for these small animals."[2]

Waste disposal is a paramount problem in any city of considerable size, as we can all appreciate who live in the city. How do termites dispose of excreta?

They found a simple, practical solution long before human engineers grappled with the problem. They learned to "recycle" garbage, and many species actually use their feces to build their own homes, shocking as it may sound. The *Apicotermes* fashion their homes in this manner, converting their feces into a work of art, using it as building bricks. Other species merely use their excreta as a binder for soil pellets, grains of sand and wood particles.

Another "first" for the termite colony is the technology of papermaking. Termites use paper pulp, composed of masticated wood mixed with saliva or excrement to build the outer walls of their dwellings, and for the construction of their living, breeding and storage chambers, including the royal cell.

The amazing termite is truly one of the creatures of nature which evolutionary theory hasn't even begun to explain. How can it?

This little creature, working harmoniously, with total coordination, also builds ingenious roads and galleries, sometimes paving the roadways with soil particles moistened with saliva. Some species using hardened drops of excrement as paving stones.

Says Karl von Frisch:

> But the major problems of termite architecture concern the marvelous structure of their mounds, and so far very little has been discovered about the way these are built.[3]

He adds:

> If we imagined for a moment that termites were as tall as human beings, their tallest hillocks, enlarged on the same scale, would be nearly a mile high, four times the height of New York's Empire State Building. How can a planned construction of such mighty buildings be brought about? Or the ingenious ventilation systems? Or the meticulously modeled exterior skin of the small nest of *Apicotermes*

with its ventilation slits and the spiral staircase inside it? *Where is the architect?*[4]

A provocative question! Where indeed is the Architect? Who imparted to these little creatures the remarkable skills which they possess? Did blind random evolution do the trick? Was it an accidental development over millions of years?

Says von Frisch:

> And yet their finished structures seem evidence of a MASTER PLAN which controls the activities of the builders and is based on the requirements of the community. *How this can come to pass within the enormous complex of millions of blind workers is something we do not know.* One can try circumlocution with learned words, but I think it is better to say, quite simply, we do not understand. Here, as so often in the science of life, the investigating human spirit *must bow before the unknown.*[5]

The Brush Turkey

Another impressive mound builder is the brush turkey of the forests of eastern Australia. Over several weeks, *Alectura lathami*, his scientific name, gathers rain-soaked leaves, branches, twigs, throwing it with his feet into a pile behind him. When the structure is 4–5 feet high and 9–12 feet in diameter, and the temperature inside it becomes a constant 35 degrees Centigrade (95 degrees F.)—the cock checks the interior temperature of the mound almost daily—he calls the hen who then lays her first egg in a deep hollow scratched into the heap.

After all the eggs are laid within a few weeks, the cock continues managing his incubator, testing and regulating its temperature, until all the eggs have hatched. Eventually, when the chicks work their way to the surface, it is ironic that the cock doesn't even seem to recognize his own offspring! It's as if he really didn't know what he was doing all this time, preparing for their safe arrival into the world!

The mallee bird, or towan, is another species of megapode ("large-footed" birds) and is called the "thermometer bird" because it spends ten to eleven months of each year regulating the temperature of its nest. This is almost a year around occupation and requires constant vigilance on the part of *Leipoa ocellata* since the daily and seasonal fluctuations of temperature in the arid region of central Australia, where it lives, are very great. Hard work is required.

The mallee bird begins nest building in April and digs a pit about a yard deep, filling it with vegetation and sand. The compost below starts fermenting, and four months later the desired constant temperature of 34 degrees Centigrade (93.2 degrees F.) is reached.

The incubation period of the new chicks is another six to seven months. To keep the temperature of the incubator just right, the adult birds check it almost daily, eliminating excess heat in spring by making ventilation shafts, or adding sand to the mound to lessen solar radiation in summer, and dismantling the dome in the autumn. The thermometer bird thus keeps the temperature within one degree of 34 degrees Centigrade!

Here obviously is another puzzle for evolutionary theory to account for. How such an incredibly delicate incubation system could have developed by blind chance stretches human credulity to the breaking point!

Bird's Nests and Woodpecker's

The variety of birds, and the variety of their nests and building materials, is in itself a very extensive and complex field for study and observation.

Spiders' silk, feathers, hair, straw, leaves, twigs, clay, mud, fibers, string, excrement, straw—each is used by various species of birds, and each species builds its own nest according to rules and hereditary laws laid down long, long ago.

Nests vary from the eagle's eyrie to the spherical nest of the leaf warbler, from the cup-shaped, highly dense nest of the hummingbird, built to preserve heat, to the hanging nest of the penduline titmouse with its lateral entrance hole.

Other birds prefer to nest in holes in trees, such as the woodpecker. The woodpecker is specially equipped for boring holes in trees and woodworking and carpentry, because he has strong claws and stiff tail feathers, enabling him to move up and down a tree trunk with ease, and because his beak is unusually strong. With it he can chisel his own breeding cavity in wood as hard as that of a sound beech tree. His beak not only chisels the wood, but also removes wood chips. The bones in a woodpecker's skull are specially constructed so that the constant pounding and hammering with his beak cannot injure his brain.

We could elaborate on the story of the woodpecker, and its fascinating physiognomy, its powerful beak and long, barbed, harpoon-like tongue, and ask how evolutionary theory could account for such specialized instruments by "random mutation." But it is enough to say that "woody woodpecker" poses another dilemma for the evolutionist. With his special beak, the woodpecker rains a barrage of stinging hammerlike blows to evolutionary theory, giving evolutionists one of their most agonizing headaches in years.

Dam Builder Par Excellence

Among the most impressive wonders built by man are the huge hydroelectric dams such as Grand Coulee on the Columbia River in the state of Washington.

But did you know that the busy little beaver built dams which are far more ecological, beneficial to nature, and in the long run, perhaps far more useful, than the mighty monuments built by man himself?

Beavers are the original experts in the art of hydroengineering and performed tremendous feats in this area long before man built his first crude dam.

Each beaver dam varies in accordance with local conditions. Ramming strong sticks into the bottom of a stream or river bed, pushing twigs into the interstices, adding larger sticks and branches, crosspieces and heavy stones, and covering the edifice with mud and clay in order to make it watertight, beavers have constructed dams 400 feet long, four feet high, forming a sizeable lake behind them. They have built dams of several hundred yards length in the Mississippi basin. Perhaps the largest ever built is one on the Jefferson River in Montana. It is over 2,000 feet long and can bear the weight of a rider on horseback.

Such dams require teamwork in construction as well as building skill. Beaver families work together efficiently. With chisel sharp incisors, they are able to chop down sizeable trees, and then drag them in extraction lanes to the water. When the ground is level, they have been known to dig canals to the lake, sufficiently deep to transport their timber.

The beaver's lodge, or dwelling, with all its entrances underwater, and a feeding chamber close by, is usually surrounded by water.

"Young beavers," says Karl von Frisch, "reared in captivity, which have never seen a beaver pond, have been observed felling trees in their compound as if they had been taught their job by experienced beaver craftsmen. They also erected a typical lodge from branches and stones and whatever finer materials they could find, and built a perfect, watertight dam in moving water, without mistakes or false starts."[6]

How did beavers develop this instinct for dam-building? How did it become "automatic" to them? How was it ingrained upon their brains?

Three hundred years ago there were an estimated 60 million beavers in the United States. Their dams were very effective in reducing flooding due to spring runoffs. Thanks to the beaver, and their building habits, our farmlands are richer and more productive. Ecologists believe beaver dams are responsible for some of our richest and best farmland. One ecologist who has studied beaver history in Vermont attributes the decline of agriculture and the mounting flood toll in that state to the absense of the beaver.[7]

This 40-pound little member of the rodent family carves toothpicks out of evolutionary theory!

Architects and Builders

In this chapter we have examined some of the marvels and mysteries of animal architecture and engineering. We have seen that the animal world developed amazing inventions which anticipated human engineering feats by aeons of time.

We have seen the beauties of the coral reef; the gossamer

The busy little beaver, weighing about 60 pounds, with his sharp incisors fells trees like a lumberjack (above) and constructs masterfully engineered dams. The original hydro-engineer, the beaver plays a vital role in ecology.—*Ewing Galloway photos.*

delights of the spider's web; the incredible complexity of the home of the termites, with remarkable ventilation systems, roadways, storage chambers, fungus gardens, water wells.

As human beings, we tend to be proud of the accomplishments of our inventors–the architectural triumphs and engineering feats which attest to the intelligence and creativity of man.

But isn't it time we took a humble bow before the even more remarkable engineering achievements attained by the insects, birds and mammals that inhabit the world alongside us?

Minute workers, cooperating in the construction of harmonious dwellings inhabited by millions of minute denizens–all without the benefit of blueprints, plans, and without any directions from an architect.

How do they do it?

When he beholds the marvels of animal architecture, Karl von Frische declares:

> There are biologists who are convinced that they, or future generations of scientists will ultimately find the key to life in all its manifestations, if only research perseveres. They are to be pitied. For they have never experienced that sense of profound awe in the face of the workings of nature, some of which will forever elude comprehension, even by the mind of man.[9]

Even so, evolutionists who cannot see the masterful hand of the Creator, in the sublime and awesome profundities of nature, are truly to be pitied. For they, too, have never experienced the awe and rapture of those who know that there is a Power greater than man who designed the marvels and mysteries of nature, in all their glory, splendor and majesty!

The craftsmanship, carpentry skill, engineering ability, the architectural exploits and innovations, which resound in the animal world, are merely reflections of the Supreme Architect and Master Craftsman and Super Builder of the entire cosmos!

Chapter Seven

The Mystery of Adaptation

Evolutionists, like their Creationist counterparts, unite in wonder at the marvelous works of nature. But adaptation, itself, is one of the greatest mysteries of all!

Just what is adaptation? Answers the *Encyclopedia Britannica:*

> In biology, a process by which an animal or plant becomes fitted to its environment; it is the result of natural selection acting upon hereditable variation. Even the simpler organisms must be adapted in a great variety of ways: in their structure, physiology, and genetics; in their locomotion or dispersal, means of defense and attack; in their reproduction and development; and in other respects.
>
> Accurate adaptations may involve migration to, or survival in, favourable conditions of, for example, temperature. Alternatively, organisms may manufacture their own environment, as do the mammals, for example, which are precisely adjusted to their optimum temperature. To be useful, adaptations must often occur simultaneously in a number of different parts of the body.[1]

Some of the unique and peculiar adaptations in nature include animal coloration, Amazonian forest arboreal animals, Antarctic lichen adaptations, amphibian leg bones and locomotion, animal communication modes, bivalve foot structure, camel feeding behavior, hummingbird feeding behavior, salmon spawning patterns, structural yielding for diving in seals, whale feeding habits and digestion, disease and host-parasite relationships, ruminants' digestive mechanism, insect pollination, mimicry, changes in eye position, seed dispersal, etc., etc.

If adaptation is a law of nature, then it is strange that so many animals have features that seem to be poorly adapted to their environment! For example, the enormous antlers of the Irish elk, and the ponderous tusks of the mammoth, had many disadvantages. These animals are extinct, but scientists are uncertain as to the exact cause of their demise.

The curious talent of some creatures to camouflage themselves in the face of danger is also difficult to explain by natural selection. Evolutionists are hard put to explain why the well camouflaged grasshopper betrays his location by chirping. Some of their explanations for adaptation border on the ridiculous.

One theory was put forth by George Gamow and Martynas Ycas, who wrote in 1968: "Some of the reptiles in the colder regions began to develop a method of keeping their bodies warm. Their heat output increased when it was cold and their heat loss was cut down when scales became smaller and more pointed, and evolved into fur. Sweating was also an adaptation to regulate the body temperature, a device to cool the body when necessary by evaporation of water. But incidentally the young of these reptiles began to lick the sweat of the mother for nourishment. Certain sweat glands began to secrete a richer and richer secretion, which eventually became milk. Thus the young of these early mammals had a better start in life."[2]

Can you imagine such immense changes that would be required genetically, physiologically, anatomically, biochemically and etbiologically to turn a sweat gland into a mammary gland, and get the young to use it instinctively? Marsupial babies at birth actually have to crawl up the mother's abdomen, find and attach themselves to the nipple (or was it a sweat gland?) in her pouch *all by themselves* in order to survive!

What are some of the striking marvels of adaptation which evolution is hard put to attempt to explain?

Take the camel. The Arabian camel has one hump, the Bactrian camel has two. The wide-spreading soft feet of the camel are well adapted for walking upon sand or snow. Horny pads that exist on the chest and knees of the camel support its weight when kneeling.

Camels can live on the coarsest and sparsest vegetation, eating thorny plants, twigs and dried grasses that other animals would refuse to consider.

Camels accumulate stores of fat in their humps, and when conditions are adverse they draw upon these for sustenance and for the manufacture of water by the oxidation of the fat. They do not actually store water in so-called water cells. Because of their peculiar adaptation, camels can go for 17 days without water and survive. But that is not all. In order to survive hostile deserts and bleak environments, camels have a double row of heavy protective eyelashes, haired ear openings, and the ability to close their nostrils and possess keen senses of sight and smell. Thus they can withstand raging windstorms blowing across the desert sands.

These remarkable adaptive features of the camel uniquely suit this creature for life in the deserts of the Middle East and Africa. But why did the first creatures, that supposedly evolved into camels, begin to change in a fashion that would equip them for this hostile environment? Why, indeed? But of course we are not supposed to ask evolutionists *why*—to them *why* is unscientific and meaningless! *Why* implies meaning and there is no real meaning to life according to evolutionists.

Adaptive Coloration

Coloration in animals serves many vital purposes. Coloration serves to draw the attention of other organisms, attracting animals such as insects that carry pollen to brightly colored flowers, or to repel animals. A tide pool blenny drives other fish from its territory by displaying its brightly colored chin. Coloration sometimes helps conceal the location or identity of an organism, often by providing an organism with color to appear like its general background. Cryptic coloration, or general background resemblance, is frequently employed by both predators and prey in order to avoid detection. Also, organisms may mimic specific objects in their environments and convey false information as to their identity.

Fish eggs and planktonic larval fishes that exist in the blue open sea are usually transparent and possess minimal pigmentation, thus reflecting their background in coloration. The plain pink eggs of the sand grouse are well concealed when they are laid on leaves of a similar shade of pink that have fallen from a particular species of tree. The parents consistently place the eggs on these leaves, thus providing for their protection.

Fishes are noted for their ability to match their background. The flatfishes, for example, have a remarkable ability to match the pattern of the surface on which they are resting. Others, such as the mosquito fish, show long-term changes in coloration according to the darkness of their environment, in order to avoid being eaten by predators.

Other creatures, such as the decorator crabs, use portions of algae and sponges and place them on the upper shell to cover their own coloration.

Interestingly, camouflaged organisms must also "track" or adjust to any changes in the coloration or appearance of their model. For instance, the chameleon must change from a brown to green background as it moves from a brown to a green environment.

Coloration is a fascinating subject and plants and animals have used it intensively for purposes of concealment, attraction, advertising their presence, repulsion, courtship, warning, or combinations of these.

Evolutionists have been hard pressed to explain the how and why of coloration, how particular species "came up with" a particular type or use of coloration, and "why" they developed the particular type of coloration in the first place. It is one of the ongoing mysteries of evolutionary theory! But the variations can logically be explained from the viewpoint of a Creator putting them all together in a balanced and interrelated global ecosystem.

The Amazing Seal

Consider, for a moment, the incredible seal which we have all seen perform at such places as Marineland and Sea World.

Acrobatic, highly intelligent mammals, the seal was especially designed for life in the water. The seal's body is streamlined, allowing the seal to pass through the water with the least amount of friction. External ears are reduced in size or absent, aiding in streamlining the creature. The flattened head is an advantage during diving. The muscled but flexible neck allows the animal to capture its prey in water with great ease, as well as toss basketballs through a hoop to entertain crowds of spectators.

The eyes of the seal, large, located forward and close together, can accommodate rapidly when the animals move from dim to bright light, and the ears and nostrils can be closed while diving. All in all the seal is efficiently designed for propulsion through the water, and submarine designers have taken tips from the streamlined smoothness of the seal in designing the most modern nuclear submarines.

The skin of the seal is tough and thick, and its blubber layer provides a source of energy when needed for lactation or when fasting. It also provides the animal with greater bouyancy and insulates the body so that it remains at a nearly constant temperature.

Seals are air breathers. Therefore they must carry as much oxygen as possible when diving. They can do this by increasing the volume of blood and decreasing their metabolism. In the elephant seal, the heart rate decreases from about 85 beats per minute when on the surface to about 12 beats per minute during a dive. The drop in heartbeat conserves the oxygen in terms of the amount being carried in the bloodstream.

Most dives last less than 15 minutes and are deep vertical dives. Since there is no exchange of gases with the environment while submerged, seals are adapted to carrying increased amounts of carbon dioxide when diving.

Seals are also specially designed to withstand enormous pressures when diving. Weddell's seal, for example, can dive as deep as 1,100 feet–more than four times as deep as a man in a diving suit. One Weddell's seal dove for 43 minutes and 20 seconds, and an elderly bull reached a depth of 2,000 feet.

How can the amazing seal accomplish these feats of unbelievable skill and ability? "Exactly how these animals can accomplish such feats is unknown,"[3] admits the *Britannica*. Part of the answer is revealed in the unique structures in the body of the seal, built to yield to such pressures, rather than resist them. But how these marvelous structures slowly evolved over millions of years—that, too, remains an unsolved enigma to evolutionists who desperately wished they had the answer!

The Creationist, of course, is faced with no such problem. He recognizes God as the omniscient, omnipotent Creator who designed the marvelous aptitudes and structures within the seal. These wonders bespeak the glory and majesty of the Creator who fashioned them. This answer may not satisfy an evolutionist who demands to know *how* the structures were "created"—but that is his problem.

Fish Migration

Another peculiar adaptation found in nature is the homing instinct found in trout and salmon. Homing to the site of birth for reproduction appears to be a universal trait among the Salmonidae. Life cycles may vary greatly among closely related species or even between populations of the same species! For example, some rainbow trout go to sea and return as large silvery steelhead trout. A single stream may contain rainbow trout that mature, spawn and complete a life cycle within 300 feet of the site of their birth, as well as anadromous steelhead rainbow that migrate to the ocean on a two to three year journey spanning several thousand miles before returning to the place of their nativity.

One species of freshwater fish reverses the cycle, however. This particular species spawns in a marine environment and the young migrate to fresh water to mature.

What is the secret of the migrating fish's homing instinct? Says the *Britannica*, in the 1974 edition: "It is now generally accepted that the sense of smell plays the major role in guiding an anadromous trout or salmon to its precise natal stream once it enters a river drainage from the ocean. How it finds the mouth of the river system leading to the natal stream from the open ocean is not yet understood; celestial navigation and detection of fields of gravity by some unknown means have been hypothesized."[4]

In sum, the process is "not yet understood." The same source goes on to point out the amazing fact that cutthroat trout in Yellowstone Lake, Wyoming, have been found to be able to return to their spawning stream after experimental blocking of the senses of smell and sight!

Evolutionary adaptation and natural selection have never been able to explain this mysterious homing ability. Given enough time and money, they may hope someday to do better. But as of the present, explanations are woefully short of the mark. How much more sensible it is to recognize in these marvels of nature the handiwork of the Creator God!

Miracles of the Ocean

The Great Barrier Reef, a vast coral arm lying off the shore of northeastern Australia, 1250 miles long and covering 80,000 square miles, is nature's wonderland. The reef itself, created inch by painstaking inch by coral polyps, teems with swimming, crawling, floating creatures, from tiny fire-fish to giant clams more than four feet across.

The creatures that built the reef are hardly bigger than the head of a pin—billions of them. With a mouth, tentacles, and inside cavity, the polyp's tissues harbor thousands of algae which multiply the polyp's oxygen supply in exchange for room and board.

Among the reef's inhabitants is the fearsome stonefish, about one foot long, shaped something like a squashed brown triple decker ice cream scoop. This scabby, wartlike, bristly creature, with razor sharp spines down its back, each one connected to two poison sacs, is the nemesis of all reef waders.

Also living in the reef is the 18-inch porcupine-toady; when calm, it resembles a sole, but when alarmed it turns into a dark-green balloon, bristling with venomous cactus spikes. And another denizen of the reef is the little anglerfish, casting a line in front of its mouth—a miniature fishing pole, no less—with a hunk of flesh resembling raw meat at the far end.

Found in many parts of the ocean, *Physalia physalis*—the deadly Portuguese man-of-war—is one of the sea's least understood creatures. Ranging from the Caribbean to Nova Scotia, and into the Mediterranean, and a smaller cousin cruising from California to Australia, this iridescent blue and purple ocean-going blob, shimmering like a dazzling parachute, looks beautiful and innocent enough from the surface. But trailing the billowing jellylike mass that floats on the surface is an array of excruciatingly poisonous tentacles studded with thousands of stinging cells containing a venom almost as powerful as that of a cobra. These dangling streamers slowly twist and reach a depth of 60 feet below the surface, searching for prey.

The man-of-war's venom is a neurotoxin—a protein material that attacks the nervous system. The man-of-war's sting means sudden death to the small fish that become ensnared by its tentacles, has sent bathers to the hospital suffering from horrible agony, and has killed others.

This fascinating creature's tentacles, once they capture food, contract and "reel in" the prize as a fisherman reels in his line. The paralyzed food is digested by hundreds of red, orange and pink gastrozooids, or feeding polyps, acting like a community stomach.

How does the man-of-war attract prey? As the tentacles of the floating creature sway and heave up and down in the surging sea, a small bright, blue and silver striped fish, the *Nomeus*, darts in and out among them, completely at home. The *Nomeus*, or man-of-war fish, grabs pieces of fish and crustacea from the tentacles, eating them, and sometimes leaves the protective environment of the tentacles, swimming in larger and larger circles, attracting larger fish. When a bigger fish sees *Nomeus*, and attempts to make a meal of it, the tiny fish darts back into the haven of *Physalia's* tentacles, which look like a field of seaweed to the hungry intruder. The pursuing fish is caught off guard, stung by the tentacles, and becomes a meal itself in the game of hunt and be hunted.

How did the man-of-war and tiny *Nomeus* develop this fascinating symbiotic relationship? At first scientists thought the little fish was simply too quick to be caught in the tentacles of its deadly companion. But Dr. Charles E. Lanex, marine-biology professor at the University of Miami's Institute of Marine Science has proved otherwise. He and his colleagues determined how much toxin was needed to kill fish the size of *Nomeus* and then gave *Nomeus* ten times that amount. The fish swam away as if nothing had happened, immune to the neurotoxin.

The only natural enemy of the man-of-war appears to be the giant loggerhead turtle, weighing hundreds of pounds. This turtle can zap right through an entire fleet of men-of-war, snapping up and devouring their jellylike floating bodies, impervious to the stings of the tentacles.

The strange man-of-war, and its sidekick, *Nomeus*, have achieved a miraculous type of adaptation. But how was it done? Evolutionary theory must admit ignorance. How this symbiotic relationship ever got started and when are unanswered questions which evolutionists have hardly even begun to think about!

Bird Migration

Another of nature's amazing marvels of adaptation is that of bird migration. In autumn, the tiny blackpoll warbler flies from its nest in Canada to Brazil, a distance of 4000 miles. The golden plover wings almost 8000 miles from the edge of the Arctic Ocean to far-off Argentina. The champion migrant of them all, the Arctic tern, spends the summer in the Arctic regions and spends winter in Antarctica—making a round trip of roughly 22,000 miles!

How do they do it? That is the mystery that baffles the world's top naturalists. How can the Arctic tern leave its nest at the age of six weeks, navigate accurately and find its way to Antarctica, 11,000 miles away, and then find its way back home next summer? We don't fully know.

How do birds steer, at day and night? What provides their unerring sense of direction for thousands of miles? How did the first bird that began to migrate, possibly millions of years ago, we are told, develop the skills to accomplish it, since none of his

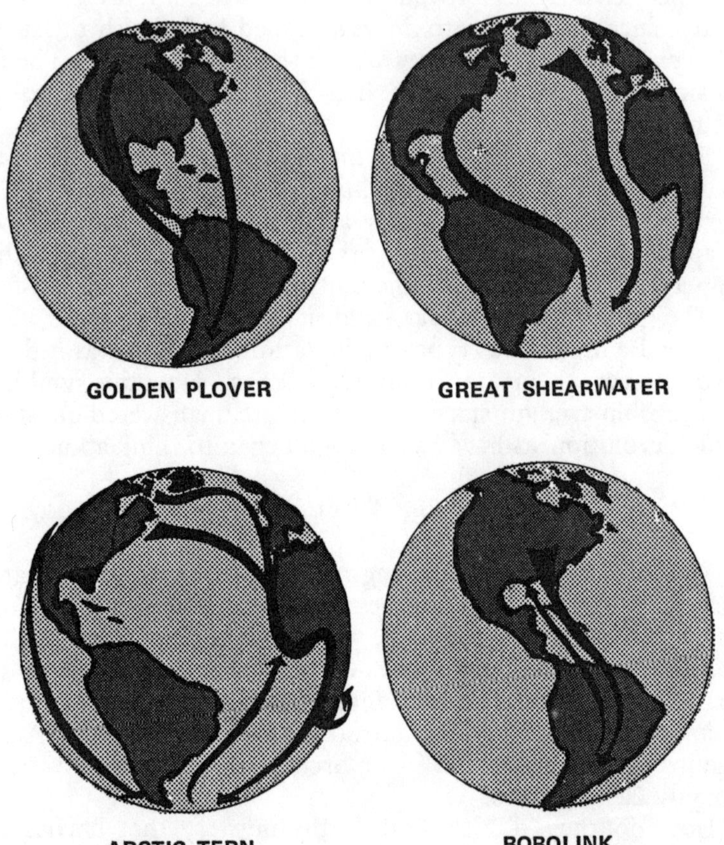
GOLDEN PLOVER
GREAT SHEARWATER
ARCTIC TERN
BOBOLINK

THE MARVEL OF MIGRATION

Above are four examples illustrating the marvel of migration. The Golden Plover makes an 8,000-mile trip entirely on its own. The Great Shearwater commutes from the tiny island of Tristan da Cunha to the North Atlantic — and back to this tiny dot of land. The Bobolink is the top migrator among land birds, averaging 7,000 miles in its jaunt from Canada to Argentina. The Arctic Tern is the champion long-distance migrator — which has been known to travel 14,000 miles.

Animals and their travels form one of the great wonders of our earth. Scientists know that eels, elephants, bats, turtles, plankton, whales — among many others — migrate in some form.

Locusts migrate sporadically. Every few years lemmings migrate. Horseshoe crabs migrate periodically into shore. Even ladybird beetles migrate. Monarch butterflies migrate hundreds of miles — south in the fall, north in the spring. Adult eels swim downstream. King Salmon may migrate 1000 miles up the Columbia River. Toads and frogs hop their way around the world. Big turtles migrate hundreds of miles through the ocean.

But the best-known migrators are birds. Ornithologists still must speak of the "mystery of migration." It has been estimated that about one third of all bird species migrate. In the diagrams above are the routes of four of them. Below are listed twelve more migrators.

Bird	*Migration Path*	*Distance in Miles*
KIRTLAND WARBLER	MICHIGAN, U.S.A. — BAHAMA ISLANDS	1200
BLUE GEESE	NORTHEASTERN CANADA — LOUISIANA, U.S.A.	1700
LESSER YELLOWLEGS	MASSACHUSETTS, U.S.A. — MARTINIQUE, W. INDIES	1900
SHINING CUCKOO	NEW ZEALAND — SOLOMON ISLANDS	2000
SEMI-PALMATED SANDPIPER	MASSACHUSETTS, U.S.A. — VENEZUELA	2400
BLUE-WINGED TEAL	QUEBEC, CANADA — GUYANA	3300
MANX SHEARWATER	VENICE, ITALY — WALES, ENGLAND (BY WATER)	3700
BLACKPOLL WARBLER	CANADA — BRAZIL	4000
BRISTLE-THIGHED CURLEW	TAHITI — CENTRAL ALASKA	5500
WHITE STORK	GERMANY — SOUTH AFRICA	8000
BARN SWALLOW	NORTHERN CANADA — NORTH CENTRAL ARGENTINA	9000
WILSON'S PETREL	ANTARCTICA — NORTH ATLANTIC	9000

predecessors had such ability? Where did the first Arctic tern find a compass and road map to fly thousands of miles and back again to the exact same spot?

The German ornithologist Gustave Kramer determined that birds oriented themselves according to the patterns of the sky. When the sky was darkened, they lost all sense of direction. He then rigged up a light to imitate the sun, and had it rise and set in the wrong location. This caused the birds to orient themselves according to the course of the fake sunlight.

Naturalists now think that birds can calculate geography from the slant of the sun, despite the complexity involved since the sun changes its position with the time of the day and the time of the year, as well as with a bird's change in location on the earth. Thus birds must also have a delicate sense of time.

Biologist G.V.T. Matthews of England showed mathematically how much calculation was involved for birds to guide their flight by the sun, since their point of reference must continually shift. It was incredible! Wrote Max Eastman of the feat: "His demonstrations involve so much mathematical calculation that you would think only an IBM machine on wings could get anywhere with such a shifting point of reference. Nevertheless he is convinced the migrating and homing birds are equipped by instinct for such a feat."[5]

Thus far nobody had been able to explain how birds also navigate by night. However, E.G.F. Sauer of the University of Freiburg, Germany, took up the gauntlet. He studied tiny warblers that fly long distances, mainly during the night. He placed a group of warblers where they could only see the starry heavens, and each took up a position pointing in the direction of its migration. Dr. Sauer was thorough. He even placed the warblers under the dome of a planetarium, with an artificial replica of the night sky, and again, they took up the proper orientation for their migration. When he rotated the planetarium sky, putting the stars in a false position, the warblers were fooled and oriented themselves according to the position of the stars in the apparent night sky.

Dr. Sauer is amazed at the little garden warbler which weighs less than an ounce, but which can wing its way, all alone, from Germany to Africa.

How can such elaborate instincts be inherited? It is, as of the present moment, still an unfathomed mystery. Consider for a moment: Tiny birds, with their very tiny brains, learned to navigate the far flung reaches of the earth long before man was able to do so with compass and sextant. Birds—by pure inherited instinct—have the ability of a giant computer to sort out navigational mathematics, make rapid calculations subconsciously, and correct any navigational errors, winging their way across thousands of miles of trackless ocean, by night and by day, in fair weather and in foul. How did they come by that incredible instinct? How was such a complex and intricate ability "slowly evolved" by blind evolutionary progress? How indeed! The marvel of bird migration leaves evolutionary theory lost, dazed, befuddled, without a sense of either direction or time!

Adaptation Reflects Purpose

A telescope, a microscope, a camera, whether it is a specialized television camera or a polaroid, all are inventions of men that reflect a human purpose. Each of these tools is comparable to the human eye, in that they aid our ability to see. They were obviously designed with a purpose in mind by a creator—in this case, man himself, a teleological being.

A telephone, radio, or phonograph, is in a sense an extension of the human ear and permits us to hear things we would ordinarily be incapable of hearing. They were invented by man's genius to serve a purpose.

If we compare these human inventions with the human ear itself, or the human eye, how can we escape the fact that these, too, are goal oriented, purposeful inventions of an Almighty Creator who designed them and gave them to us?

An eye, an ear, a hand, each is a complex tool serving a particular function. They were made for a purpose. But evolutionists refuse to admit that such is the case.

The Mystery of Adaptation

George Gaylord Simpson, a leading evolutionist, says in his

book *This View of Life*, "Adaptation and the apparent purposefulness of evolution are basic problems that a successful theory *must* solve." He goes on to claim that natural selection, operating on the basic building blocks provided by mutations, paves the way for such evolutionary progress. Natural selection weeds out the undesirable, disadvantageous mutations and genetic combinations and multiplies those that are advantageous in existing circumstances.

The main elements of evolution, Simpson tells us, are the genetic systems within organisms, composed of discrete genes and chromosomes, which are shuffled and combined in various ways by the sexual processes in most organisms. Mutations introduce wholly new variations which are then fed into the recombination process.

Interbreeding animal populations have genetic pools, which include all the genetic units distributed throughout the interbreeding population. Recombinations of existing genes, however, does not foster evolution. Such recombinations only distribute genetic characteristics among the basic population which are already in existence in the group. How then is the genetic pool changed in order to foster evolution?

Mutation, says Simpson, *fluctuation* in genetic frequencies, inflow of genes from other populations, and differential reproduction are the factors contributing to evolution. The first three of these however are essentially random occurrences and are not oriented toward adaptation of an organism. They are usually inadaptive.

Differential reproduction however is the key to the process, according to Simpson. By this term he refers to consistent production of more offspring, on an average, by individuals with particular genetic characteristics than by others without said characteristics. This is what is called natural selection and leads to nonrandom adaptation of an organism.

Having claimed that this is the essential key that unlocks the mystery of evolution, Simpson then admits: "The theory just outlined obviously does not yet answer all questions or plumb all mysteries, even when the details here omitted are taken into consideration. *It casts no light on the ultimate mystery—the origin of the universe and the source of the laws or physical properties of matter, energy, space and time.*

"Nevertheless, *once those properties are given*, the theory demonstrates that the whole evolution of life could well have ensued. . . ."

Simpson then boldly adds: "There is no need, at least, to postulate any non-natural or metaphysical intervention in the course of evolution."[6]

First, notice how the basic issue of origins is nicely skirted in this passage. The question of ultimate Creation, then, Simpson avoids, calling it the "ultimate mystery." Throughout this book, however, we face that issue, and show that logic impels us to the conclusion that the only rational explanation for the origin of the universe, the laws and physical properties of matter, energy, space and time is God.

But what about the second part of Simpson's statement? Once these properties are given, does the theory of natural selection demonstrate that the whole of life could have ensued as a natural consequence of those primordial properties and successive configurations of the cosmos?

Can natural selection really explain the amazing examples of adaptation we see around us in the animal world?

Teleology in Nature

According to evolutionary theory, anything in nature that looks purposeful, predetermined is actually an illusion. There is no plan or purpose in nature. They admit, as Darwin concluded, that all dominant forms of life tend to become adapted to many and highly diversified places in the realm of nature. Simpson says there are beyond any doubt directional forces in evolution, trends and common tendencies. Evolution is regulated by forces that change continuously in intensity, direction and combination, producing different results in different instances. But, he says, these forces are interwoven with historical processes and are subject to historical causation—they are not absolute or unchanging or metaphysically predetermined. Thus there is no evidence, he is saying, that a God has predetermined the course of evolutionary change in life.

Looking at the fossil record, Simpson says that natural selection is entirely consistent with that record and therefore must be accepted. Natural selection is an interaction between an organism and its environment and thus obviously plays a role in the continuing change of organisms.

But such reasoning still misses the point. The question we must ask is: Can natural selection or evolution by random chance account for the amazing adaptations of creatures in the world today? Can natural selection account for certain brilliantly contrived features of plants and animals?

What about elements within living things which seem to serve a particular function? What about a bird's wings, a man's brain, the gills of a fish?

Fishes have gills in order to breathe in water; birds have wings in order to fly; men have brains in order to think and reason. That is obvious. That is teleology in nature—apparent purposefulness. But the real questions remain unanswered: Why did primordial creatures without wings develop wings since they didn't need them in order to survive? Why did ancient water-going creatures develop gills in order to breathe in the water? What need did they have for gills if they were adequately surviving without them? Why the mysterious change? Why didn't the first fish that randomly mutated gills drown because the gills had not been perfected yet? What was the pattern of the evolution of a gill—a brilliantly designed mechanism for breathing in water? Was the gill designed by a Supreme Architect? Or was it the product of time and chance and circumstance?

These questions seem almost childish in their simplicity. But they are basic, fundamental, crucial.

Evolutionists all know exceedingly well that no organism "evolves" a new organ because of "need." Evolution is basically nondeterministic, random, shaped only by time, chance, and random circumstance. Thus an animal that didn't have wings, but needed wings in order to survive, simply became extinct—perished.

How then can evolution really adequately explain such a thing as a bird's amazing beak, or feathers, or the hand of a man, all so wonderfully designed, clearly made for a purpose? When it comes to explaining any such remarkable adaptation, evolutionary theory flounders. The best answer, in each case, is a weak, timid, "We don't know *how* these organs were formed, neither do we know *why* they evolved, but since they exist, they must have evolved!"

When we study the amazing adaptations of living things on the earth, shouldn't we conclude logically that adaptation reflects the purpose of the Creator? These same points were carefully enunciated by Sir Charles Bell in his contribution to the *Bridgewater Treatises* published in 1833 to 1840. Bell asserted: "It must now be apparent that nothing less than the Power, which originally created, is equal to the effecting of those changes on animals, which are to adapt them to their conditions: that their organization is predetermined, and not consequent on the condition of the earth or the surrounding elements."[7]

Since Bell's time, of course, investigators have come to see that God built *within each Genesis kind an amazing ability to diversify and to adapt to environmental conditions*. Not every adaptation reflects an original Creation of God. Rather, the *inherent* capacity for multiple adaptations in a single species, which lies in the genes and chromosomes of the organism, is what reflects the creative genius of God. This point needs to be carefully understood.

Nevertheless, evolutionists even deny this explanation. Says Simpson of Bell's treatise, "But now that we know that evolution is a fact, we can no longer accept his simple solution of the problem of adaptation as reflecting the purpose of a Creator manifested in the separate creation of each species of animal or plant."

Simpson then makes the astonishing statement: *"Whether or not we can explain the evolution of adaptation has no necessary bearing on the truth of evolution."*[8]

Read that again. According to this evolutionist, it doesn't matter whether or not we can explain adaptation in terms of evolutionary theory, it is a fact nonetheless. He then refers ambiguously to other "proofs that have now accumulated, quite aside from attempted explanations of adaptation."[9]

But these so-called other "proofs," as this book shows, are just as nebulous, weak, and insufficient to prove evolution as the attempts to explain the process of adaptation itself!

Evolutionary theory, then, is left floundering aimlessly, helplessly, unable to adequately explain either the simplest adaptation or the most complex adaptation.

Despite this failure, we find that evolutionists are unwilling to accept the hypothesis of God, or a metaphysical explanation for Creation, and adaptation, because of a *prior* bias and antagonism toward the idea of a God ruling the universe.

Simpson goes so far as to state, "Of course, an explanation might be metaphysical and nevertheless true. It is, however, an obvious lesson from the history of scientific progress that in science *one should never accept a metaphysical explanation if a physical explanation is possible or, indeed, conceivable.*"[10]

How can highly intelligent men, supposedly logical and rational, virtually insist on seeking physical solutions to all problems, playing mathematical games of evolutionary dice, when the simplest, most elementary logical processes of the human mind should impel them to a conclusion that the multiplied miracles of adaptation demand the existence of a Supreme Designer and Architect who lovingly and studiously fashioned each one of the marvelous living kinds!

I took a day to search for
God,
And found Him not. But as I
trod
By rocky ledge, through
woods untamed,
Just where one scarlet lily
flamed,
I saw His foot print in the
sod.
Bliss Carman—*Vestigia*

Chapter Eight

Evolution Hopelessly Entangled in the Web of Life

All life on earth exists in what we call the "biosphere"—that portion of our planet containing the oceans, land and atmosphere where life can survive.

The word *biosphere* was coined by Lamarck in 1809 to denote the whole zone at the surface of the earth occupied by living things. In proportion to the planet as a whole, the biosphere is only a *thin film* covering the surface of the earth.

The biosphere is a marvelously intricate system that unites millions of varieties of plants, animals and micro-organisms. Influencing the biosphere are the annual seasons, the daily rotation of the earth, changes in the wind and weather, the earth's magnetism, the chemicals in the atmosphere, in the oceans, and in the land, as well as the shape of the land.

One cubic foot of seawater may contain as many as 12 million living unicellular plants called diatoms and dinoflagellates—often called phytoplankton, the "meadows" of the sea.

It was once believed no creatures could live below 1,800 feet of the ocean—because of the great pressures at that depth. However, studies have shown that animals can live at *any ocean depth* so long as the fluids inside and outside the body of the creature are at the same pressure. Explorers in bathyspheres have found animals at the greatest depths of the ocean, some seven miles down!

On land, the tropical rain forest is the richest and most diverse region of living creatures. No plant or tree is likely to be the same as its neighbors. In North Queensland, Australia, 141 different species were found among 1,261 trees counted on a little more than one acre. In a 6-square-mile district in the Panama Canal Zone, some 20,000 different species of insects were catalogued!

Can evolutionists account for the existence and survival of an estimated *three million* different species of plants and animals on the earth? Can evolution account for the tremendous array of life we see about us?

The Pyramid of Life

Write Lorus and Margery Milne, famed naturalists, "All nature is a web, each animal and plant a separate point where the strands come together. Pull at any individual, and the whole web is affected."[1]

All life on earth can also be arranged in the form of a great *pyramid.* At the bottom of this pyramid are algae, bacteria and protozoa. Feeding upon these are slightly larger creatures—shrimp, insects, minnows. Feeding upon them are larger creatures, such as birds, large fish, reptiles, amphibians, and mammals. Feeding upon them are still larger animals—large fish, sharks, predatory lions, cougars, etc. At the top of this vast, complex, interrelated pyramid stands man.

The great pyramid of life is intimately tied together in a vast complex system of interdependency. The whole pyramid is dependent on the supply of oxygen and carbon dioxide and nitrogen in the atmosphere, and upon water and a host of minerals upon the earth.

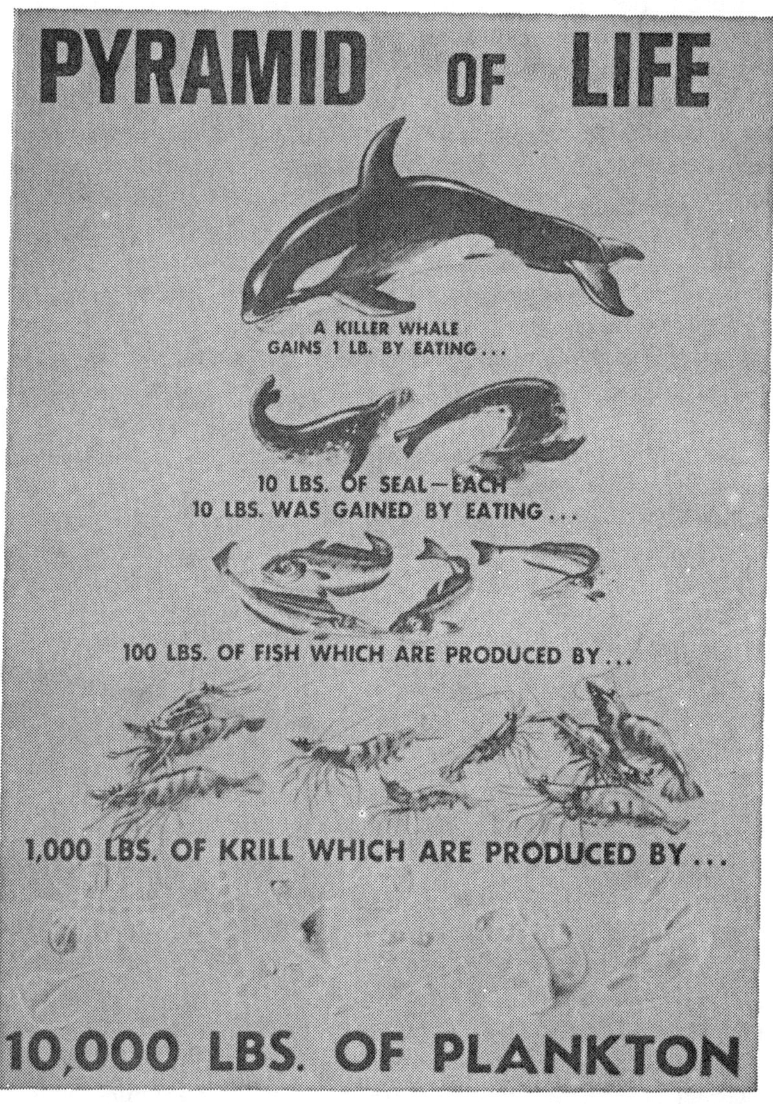

All life is interrelated as this sea life food chain illustrates. Can evolutionary theory account for this highly integrated and complex life interdependency?

Most people fail to realize how the air, water and land are delicately tied together in great natural cycles involving life itself—cycles which are largely caused by life, and upon which life itself depends! All nature is a vast network of interlocking parts which function together as a system to sustain all life! Some of the most important of these cycles are the carbon, oxygen and the nitrogen cycles.

Writes Gordon Rattray Taylor, "Interestingly, scientists are looking at the whole earth, with its land-masses, seas and atmosphere, as *a single system* in which energy and material are transferred from one part of the system to another at varying rates, which somehow balance out in the long run. The interesting thing is that they *balance out at a level at which life can exist.*

"It would not take very large shifts of any of the variables to make life as we know it impossible."[2]

For example, if the earth's atmosphere contained just five percent more oxygen, say scientists, the added oxygen would cause forest fires and prairie fires to rage. With the destruction of these natural habitats, many species of plant and animal life would perish.

What are some of these great natural cycles? How do they work? Why are they in *perfect balance* for the existence of life? Can the theory of evolution explain it?

The Carbon Cycle

Consider the carbon cycle. All plants and animals are interrelated in the carbon cycle. Plants extract from the air the carbon dioxide expired by animals. Plants produce carbon dioxide in their respiration also, but in relatively smaller amounts. The carbon dioxide absorbed by plants is used in synthesizing food. This process of photosynthesis produces two by-products, water and oxygen. Oxygen produced in this manner is used by all animals (except those few which liberate energy anaerobically), and also by plants, in the respiratory process by which they oxidize food substances to release energy required for living processes.[3]

How important is this carbon cycle? Says naturalist Peter Farb: "The carbon cycle is of *the utmost importance* because all of the carbon contained in the atmosphere, if not replenished by the cycle of matter, would be utterly exhausted in about fifteen years. A single large tree locks up in its massive structure the equivalent of carbon found in the total atmosphere over as much as twenty acres of the earth's surface. Were this carbon not returned to the soil . . . a forest might exhaust much of the earth's supply of carbon."[4]

If carbon were not replenished in the atmosphere and in the soil, where plants could absorb it into their tissues—if all the carbon became buried in rocks and mud—it would become unusable for life. Most plant life would ultimately perish. This, in turn, would result in nearly all animal life being destroyed!

Carbon dioxide is vital to life. Plants need to get it from the atmosphere in order to perform photosynthesis. Although erupting volcanoes give off some CO_2, most of that which is in the atmosphere was given off by animals in the process of respiration. Thus plants depend on animals for carbon dioxide, and animals depend on plants for oxygen. Here is another marvelous cycle. Fortunately for all of us, there is just the right amount of carbon dioxide in the air—for if there were too little, plants could not survive (and if they couldn't survive, neither could we!). But if there were too much, the excess carbon dioxide would absorb the redder wavelengths of the light from the sun, cutting off the supply of light and thus reducing photosynthesis in plants!

Since living tissue is largely composed of carbon molecules, it is plain how important the carbon cycle is to life. Did this complex, vital cycle in nature just "happen"? Did blind, dumb, inanimate matter just "stumble onto" this exceedingly intricate and vital relationship by some "lucky accident"?

The Oxygen Cycle

The only reason the world does not run out of oxygen is the fact that plants breathe in carbon dioxide, retain the carbon, but release the oxygen atoms back into the atmosphere. If we had no plants, life would eventually perish because the world would run out of usable oxygen.

Writes G.E. Hutchinson, "We know that the present supply of atmospheric oxygen is continually replenished by photosynthesis, and that if it were not, it would slowly be used up in the process of oxidation . . ."[5]

Some scientists have estimated that the oxygen supply of the earth would be used up in 2,000 years if it were not replenished by the photosynthesis of plants. Up to seventy percent of our oxygen is supplied by diatoms and other algae in the sea; the other thirty percent comes from land vegetation, mainly forests. Most of us take oxygen for granted. We forget that upsetting the oxygen balance could eventually mean disaster! But the really interesting thing is that oxygen—which is needed by life—is produced by life.

As one writer put it, "The extraordinary fact is, the earth supports life only because there is life there—or rather, it is life which supports life."[6]

Consider that remarkable fact! Were it not for the life that is on the earth, the earth could not support life. If plants did not produce oxygen in the atmosphere, there would eventually be none. The oxygen in the atmosphere would combine with other elements. Oxygen dependent animals would die. Plants, dependent on the carbon dioxide produced by those animals, would also die. Thus the existence of life depends on life.

If it takes life to support life, then how did life get here originally? Without God, it is an unanswerable paradox!

Since life could not exist if there were no life, how could it have evolved from the *not*-living? How can something come into existence if it requires its own prior existence to exist? It cannot.

In the Precambrian, the lowest strata showing evidence of life, we have evidence that the first life was algae and bacteria (probably anaerobes not needing oxygen). Animal life came later when the oxygen supply was increased. An evolutionist could point this out and say, "See, no need for God here." But wait.

An evolutionist could say all the other cycles developed with the ecosystem that evolved in response to the progressive development of life forms. Fine. But the point is, the workings of these cycles *all had to be planned in advance.* Such incredibly delicate and complex cycles would hardly be the product of accident. To believe they resulted by sheer chance is like believing all the delicate functioning parts of an industrial plant, with mining, manufacturing, merchandising, all happened by accident, with no forethought or planning.

The Nitrogen Cycle

Another important cycle in nature is the nitrogen cycle. Although we live in an ocean of air that is 78 percent nitrogen, and nitrogen is vital for life processes, that airborne nitrogen would be useless until it is incorporated into a chemical compound that can be utilized by plants and animals! Nitrogen is found in proteins, enzymes, hormones, vitamins and nucleic acids. But if free nitrogen in the air is useless to most plants and animals, how does it become a part of living tissue?

There exist a host of sea and land organisms which are able to "fix" atmospheric nitrogen—that is, incorporate it into usable chemical compounds for plants and animals. The largest natural source of "fixed" nitrogen are *terrestrial microorganisms.*

The nitrogen cycle is a fascinating one. Specialized bacteria actually extract the nitrogen from the air and convert it to nitrites, nitrates, and ammonia. They generally live on the roots of certain plants and make the nitrogen usable to the plants. Animals get their supply, obviously, by eating the plants, or eating other animals which have eaten the plants. The animals die, and decay, and return their nitrogen to the soil, making it available to other plants! Thus the cycle goes round and round. If one link in the cycle were missing, or broken, the whole chain of events would be disrupted. The result would be calamity!

The nitrogen cycle is a complex one. Amazingly, nitrogen-fixing bacteria can accomplish *at ordinary temperatures and pressures* what requires *hundreds* of degrees and *thousands* of pounds of pressure in a synthetic ammonia reactor! Precisely how this is accomplished is not yet known.

Microorganisms that can fix nitrogen include those that are "free living," and those associated with plants. It is an interesting relationship. John Storer explains it this way:

> One group of plants, the legumes—clovers, beans, locust trees, and other pod bearers—joins forces with bacteria to form a sort of *chemical laboratory* in the earth. . . . They (these legumes) offer a home in the soil to nitrogen-fixing bacteria which enter their roots and cause them to swell into lumps called nodules, where the bacteria live in *colonies* of many millions. Taking their energy from the sugar in the plant roots, the bacteria gather nitrogen from the air to form nitrogen compounds, which they store in the nodules.
>
> When the roots die, the nitrogen is left in the soil, and with this enrichment the plant community bursts into full life.[7]

The plants give nourishment to the bacteria, which in turn synthesize nitrogen from the air into compounds the plants need for growth. Both parties benefit from this partnership! However, the bacteria cannot establish itself on the plant's root unless the root secretes a substance at a certain state in its growth. But *why* does the root do that? Does it "know" the bacteria need a "home" specially prepared for them? Can evolutionists explain this amazing relationship on the basis of pure "chance"?

But there is even more to the story.

Other bacteria perform the role of "denitrification." They exist to return nitrogen to the atmosphere from the soil. Without them, most of the atmospheric nitrogen would become locked up in the ocean and in the earth and the nitrogen cycle would be broken. If nitrogen built up in the seas and rivers continually, blue-green algae would rule the seas, rivers and lakes, blossoming in wild abandon.

As such blooms of algae died and decayed, they would use up all the available oxygen in the waters, and thus destroy all fish life and other animals dependent on oxygen.

It is fortunate for all of us that the nitrogen fixing bacteria and denitrifying bacteria are both numerous and abundant. Were it not for these fantastic little creatures, each performing a specialized task in the nitrogen cycle, plants and animals could not exist!

Is this merely "coincidence"? Is this merely a lucky, fortuitous "accident" of evolution? Can your mind conceive of such a perfectly balanced ecological system, so complex and intricate, involving so many, many different kinds of life, just gradually evolving all together, accidentally, through millions of years?

There are just *too many* "coincidences" and "lucky accidents" and "fortunate breaks" for evolutionary theory to account for!

Interdependence of Life

All life on earth is part of a giant web, composed of many interconnected strands. If one major strand is broken, the whole suffers.

This vast interdependency of nature involves not only the broad interdependency of plant life and animal life, but also is manifested in numerous specialized creatures that depend on each other!

Writes Fairfield Osborn: "The most basic truth regarding our earth-home is that all living things, in some manner, are related to each other."[8]

There is orderliness in all nature. No creature or plant lives or dies to itself.

For example, a caterpillar may be looked upon as a pest by farmers. But this little creature which subsists by eating the leaves of trees and bushes eventually becomes a flying insect. Says Storer: "Then it will repay with interest the damage it has done to the plant, for it becomes a partner in the plant's life process, carrying pollen to fertilize the blossoms. Insects make possible the continued existence of many plants.

"Nearly all fruits and vegetables used by man are directly dependent on this partnership with insects."[9]

This interrelationship between insects and plants poses some serious questions for evolutionists. If fruits and vegetables are dependent on insects, *how* could they have survived before there were any insects? Likewise, if insects are dependent on such plants, *how* could they have survived before those plants came into existence?

It is mind boggling. We see a definite orderliness in the web of interrelationships between animals, plants, soil and climate. Vegetation in every part of the world is governed by the climate that supplies its moisture, warmth and sunlight. And living creatures, in their turn, are controlled largely by vegetation.

This remarkable *orderliness* in nature's ecosystems is further evidence that there has to be a God who set the whole biosphere in order. There had to be someone who *designed* it—a Supreme Designer!

The very word ecology, which describes the science of the relationships of living things and their environment, comes from the Greek *oikos,* meaning "household." Thus ecology is the study of "households." But can your mind conceive of a household existing without a builder, a designer, a "householder"?

Nature's "Co-ops"

In the soil, no life is self-sufficient. The threads of the lives of its inhabitants during their brief existences cross and recross to make up the fabric of soil life.

Writes Peter Farb in *Living Earth:*

> In observing life underfoot, we cannot fail to note the endless variety of partnerships that have been entered into. Many of the plants and animals have joined their resources and created *completely new entities.* There are the tree roots that have allied themselves with mycorrhizal fungi, and legume roots that work in partnership with bacteria to obtain nitrogen from the atmosphere. Other kinds of fungi are cultivated by termites and ants. The lichens demonstrate how an alga and fungus can *combine* so that they may colonize a new habitat, bare rock.[10]

Read that paragraph again. Can evolutionists explain how plants and animals could "join" resources to create "completely new entities"? Why "join" if they had evolved independently in the first place? How could they "join" if each was oblivious to the existence of the other? If they were aware of each other, can evolutionists explain mere matter becoming conscious of itself—and being intelligent enough to plan and develop well-organized botanical communities?

Can "tree roots" consciously or unconsciously conclude that they should evolve a special relationship with mycorrhizal fungi? Was all this sheer chance? Did plants and animals form partnerships by accident? Did algae and fungi "learn" to "combine" so they could colonize bare rock?

Evolutionists simply cannot answer these questions without resorting to non-materialistic modes of thought. Admits Farb, "The living together of diverse organisms is *still a complex problem* in biology and many of the mechanics of it are obscure."[11] He continues, "The truth, whatever it is, is buried in the mysteries of time, and an answer may not be forthcoming for uncalculable ages."[12]

Evolution has stumbled against some very complex, inexplicable problems to which it has no answers.

How can evolutionists explain such incredible relationships among various forms of life? Which "partner" evolved first? If one evolved without the other, how did it survive alone?

The secret of survival appears to lie in "mutual cooperation" rather than competition. Cooperation among plants and animals characterizes the dark jungles and the arid deserts of the world. Says Farb, "Today we are not witnessing many forms of plant life struggling with each other, but rather *well-organized botanical communities.*"[13]

How contrary to the "survival of the fittest" evolutionary doctrine of Charles Darwin!

Life is not essentially "competitive" on the earth. Rather, it exists in well organized botanical and zoological gardens of communities!

Symbiosis—or, "Living Together"

When plants and animals live together, they have a relationship called symbiosis—a strange word which merely means "living together."

A fascinating example of symbiosis involves the South American parakeet which only breeds in nests of one species of termite. While constructing its own hollow, the parakeet destroys about half of the termite nest. At first the termites attack the invader, but then for some unknown reasons adjust to the new situation. They cease molesting the parent bird. They ignore the vulnerable young.

Writes Peter Farb: "What is so remakable about this relationship is that the parakeet depends completely upon this single kind of termite, yet it inexplicably destroys half of the termite's nest and thus its own potential nesting site for the next breeding season. The termites are capable of preventing the successful breeding of this injurious parasite, *yet they do not do so.*"[14]

Why?

Frankly, if evolution were true, such a relationship wouldn't make any sense! If each species is in a struggle for survival, and everything it does is for its own survival, termites would not tolerate the invasion of the South American parakeet! They would attack the bird's nest, and kill the young. But they don't. Apparently they haven't yet heard of Charles Darwin or his cherished theory!

Doctor Fish

Numerous little 2–4 inch wrasses, or "doctor fish," as they have also been called, play a vital role in the health of coral communities in the sea. One scientist watched for six hours while these underwater doctors scrubbed and sanitized some 300 different visitors at their "cleaning station."

These little fish supply a real service to the larger fish, and in return they receive immunity from the attacks of their own predators. None of their natural enemies desires to chase them down the mouth of a moray eel or a giant sea bass.

How important are the cleaner fish to their larger cousins? To find out, researchers removed all the known cleaners from a particular area of a reef. From that time the denizens of the deep of that region began developing sores, infections, swellings and some died.

Stated Douglas Faulkner, in *National Geographic*: "Parasitic infections afflict fish in all the world's oceans and seas. Biologists theorize that the wrasses' services in removing these growths contribute substantially to the health of marine populations.

"In areas lacking cleaners, the young of many species take over the function, though not without risk. A hungry predator may simply swallow one of these amateur doctors. The true professionals, on the other hand, seldom if ever are eaten by their patients."[15]

Why don't the larger fish attack and eat the "cleaner fish"? Do they somehow "know" that if they did, they would eventually become covered with sores, infections, and die? How did they "evolve" this incredible insight? Do fish have this kind of *intelligence?*

Can you imagine the first cleaner fish, supposedly millions of years ago, which swam up to a large cousin and began to scrub and sanitize him? What would have happened? If the larger fish had not yet "evolved" the "knowledge" that he should allow the cleaner fish to scrub him, he would have eaten him!

And that would have been the first and last cleaner fish! The first "amateur" cleaner fish would have been eaten and there would be no "professional" cleaners alive, today, performing their vital role in coral reef ecology.

The MEANING of the Web of Life

Clearly, the science of ecology demonstrates that all life is mutually dependent. Man and animals could not exist for long without plants and photosynthesis. Flowering plants would soon perish were it not for pollinating insects. Life as we know it would be impossible were it not for nitrogen-fixing bacteria, and denitrifying bacteria.

You may have never thought that your own life depended on forests, trees, blue-green algae and phytoplankton—but it does—for both oxygen and food.

All plant and animal life on earth is intricately interwoven and interrelated—like a patchwork quilt. Nothing exists totally unto itself. Every form of life performs a role for others in the ecology of the earth.

Many scientists themselves have marvelled at the mysteries and intricate balance between living things.

Joseph Krutch, a famed naturalist, wrote in a moment of candor: "If it really is true that he (man) is merely the inevitable culmination of an improbable chemical reaction which happened to take place once and once only and involved 'merely material' atoms, then the fact that he has been able to formulate the idea of 'an improbable chemical reaction' and to trace himself back to it is remarkable indeed. *That chemicals which are 'merely material' should come to understand their own nature is a staggering supposition. Is it also a preposterous one?*"[16]

A good question!

Can evolutionary theory adequately explain the origin of the great cycles of nature which are dependent upon life, and upon which life itself depends?

Can it explain the interdependency of plant and animal life, flowers and insects, and the existence of "partners" in nature? Can it explain the fact that so many creatures *assist* each other in survival by Darwin's "survival of the fittest" doctrine?

The web of life entangles evolutionary theory in helpless futility.

Chapter Nine

Color, Camouflage and Nature's Amazing Inventions

Nature's creatures are the most amazing inventors of all time! Some animals—such as the octopus—discovered "jet propulsion" long before man invented the jet airplane.

Termites, tiny little creatures that are a pest to home builders because they eat wood, build intricate, huge "metropolises" complete with air conditioning, satellite suburbs, and storage areas. They even bring water to their homes by digging wells 120 feet deep!

Animals used camouflage to escape detection by enemies long before human soldiers learned to camouflage their weapons during war.

Color is not just something beautiful to look at. It is very important in Nature's scheme. The tide pool blenny drives other fish from its territory by displaying its brightly colored chin. Decorator crabs use parts of algae and sponges, putting them on their own upper shell to mask their own coloration.

Flatfish have an uncanny ability to perfectly match their background, the pattern of the sea bottom on which they rest.

Ingenious tricks and camouflage provide protection for smaller creatures; but predators themselves often resort to similar tricks in the never ending struggle of eat or be eaten.

Man's own efforts to disguise and camouflage his military weapons seem feeble in comparison with nature. The main method of concealment used by nature's creatures is simply matching the background. Meadowlarks disappear in a hay field, a woodfrog vanishes among dead leaves, a green tree frog hides in green air plants growing on trees.

Some creatures change their costumes to match the seasons. Wet and dry season broods among some butterflies show marked differences. The wet season dead leaf butterfly has a more dazzling pattern than the dry season brood. The arctic fox discards his brown summer coat for a bright white winter coat to match the winter's snow.

You may have noticed that a deer fawn has spots that help to conceal it among tiny shafts of sunlight in the summer. But in the winter a more uniform coat is needed, so the deer sheds its white hairs for brown ones as winter approaches. Since there are no leaves in the winter to cast tiny shafts of sunlight patterns, the brown coat is more protective.

Some of the artful camouflage tricks of nature make its creatures resemble magicians or quick-change artists. Within two or three minutes an American Anolis lizard can change from pea green to dark brown. The surgeon fish and the Nassau grouper can also change coloration very quickly. The surgeon fish is mostly black as it swims among coral reefs, but when it swims into clear water it quickly changes to a pure pale blue-grey which makes it very difficult to see.

The Nassau grouper can change to six or eight different appearances within a few short fleeting minutes. Usually very dark, it may turn several shades as a swimmer approaches, or adopt a strongly banded appearance, or turn almost white as it darts out into the open waters to escape.

Some harmless animals "mimic" dangerous distasteful animals in order to escape being eaten by predators. Many times one creature deliberately poses and acts like another. Some spiders hold up their two front legs giving the appearance of ants which have only six legs. Many moths look like wasps and hornets and act like them too. The hummingbird moth can even deceive humans as it hovers in front of flowers like a hummingbird!

Why are male birds usually more brightly decorated, and have more brilliant feathers, than the female birds of the species?

The bright plumage may help attract a mate, or deter a rival, of course. But another reason is that the male birds usually keep far away from the nest where the female tends the young. This directs the attention of enemies to the male bird, away from the actual nest where the young are, and where the female blends into the background with her "ordinary" looking camouflage.

The huge "eyespots" on the head of some swallowtail butterflies are nothing but deception. The huge "eyes" give enemies the impression that the butterflies are much bigger and more dangerous than they really are.

The amazing camouflage artists in nature are another evidence of the Supreme Artist—the Creator God who endowed them with these incredible, fascinating abilities.

Similarly, the inventiveness of nature's creatures bespeaks the Supreme Genius of the Original Inventor of all things.

Did you know, for example, that the whirligig beetle, which is found all over the world in pools and lakes and rivers, has an amazing trait? This little creature, insignificant of itself, is equally at home in the air, on the water, or underwater. It can fly from pond to pond, and when it finds a new home, it uses its wings as a parachute, dropping gently to the surface of the water. When diving underwater, it takes with it, under its wings, an air bubble. On the surface of the water, it uses its two rear legs as oars to scull over the water.

The whirligig beetle is an aviator, parachutist, surface craft operator, and skin diver, all in one!

Long before Adam and Eve learned to sew, tiny ants, a species of Oecophylla, stitched leaves together in a spectacular fashion. Several ants, working as a team, pull the edges of two leaves together. If the leaves are too far apart, they form a living chain, each ant gripping the one behind with its hind legs. Then other ants join the sewing party, each carrying a grub between its jaws. The grubs emit silk, and are passed back and forth like shuttles until the two edges of the two leaves are securely fastened together by the silk strands.

Another amazing architectural feat of the animal world is tunnelling. It may seem simple, digging a tunnel, but not so at all! Moles for example are equipped with their own built in shovel, hoe, pick-ax, and garden fork. Their front paws combine a fork and shovel, and they are able to burrow into ground hard enough to require a pick to break!

Tunnelling requires more than just digging apparatus, however. It requires mathematical precision and engineering skill to be able to calculate position at every moment while working underground, blind, with no light, and nothing but dirt all around! A blind mole can bore a new tunnel and make it connect precisely with a pre-existing tunnel several feet away! Nobody knows how he does it.

Nor were Adam and Eve the first gardeners on earth. Did you know that some species of ants and termites raise their own gardens for food? The leaf cutter ants cultivate a fungus in special chambers in the ant nest, and feed on the fungus gardens.

Some species of termites also cultivate mushroom beds within their colonies. The fungus serves the termites by pre-digesting vegetable matter such as wood which the termites themselves are unable to digest.

The giant clam of the Indian Ocean, which grows to be several feet across, is also a capable, ingenious gardener. Many single-celled green plants live within its tissues and form part of its food. When the clam opens its shell to expose itself to the sunlight filtering down from the surface of the shallow sea, the sun's rays enable the green plants to manufacture sugars and starch, causing the plants to grow and multiply. The plants are aided by the clam in another way. The clam has transparent lens structures which even focus the sunlight on the plants!

The wonders of nature defy human description. Bats navigate by means of echo-location. Electric eels, with electric cells capable of generating 220 volts, are capable of causing great pain to men. Dolphins and porpoises have a sonar system and use it as a depth-ranger as well as for detecting obstacles in the water.

To combat the radar or echo-location systems of bats, there are certain moths which give out sounds which disrupt the echo-location of pursuing bats—nature's own radar-jamming devices!

We look at the tanks, armored cars, shields, and helmets of human armies, and then note that armor appears often in the animal kingdom—the armadillo even looks like a tank! Turtles and tortoises are renown for their heavily armored shells.

Human ingenuity and engineering were anticipated by nature many times over—the snorkel, the flying aircraft, the submarine with its periscope, artillery and chemical warfare, are all found among Nature's denizens.

The snorkel, which enables a submarine to replenish its air without surfacing, was anticipated in the hippopotamus and crocodile which have eyes and nostrils set high upon the head so the animals may remain submerged and still breathe and see above the surface.

Numerous aquatic animals have long breathing tubes which they push above the surface of the water to take in air. One of them is the rat-tailed maggot (the larva of a hoverfly). It can live in turgid water with its telescopic tail. While resting on the bottom of a pool, it can extend its breathing tube up beyond the surface to breathe.

Birds of course are the first heavier than air flying machines. They are able to soar, glide through the air, hover in place, and even able to migrate for thousands of miles without running out of fuel or energy or losing their sense of direction.

One of the champion migrants is the tiny blackpoll warbler. Every autumn it flies unerringly from its Canadian nest all the way to Brazil, a distance of over 4,000 miles.

The golden plover wings its way a distance of almost 8,000 miles from the edge of the Arctic Ocean in the north to far-off Argentina in the south. The blue-winged teal flies from Quebec, Canada to Guyana every year, a distance of 3,300 miles. The bristle-thighed curlew makes an annual round trip from Tahiti to central Alaska, flying 5,500 miles each way.

Even the unheralded barn swallow migrates yearly from northern Canada to north central Argentina, a distance of no less than 9,000 miles.

The top migrator among land birds is the little bobolink which averages 7,000 miles in its journey from Canada to Argentina.

The greatest migrator of them all, in terms of mileage, is the Arctic Tern. It leaves its nest at the age of six weeks in the Arctic, and flies nonstop to the region of Antarctica, 11,000 miles away, and finds its way back home the following summer. How it is able to navigate successfully for 22,000 miles scientists do not know. But migrate they do, and very successfully, too!

It has been estimated that perhaps one third of all bird species migrate. But evolutionary theory has not been able to explain the why or how of bird migration—or even less why the *first* bird that migrated attempted to do so—or how that first bird navigator was able to find his way accurately—or how many birds attempted to learn the secret of migration, and failed, and died in the dismal attempt, thus becoming extinct!

What about speed? How fast can animals travel? We humans are fascinated with speed. Millions watch in fascination as men strive to break a speed record and win a race, such as the Indianapolis 500 or the Grand Prix.

Animals also are "speed kings." Theoretically dolphins shouldn't be able to swim faster than ten knots, but they have been clocked at twenty knots or more for up to a half hour! Research and studies have showed that the skin of dolphins has a soft outer layer filled with vertical ducts containing spongy water-logged tissue. Tests showed that this design reduces friction of water and reduces drag by as much as 60 per cent!

Swordfish, marlin and sailfish have been clocked up to about 70 miles per hour. Flying fish have been timed at 35 miles per hour and can fly up to a quarter of a mile before descending to the sea.

How fast can birds fly? The cloud swift has been measured up to 200 miles per hour. A peregrine falcon can reach 180 miles per hour when diving upon its prey. The racing pigeon in level flight has been clocked up to 94.3 miles per hour!

When we observe the many marvels, mysteries, and fascinating creatures in the Natural Realm, we see a glimpse of the wonderful and ingenious Mind of God, the Creator. The marvels of Nature reflect the majesty of the Creator who designed them, and placed them on the earth!

In the light of these mind stirring, inspiring features of the world around us, how can anybody say there is no God?

Chapter Ten

"Should We Burn Darwin?"

Just what do we mean when we talk about "evolution"? Does the Bible tell us that the theory of the evolution of life is wrong? Or could God have created all things through an evolutionary process?

There are four major beliefs. The materialistic approach states that all things, including life on earth, slowly evolved without divine or outside interference or guidance.

The theistic evolution approach states that God did create all things, but He did so in an evolutionary manner. Another concept is the "progressive creation" approach. It says that God created all things and every form of life. He did so over millions of years, probably, in a gradual, progressive manner, leading up to man, the crown of His creation.

The fourth concept is the "sudden creation" theory. It states that God created all the universe and all life forms instantaneously, by divine fiat, over a period of six days, approximately 4,000 B.C. Many "creationists" subscribe to the latter theory.

Besides these four main categories of belief, there are no doubt many sub-categories, with varying degrees of divergence.

Which of these theories is most logical? Which is right? Is there any way in which we can know?

In order to obtain a better view of the problem, we must clearly define just what we are talking about when we say "evolution."

Automobile manufacturers in Detroit sometimes refer to the "evolution of the automobile." We hear expressions from time to time about the "evolution of the airplane," or the "evolution of the steamboat."

Technically, however, none of these things actually "evolved," in the biological sense of the word. It would be more accurate to speak of the "development" of the automobile, the airplane, or the steamboat.

Nevertheless, if you walk through an automobile museum, and see the early Stanley Steamers, the Model "A" Fords, the early Chevrolets, and progress until you come to the modern automobiles, including the Ford LTD, the Mercedes Benz, the Jaguar XKE, and Toyota Celica, you will no doubt see a "natural progression" or "evolution." The latest models will be much more powerful, sleek, and hopefully efficient than the earlier models.

Thus in the case of the automobile, for example, we see "evolution"—but of course automobiles all have designers, creators, and thousands of men involved in their assembly. They did not "evolve" by blind chance; they are not the product of accident; the glass, rubber, steel, leather, and other metals did not "put themselves together." The batteries, hydraulic systems, brakes, radios, air conditioning systems, transmissions, gas tanks, trunks, seat cushions, etc., did not design and fashion themselves out of the raw materials in the earth!

Is it any more reasonable, then, to think that the beautifully designed forms of life on earth somehow designed, fashioned, and manufactured themselves out of the raw materials available?

Two Theories of Evolution

There is a General Theory of Evolution, which states that all life forms evolved from simple, remote ancestors. There is also a Specific Theory of Evolution, which attempts to trace evolutionary progress of a specific organism and its variation and mutation down through geologic history.

Julian Huxley, in *Issues in Evolution*, put the General Theory this way: "Evolution is a one-way process, irreversible in time, producing apparent novelties and greater variety, and leading to higher degrees of organization, more differentiated, more complex, but at the same time more integrated."[1]

Charles Darwin, the modern father of evolutionary theory, defined evolution as "the belief that all animals and plants are descended from some one . . . primordial form."[2]

How does this evolution ostensibly occur?

Let's take a look at the theories which have been presented, and examine some of the supposed "evidence" to support evolution.

Acquired Characteristics

More than one hundred and fifty years ago the French evolutionist Lamarck sought to explain how evolution worked. His theory was that environment caused an animal to acquire certain characteristics, and these were passed on to the offspring. Thus, when drought struck Africa, giraffes had to develop long necks to get to the leaves way up in the trees. Gradually, therefore, the ancient giraffes developed long necks.

Why other animals living in drought-stricken areas did not also grow long necks was never explained. And why the giraffe today lives on the plains and also eats grass was ignored.

Lamarck also had an explanation for the long legs of the flamingo. Supposedly, its ancestors had short legs; but since the flamingo loved to wade out into the water to get its dinner, gradually, over eons of time, its legs grew longer. Strange, that those ancient flamingos did not find some easier way to get their dinner—such as learn to eat insects instead of fish, or learn to swim like a duck!

Lamarck's theories have been rejected by most evolutionists today. Darwin himself declared, "Heaven forfend me from Lamarck's nonsense."[3] Scientists have long since come to see that acquired characteristics are not inherited by offspring.

For instance, if a person cuts off his arm, his children will not be born armless. If he plucks out his eyes, his children will not be born missing their eyes!

It was August Weismann, who dealt the deathblow to Lamarck's theory. He reared twenty-two generations of mice and amputated their tails. Sad for the theory of Lamarck, the mice of the last generation grew tails just as long as those of the first generation. Not a single tailless mouse was born!

Nonetheless, theories of science die hard. Many scientists had firmly believed that Lamarck was right. In the early 1920's an obscure Viennese scientist Paul Kammerer wrote a book purporting to show environment could definitely change heredity. For a time his discoveries and experiments were widely hailed, the British acclaimed him, the Russians rolled out the red carpet when he visited Moscow.

But then others began putting Kammerer's experiments to the acid test. Doubts grew. Finally, an American scientist investigated the circumstances and findings of Kammerer's experiments, and found that someone had perpetrated a hoax. Whether it was Kammerer himself, or whether he had been a tragic victim of the hoax was debatable. But the greatly shaken Kammerer chose to commit suicide after the exposure!

Darwinian Evolution

Darwin, of course, is widely regarded as the true father of the theory of evolution. Although his claim to this title is certainly open to question, it cannot be denied that his theory of *natural selection* created an uproar when first published, and has since been embraced by most of the world, at least in part.

Darwin's theory was based on two primary observations—first, the existence of variations among living things; second, the perpetual struggle for existence among living things.

Darwin taught the doctrine of the survival of the fittest. Those animals more fit to cope with their environments were the ones to survive; those not so fortunate, perished in extinction! And in this way, according to Darwin, animals evolved into more fit, higher forms of life.

The world was enthralled. Darwin's name went into the history books. But his theory has run into stormy weather. Whereas American scientists tend to praise Charles Darwin, French scientists have attacked his theories for many years.

A few years ago, in fact, the French magazine *Science et Vie* ran a two-page title asking seriously, "Should We Burn Darwin?" The author of the article concluded that Darwin's theory of evolution and natural selection belonged to the past–it is obsolete. Today, almost all French specialists have strong reservations as to the validity of Darwin's theory of natural selection.[4]

Hugh de Vries many years ago declared: "Natural selection may explain the survival of the fittest, but it cannot explain the arrival of the fittest."[5]

Thus Darwin's theory begged the question of the arrival of species, merely giving a partial explanation of how animals and species survive.

Natural selection, or even artificial selection through breeding, has no power in creating anything *new*. The most fundamental problem with the theory of natural selection is that it cannot originate *new* characteristics–it only selects among characteristics already existing.

As early as 1921 the weaknesses in the theory had become obvious. One scientist, in an article appearing in *Nature*, September 29, 1921, declared: "A new generation has grown up that knows not Darwin"!

The Species Problem

One of the major problems perplexing evolutionists today is that of the existence of "species."

The plant kingdom has about 300,000 species, with 200,000 of them being found among the flowering plants. There are about one million classified animal species, with an estimated two million more yet to be described. Of the million known animal species, there are about 750,000 insects, and of these, about 650,000 are beetles.

But just what is a "species"? There is little agreement. The *generally accepted* definition of a species limits members of the same species to those which are capable of interbreeding, having offspring fully fertile, and usually separated from other species by differences of structure and appearance.

Historically, some scientists mistakenly equated their ideas of "species" with the *kinds* of animals mentioned in the book of Genesis. They *assumed* that what they labeled a "species" always reproduced after its own species, and therefore believed it was identical with the "Genesis kind." Then, when a new variety developed from that particular species, and did not interbreed with the parent stock, scientists assumed that a new "species"—or *kind*—of animal had arisen. They erroneously concluded that this discredited the Biblical statement that each kind reproduced after its kind.

The fallacy of such reasoning is obvious. Genesis "kinds" are not necessarily the same as "species." In fact, the evidence shows that in many cases there is a *vast* difference between what scientists label a "species" and what the Bible calls a "kind."

For example, the Bible speaks of the "owl kind" (Lev. 11:17), but modern taxonomists speak of the owl as a complete "order" in their classification systems.

What are called "species," today, are in many instances mere varieties and not new "kinds" in the Genesis sense of the word. We must not confuse Genesis kinds with what scientists label as "species." That is the common mistake made by many people, today, including most evolutionists.

Although it is true that new "species" arise in nature, this fact does *not* contradict the fact that Genesis *kinds* always reproduce after their own kind.

Early in the 15th century, a litter of rabbits was released in Porto Santo island near Madeira. Since there were no other rabbits on the island, and no enemies of the rabbit either, the rabbits multiplied rapidly. By the 19th century they were strikingly different from the ancestral European stock—only half as large, had a different color pattern, and most important, could no longer breed with members of the European species. Within four hundred years, then, a new species of rabbit had developed.[6] But this fact in no way proved the theory of evolution true.

It is now well established that for a group of animals to become a new species, they must be prevented from breeding with their relatives, and thereby transmitting to them the changes in their genes that may have appeared. The normal way to prevent such interbreeding is by some form of *isolation.* In nature, this may occur as a result of separation by a physical barrier, such as a mountain range, a desert, a river, glacier, or ocean.

Geographic isolation, however, is seldom permanent. Therefore two isolated groups may eventually come into contact again and interbreed unless *genetic isolation or sterility* has arisen in the meantime.

These so-called "new species" remain very similar to the original ancestral stock. They are not really totally new kinds of animal at all in the Biblical sense. They constitute a *major variation within* the original kind of animal. The new "species" of rabbits on Porto Santo island *were still rabbits!*

Although changes in a particular species have undoubtedly combined to provide a new closely related so-called "species," evolutionists have never demonstrated that such changes ever produce an entirely different *kind* of animal! Dogs always reproduce dogs. Cows always reproduce cows, and so on.

It is important to realize that such changes or variations *within* the original Genesis "kinds" are often cited to "prove" the theory of evolution. Such relatively minor changes do constitute "changes" all right, but can be explained as variations *within* the original Genesis kind. To use such "changes" (within the Genesis "kinds" God created) to substantiate the *theory* of evolution is like calling apples oranges. It is a complete mislabeling, and leads to erroneous conclusions.

Evolutionists assume that these lesser changes will eventually —given enough time—lead to the innovation of entirely new kinds of animals.

But that is pure assumption!

Evolutionists, after years of attempts, *have never shown* that the basic "kinds" can change into another kind. How then, could they "prove" evolution?

A Few "Proofs" of Evolution Examined

In the search for proof, evolutionists at one time turned to "vestigial organs." These are "useless" organs which supposedly remain from previous evolutionary forms. At one time necessary to the organism, they have long since become useless.

But do such organs really exist, except in the minds of evolutionists?

These "useless organs" have, in the past, been called the "showpieces" of evolution. Some textbooks claim that the human body resembles an "old curiosity shop"—filled with useless relics! "In the human body there are more than 100 such vestigial organs, including the appendix, the coccyx (the fused tail vertebrae), the wisdom teeth, the nictitating membrane of the eye, the body hair and the muscles that move the ears,"[7] says one authority. The tonsils and all the endocrine organs were at one time included in this category.

As long as no function was known for an organ evolutionists freely called it a "vestigial" organ. However, in recent years, due to the findings of modern research there has been less and less emphasis on this "proof" of evolution. Some current textbooks don't even mention it. As man's knowledge increases more vital functions are being found for these "apparently useless" organs!

For example, one time scientists considered both the tonsils and the appendix to be "vestigial." Actually they are part of the body's defense system. They are composed of lymphoid tissue which manufactures white blood cells and possible antibodies which contribute to the body's resistance. The appendix may also protect the body against various types of cancer.[8]

The coccyx, which consists of several vertebrae fused together in the sacral region of the spinal column, are said to be part of a "vestigial tail." In reality these bones provide attachment sites for several muscles that support the organs of the pelvic cavity. Pictures that purport to show human beings with a tail, when the source is investigated, begin to look more like a "tall tale" than a real "tail"!

Until recently, the pineal gland, a small pea-sized organ located in the brain, had been regarded by some as ". . . a vestigial organ homologous to the pineal sense organ of the lower vertebrates."[9] The structure was classified as a rudimentary organ in man due to its small size and because it had no ascertainable function. Once again, *assumptions* have proven erroneous. Current evidence indicates that this "vestigial" organ "is one of the most biochemically active and complicated organs in the body."[10]

Supposed "vestigial" organs do *not* prove evolution. In fact, evolutionists have never demonstrated that such organs really exist. This so-called "proof" of evolution is proven to be more and more an argument from *ignorance* as time goes on!

Proof of Embryology?

Similarity between developing embryos of animals is also supposed to constitute a formidable proof of evolution. This theory declares that stages of previous evolutionary steps are "recapitulated" in the embryos of supposedly later, more complex evolutionary descendants. According to E.H. Haeckel, an early advocate of this theory, "phylogeny recapitulates ontogeny." Simply explained, this means that the evolutionary path of the animal is "recorded" in the embryo of the creature!

Haeckel asserted, "The developmental history of ontogeny of every multicellular organism recapitulates the various stages of its ancestry and thereby every organism resembles roughly at each stage of its development the form of one of its ancestors."

This theory was at one time highly regarded. It was—and still is—stressed in biological and zoological texts. Students were taught it, and tested on it.

At first zoologists paid attention only to discoveries which seemed to corroborate the theory, neglecting those which cast unfavorable light on it. The theory was held in the highest repute for years! But research continued, investigation proceeded, and gradually more and more facts came to light which did not agree with the theory.

Fatal to the theory is the fact that plants simply do not develop accordingly. And since plants and animals, came, supposedly, from a common ancestor, this is hard for evolutionists to explain. Also fatal to the theory is the fact that embryos of closely related species pursue very different courses of embryonic development.

So a compromise was made. Scientists claimed that embryonic development does not repeat *every* stage of the supposed evolutionary ancestry. But as more compromises were required, scientists became disenchanted with the theory—and today Haeckel's ontological theories have been generally abandoned. Nevertheless, evolutionists will still at times cite its teachings in school texts to buttress their arguments for evolution!

Other "Proofs" of Evolution

Claims Claude Villee, "... studies of anatomy, physiology and biochemistry of modern plants and animals, their embryologic and genetic histories, and the manner in which they are distributed over the earth's surface would provide *overwhelming* proof that organic evolution has occurred."[11]

This biologist states that comparisons of the structure of groups of animals and plants show that organ systems have a fundamentally similar pattern. He asserts that the existence of "homologous organs," or organs which are basically similar in structure, embryonic development, and relationships to adjacent structures, "is a *strong argument* for a common evolutionary origin."

Is that claim true? Could not such organs, as the wing of a bird and forelimb of a horse, be explained just as easily by means of the fact that the same Creator God made them all—He designed them for similar purposes and functions in all these animals? Similarities in design of organs could be cited as proof that these animals had the same original Designer—rather than that they evolved from the same ancient ancestor!

The same fact applies equally to similarities in the function of important physiologic processes and similarities in blood chemistry. Even though the process of respiration, digestion, circulation, etc., is the same in certain other animals as it is in humans, this does not prove evolution—it could equally demonstrate that all these animals were designed along the same lines by their original designer—God!

Although thousands of tests reveal different animals have a basic similarity between their blood proteins, and even though man's closest "blood relations," as determined by such similarities, are the great apes, this fact does not prove evolution. It merely shows the similarity between apes and men insofar as blood chemistry is concerned. But just by looking at the great apes, a person can see plainly that man resembles them more than he does, for instance, a tree squirrel, a little monkey, a rabbit, a fox, a rat, a deer, or a bird or reptile!

Geographic Distribution of Animals

According to evolutionists, "The present distribution of organisms is understandable only on the basis of the evolutionary history of each species."[13]

But is this true? To assert that certain animals and plants are present in one region of the world but are not found in another region where they could just as easily survive can only be explained by "their evolutionary history" is very misleading. Evolutionary theory is only one explanation for distribution of animals. The creation theory can also account for it. As the original Genesis kinds diversified and developed into many new varieties, they adapted to various ecological niches.

One who believes in a Creator God can easily account for the geographic distribution of animals. First, God created various animals to live in particular habitats. He created gorillas, lions, and elephants to live in Central Africa—not in Brazil. Just as God divided to the children of men their inheritances, so He divided to the animals their particular habitats (see Deuteronomy 32:8). Secondly, animals tend to dwell wherever the climate is suitable for them. This fact, however, in no way supports evolution as against creation.

The "Great Faith" of Evolutionists

When one considers the weight of the evidence, thus far observed, one begins to wonder how men who are intelligent and educated can subscribe to evolutionary theory. But they do.

Dr. Harold C. Urey, Nobel Prize-holding chemist of the University of California at La Jolla admitted that "all of us who study the origin of life find that the more we look into it, the more we feel it is too complex to have evolved anywhere." And yet, he added, "We all believe as an article of *faith* that life evolved from dead matter on this planet. It is just that its complexity is so great, it is hard for us to imagine it did."[14]

Noted evolutionist and paleontologist George Gaylord Simpson in his book *This View of Life,* admitted in regard to animal behavior:

> It is a habit of speech and thought to say that fishes have gills in order to breathe water, that birds have wings in order to fly, and that men have brains in order to think.
>
> A telescope, a telephone, or a typewriter is a complex mechanism serving a particular function. Obviously, its manufacturer had a purpose in mind, and the machine was designed and built in order to serve that purpose. An eye, an ear, or a hand is also a complex mechanism serving a particular function.
>
> It, too, looks as if it had been made for a purpose.[15]

Nevertheless, Simpson believes there is a natural, material explanation for all these things. He looks to "creative natural selection" as the answer.

Look at your hand. Manipulate your fingers. Flex the muscles of your arm. Think about the intricacy of the combination of muscles, tendons, bones, cartilage, blood vessels, blood fluid and corpuscles, and the network of nerves.

Think how these parts of your arm, hand, and fingers, all work together harmoniously, as if by design.

Consider, too, the similar interrelationships among all life forms. To produce such adapted types by pure chance recombinations of genes via mutations and natural selection—as even Julian Huxley admitted—"would require a total assemblage of organisms that would more than fill the universe, and overrun astronomical time."[16]

Yet evolutionists believe it happened. Surely they are men of incredible faith!

Chapter Eleven

Genes, Genetics and Evolution

Gregor Johann Mendel was born July 22, 1822 in the little village of Heizendorf in what is now Czechoslovakia. He was an Austrian scientist and Catholic monk. Fascinated by the study of nature, Mendel–contrary to the advice of his peers–persevered in studying botany, especially the breeding qualities of plants.

Mendel planted generation after generation of the common garden pea. He noted what occurred when he crossbred them; he kept notes on each generation, and thus discovered some of the basic laws of heredity.

In 1865 Mendel read his experimental results before the Brunn Society for the Study of Natural Science. The silence was deafening.

Up until Mendel's time scientists had been unaware of any laws regulating the inheritance of biological traits. They assumed that inheritance was the blending of characteristics of the parents, but Mendel showed that inherited characteristics are carried as discrete units which may be dominant or recessive.

Since Mendel's time, geneticists have learned a great deal about the laws of heredity. They have learned that hereditary traits are carried–or blueprinted–in the genes and chromosomes of each individual. They have learned that some hereditary traits are "sex linked"–that is, they are connected with the male or female sex chromosome.

Early in the 1900's Thomas H. Morgan began studying genetics at Columbia University. He selected the tiny fruit fly *Drosophila* for his experiments. Drosophila is easy to breed and maintain, and it has only four pairs of chromosomes. Morgan's experiments led to an even greater knowledge of heredity.

Since the time of Gregor Mendel, the laws of heredity have been firmly established. These laws state in general that because of the genetic code each kind of animal and plant must reproduce after its own kind. This discovery corroborated the text of Genesis which points out that each kind of plant and animal must reproduce "after its kind." Variation may occur but each basic kind produces its own kind through heredity.

Because of dominant and recessive genes, there may be hundreds of different varieties or breeds in a particular species. There are, for instance, 110 recognized separate breeds of dogs, ranging from tiny Chihuahuas and Yorkshire Terriers to huge Great Danes and St. Bernards. Each of these varieties could well have descended from one original Genesis *kind*, or pair of dogs!

Such variation in descent from a common ancestor is frequently cited as proof of evolution. In reality, it remains purely variation within the created kind. Without such variation, all dogs would be virtually identical; all people would be identical; all fingerprints would be identical.

Applying the laws of heredity, breeders and horticulturists are able to crossbreed these varieties and produce entirely new varieties of animals and plants; they are able to produce "crosses" or hybrids within the Genesis kind; they are able to produce new varieties of corn, wheat, cattle, roses, rice, tomatoes. But these new varieties are not entirely new animals or plants! They are still the same basic *kind* as were their ancestors—their parent stock!

The basic laws of heredity discovered by Mendel in 1865 and amplified ever since directly support the Biblical statement that each animal and plant must reproduce "after its own kind!" (Genesis 1:11-12, 21, 24-25).

"But wait a minute," evolutionists will object. "What about mutations? Aren't they an exception to that law?" "And what about 'Natural Selection?' " Don't mutations, working with natural selection, lead to evolutionary change?"

This is a very important and much misunderstood point.

What Are Mutations?

One author writes: "It remains true to say that we know of no other way than random mutation by which new hereditary variation comes into being . . ."[1] Mutations are generally accepted as the key to any evolutionary progress. To understand the role they are supposed to play, we must first understand what they are.

A "mutation" is generally defined as an alteration in the structure of a gene. Atoms are gained or lost, the DNA molecule is partially destroyed, or a gene is destroyed or removed, and a change results in the animal or plant heredity.*

Such changes can be due to environmental influence, or perhaps, they can sometimes occur "spontaneously." In some cases, however, scientists have mistakenly called "recessive characteristics," which only show up in the absence of one or more dominant characteristics, "mutations." Although a mutation may sometimes produce a recessive characteristic by destroying a gene or adding a repressor, most recessive characteristics are simply due to the working of the laws of heredity.

Radiation is one cause of mutations. Chemicals in the environment have also been demonstrated to cause mutations. There are other causes as yet still unknown.

There are two basic types of mutations. The first type are "spontaneous" mutations, which are really caused by mutagenic agents such as X-rays, ultraviolet light, nitrogen mustard, and other chemicals. The second type are "adaptive mutations." The adaptive mutations would include all "mutations" which are actually due to inherited recessive traits, which may be more suited for survival in the local environment.

---

*For instance, sickle-celled anemia in human beings is caused by the substitution of just one amino acid for another, resulting in alteration of the DNA molecule. (See *Textbook of Biochemistry*, Benjamin Harrow and Abraham Mazur, 1966, page 53.)

In a true mutation—that is, in one which is not really due to a recessive gene—one or more genes in the DNA undergo a change resulting in the production of offspring which are slightly different from the parent stock. Such events are comparatively rare.

Estimates of mutation frequency range from 50 to 60 per million births, although no thorough method has been devised to arrive at an exact average.

Will true mutations eventually lead to evolutionary progress in plants and animals? This is the basic question which must be answered!

Notice this admission of fact:

> . . . for a long time they [mutations] were regarded as Darwin himself regarded them, simply as curiosities. Darwin did not consider them important because they nearly always represented obviously disadvantageous modifications from the point of view of the struggle for existence; consequently they would most likely be rapidly eliminated in the wild state by the operation of natural selection. *This, in fact, is almost exactly what happens, in the majority of cases.*[2]

Mutations are best described as forming a wide spectrum of changes, from drastic ones which cause death of the embryo or even lethal hereditary diseases, to changes that are so slight that they are almost undetectable.

A leading authority, Theodosious Dobzhansky writes:

> Looking at mutations as genetic "mistakes" will be helpful in understanding the otherwise astonishing property of most of them, namely, the fact that mutant genes and chromosomes are *usually harmful* to the organism that carries them . . . . The clear-cut mutants of Drosophila [a fruit fly] with which so much of the classical research in genetics was done, are *almost without exception inferior* to wild-type flies in viability, fertility, longevity, and in all these features.[3]

Hampton L. Carson says, "Although absolute criteria as to what is beneficial and what is harmful are difficult to set up, the ratio of harmful to helpful mutations is on the order of a thousand to one."[4]

Practically all mutations are harmful because mutations occur at random. They are *chance* occurrences. Any chance alteration in the properties of a highly complex organism is very unlikely to improve its operation. Such alterations almost always are disadvantageous.

There is a delicate balance between an organism and its environment. A mutation can easily upset that balance. You could just as well anticipate that changing the location of the gas pedal or steering wheel on your automobile at random would improve its operation.

The destruction of a genetic factor, the substitution of a genetic factor, and the alteration of a gene thus induced would nearly always result in a less efficient organism. This is why almost all mutations are either lethal or harmful to the creatures experiencing them.

For mutations to be the key to evolution would, in effect, consistute the "survival of the unfit" instead of survival of the fittest. Since mutations are generally disadvantageous, they would tend to be eliminated by the struggle for existence and the process of natural selection. Why then do evolutionists cling to mutations as the essential agent responsible for evolution? Simply because they don't have any visible alternative.

Biologists Simpson and Beck write: "Mutations are . . . repetitive; the same ones [in different individuals] occur over and over again. Furthermore, they are to some extent reversible [because of self-repair and corrections] . . . ."[5]

Since mutations—the same ones—occur over and over again and since they are generally harmful to the organism, what chance is there that they could sustain evolutionary progress from ancient amoeba to the three million incredibly complex species on the earth today?

Since mutations are also reversible—that is, "mutant" individuals can just as easily mutate back to their original type as be formed in the first place—what likelihood is there for "evolutionary progress" to be made?

This is a real head scratcher!

Geneticists have no evidence of beneficial mutations occurring through adding on more genes, or NEW genes. But such

new genes would be absolutely required to sustain evolution!

Mutations *cannot* lead to the evolution of totally new kinds of animals because they do not involve additions of new genes to DNA molecules, but rather either destruction, substitution, or repair of already existing genes! Thus there is no hope for evolutionary progress in the occurrence of "mutations"!

Despite these problems however, evolutionists must cling to mutations working with natural selection as being the mechanism of evolution. They have no alternative.

Micromutations

Today a great debate rages in evolutionary circles. The Neo-Darwinists *believe* that new species evolve by the gradual accumulation of small mutations, called "micromutations." Another group *believes* new species and genera arise in one step—by macromutations, or major mutations, in the genetic system.

The problem with small mutations accounting for evolution is summed up in one word: Time.

Darwin himself believed these mutations occurred too rarely to be important in evolution. If small mutations are supposed to account for all the vast variety of life we see about us, then indeed time becomes a major problem to the evolutionist!

States one zoologist:

> Darwin and his followers assumed that evolution of larger differences was the result of gradual summation of the small differences involved in the evolution of varieties and species. There are, however, certain difficulties with this idea. Darwin recognized one of these—that related to *time*. The time necessary to produce the vast differences seen among the major groups of plants and animals would be *very, very great* if such a slow process were operating. . . . But certainly it is difficult to see how such vast differences have occurred within the time that seems to be available.[6]

A second problem is that to be successful in life, a creature must be a unified whole. How then, could the supposed "intermediate stages" have survived?

Take the eye, for example. It has been proposed that the cornea and lens appeared before there was a retina—or vice versa. But either way, such an incomplete "eye" would have been useless! How could such a partial, useless structure have survived, if it had gradually "mutated" piece by piece? Would not natural selection itself have caused such mutants to become weeded out? Biologists admit, "The situation . . . is unsatisfactory."[7] It certainly is!

In some cases, fish in caves have mutated to blindness. Such a mutation has lead to the development of blind varieties of fish. They cannot see the light which would lead them to the cave opening. Mating with blind partners (where blindness is genetically caused) leads to blind offspring. This, however, is completely the *opposite* of the development of sight! *One single factor* failing can produce blindness but thousands in unison are needed to produce sight!

Macromutations

But what about major or *macro*mutations? Evolutionists like Richard Goldschmidt of the University of California believe that occasionally such macromutations give rise to "hopeful monsters"—that is, new forms enabled by their mutations to occupy some new environment.

As George Gaylord Simpson described it: "All strongly distinctive types of animals originated as 'sports,' or 'hopeful monsters,' as Goldschmidt calls them, that happened to find a practicable way of life adapted to their peculiarities, rather than originating by any process that adapted them to peculiarities of the environment."[8]

What are the objections to this theory? They are numerous.

This theory, for example, also totally fails to account for the "evolution" of such a complicated organ as the eye. If even the slightest thing is wrong—if the retina is missing, or the lenses are too opaque, or if the dimensions are in error—the eye would fail to form a recognizable image. The eye would be useless! It must be either nearly *perfect*—or useless. But can you imagine such a delicate, complicated organ "mutating" at random suddenly in a creature that had no eyes?

The same might be said for the woodpecker's beak, the amazing underwater "sonar" devices of certain fish, or the feathers of a bird. Such complicated, marvelous structures and characteristics would have had to "evolve" perfectly *all at once*, or the creature could not have come into existence!

Biologists admit: "This idea also raises some *knotty problems*. Any large alteration in basic body pattern is almost invariably *deleterious and results in death*."[9]

Some evolutionists claim that "the old idea that evolution occurs as a series of small changes . . . is not concordant with modern knowledge."[10] Others strike back heatedly and claim that macromutations, or megamutations, only lead to *death* of the animal, and therefore could not account for evolution! The debate goes on and on. But the real weakness lies with the theory of organic evolution itself!

Chapter Twelve

Genesis Versus Geology?

Does the geologic record in the earth's strata prove that evolution has occurred? Do fossil remains refute the Genesis account of creation?

Says Carl Dunbar: ". . . the fossil remains of evolving series constitute *actual documentary evidence* that the changes (of evolution) occurred."[1] Granted, the fossil record reveals vast changes in the biota of the earth over long periods of time. But do these changes demonstrate the truth of "evolutionary theory" as opposed to creation?

Says another author: "The fossil record provides direct evidence of organic evolution. . . ."[2] Does this mean there is evidence that all life forms on earth today can be traced step by step back to a common simple ancestor?

Is there conclusive proof in the strata of the earth that the General Theory of Evolution is true and the case is closed?

The Fossil Record

Let's scrutinize the fossil record. Let's look at the earth's strata and see what it reveals.

A continuous chain of fossils, from simple to complex, would be the greatest discovery of any evolutionary geologist! But alas, such has never been found.

Declared A.S. Romer in *Genetics, Paleontology and Evolution:* " ' Links' are missing just where we most fervently desire them, and it is all too probable that many 'links' will continue to be missing."[3]

Added author William Stokes, in the same vein: "The fossil record tends to be *weakest* in those portions that are of most interest to evolutionists; that is, in specimens pertaining to the origin and early stages of the individual groups of organisms. Not only the whole problem of the origin of species but also the appearance of life on the earth is involved here."[4]

Charles Darwin was appalled at the paucity of evidence for evolution in the geologic record in his day. He admitted, "From these several considerations, it cannot be doubted that the geological record, viewed as a whole, is extremely imperfect; but if we confine our attention to any one formation, it becomes much more difficult to understand why we do not therein find closely graduated varieties between the allied species which lived at its commencement and at its close."[5]

Could it be that these graduated varieties simply don't exist—and never did?

In the past hundred years since Darwin's time, in spite of the vast amount of geologic research which has been done, geologists are still plagued by the problem of manifold "missing links."

Today there is no escape for evolutionists by bemoaning the poverty of the fossil record. It has become almost unmanageably rich. A super abundance of fossils have been unearthed.

Despite this abundance of fossils, however, the fossil record continues to be composed *mainly of gaps.*

Writing in *Evolution*, September 1974, David B. Kitts, of the School of Geology and Geophysics, at the University of Oklahoma, says:

> Despite the bright promise that paleontology provides a means of "seeing" evolution, it has presented some nasty difficulties for evolutionists the most notorious of which is the presence of "gaps" in the fossil record. *Evolution requires intermediate forms between species and paleontology does not provide them.* The gaps must therefore be a contingent feature of the record.[6]

These "notorious gaps," Kitts goes on, have created unresolved problems in evolutionary theory and lend no support to the "synthetic" theory espoused by Simpson. No evolutionary theory yet proposed has been able to adequately explain these embarrassing gaps. They play havoc with standard evolutionary concepts and leave Darwin's theory without any paleontological support.

Glen L. Jepsen, Ernest Mayr, and George Gaylord Simpson discuss this insurmountable problem facing evolution: "A few paleontologists even today cling to the idea that these gaps will be closed by further collecting . . . but most regard the *observed discontinuities* as real and have sought an explanation for them."[7]

If the discontinuity is real, the statement in the book of Genesis that God created plants, fish, terrestrial animals and birds "each after its own kind" is supported strongly by the geologic record.

Is Genesis right after all?

Geologists call the strata containing the earliest fossils of abundant animal life the Cambrian system. The Cambrian system is generally estimated to have occurred 600 to 440 million years ago. Before this time, in the Precambrian world, only a few forms of comparatively simple life existed. Precambrian fossils include algae, bacteria, worms, jellyfish and arthropods.

Yet astonishing as it may seem, the Cambrian strata contain fossils of exceedingly intricate forms of life—including sponges and over a thousand species of trilobites.

Says Gairdner B. Moment, professor of biology at Goucher College: "The most surprising fact about this oldest of all fossil records is that, with the exception of the vertebrates, there are representatives of all the major groups of animals, protozoa, sponges, coelenterates, annelids, echinoderms, mollusks, arthropods, brachiopods; all were there."[8]

Notice—mark well that *when the curtain first rises early in the fossil record*, a vast assemblage of complex living creatures is startlingly revealed. A full-blown armada stands before us. Biologists explain: "Nearly all phyla which leave any kind of a fossil record are well represented in Cambrian rocks—many of them by several groups, which *already* show the distinctive characters of modern classes."[9]

In the earliest strata containing abundant animal life every major division of invertebrate animal life is already found present. Why is this so if all these life forms had *gradually* evolved from a few simpler creatures? Why the apparent *sudden* appearance of all these life forms?

The Larousse Encyclopedia of the Earth states:

> One of the great unsolved mysteries of science is the missing fossil record of life which (supposedly) evolved between 600 million and 1,400 million years ago, during the late Pre-Cambrian. . . . In many places thick marine sedimentary strata (more than 5,000 feet) are known to lie beneath formations containing Early Cambrian fossils. *Diligent search* in these rocks, many of which resemble the fossiliferous beds about them, *has failed to reveal the missing record.* [10]

The record of most of the ancestors of the Cambrian Fauna are missing. However in the late Precambrian Fauna of Australia and Africa (which some workers would place in the Cambrian) are found jellyfish, and arthropods. Below this the only evidence of animal life are fossil traces of worms.[11] Most of those animal phyla appear *suddenly* in the record, at about the same time, without ancestors.

Why? Could it be because they were suddenly created?

Admits noted biologist G.G. Simpson: ". . . it remains true, as every paleontologist knows, that most new species, genera, and families, and that nearly all categories above the level of families, *appear in the record suddenly* and are *not* led up to by known, gradual, complete continuous transitional sequences."[12]

In the earliest record in the rocks, life appears suddenly—full blown, diversified, and complex! Where, then, is the hard evidence for the evolutionary theory?

It is missing. Writes Charles H.S. Ladd:

> Most paleontologists today give little thought to fossiliferous rocks older than the Cambrian, thus ignoring the most important *missing link of all.* Indeed the missing Pre-Cambrian record cannot properly be described as a link for it is in reality, about *nine-tenths of the chain of life*: the first nine-tenths. [13]

There are few types of animal fossils and they are restricted to various kinds of algae and bacteria before the Cambrian period. All the complex and hard-shelled animals, such as the trilobites which appeared in abundance at the beginning of the Cambrian had no predecessors in the Precambrian. Thus at the earliest strata where evidence of abundant animal life appears—it appears in sudden diversity and with startling abruptness.

How can this sudden appearance of life be explained? Not very easily. There is no general agreement as to where to place the base of the Cambrian. It has been placed at the unconformity below the lowest stratum containing abundant faunal hard parts. The boundary is often very discrete, giving the appearance of sudden introduction and proliferation of animal life.

A number of theories have been advanced to explain the apparent lack of Precambrian ancestors of the Cambrian faunal assemblages. However, these theories have been rebutted. For example, it was held that there was a lack of $CaCO_3$ to produce hard parts, but Precambrian carbonate rocks are abundant. It was also held that sedimentation was lacking during the transition between Precambrian and Cambrian, but transitional sequences have been discovered.

Another theory suggested that metamorphism destroyed fossils in the Precambrian. But delicate sedimentary structures are present in Precambrian rocks of all ages, and fossils therefore should have been preserved.

The simple fact is that diligent search has failed to reveal Precambrian fossils. Although continuous searching has led to the discovery of numerous "Precambrian metazoans," Preston E. Cloud, Jr., dismisses these as algae or inorganic phenomena except for the Ediacaran faunal assemblages with which he begins the Cambrian.[14]

This fact of the sudden appearance of life forms in the Cambrian is strong evidence that life in the Cambrian was created suddenly—as we would expect if life was divinely created.

But now let's take a look at the origins of various specific types of animals. Do they reveal a long, gradual evolutionary history thus documenting the evolutionary theory?

The Origin of Insects

What about flies, mosquitoes, and other insects?

Ross E. Hutchins, a well-known entomologist, is an expert on insects. He observes: "As with other animals, the clues to their past history are buried in the earth as fossilized remains, but there are vast gaps in the fossil record covering millions of years. . . ."

This authority continues:". . . and when we go beyond the the Carboniferous period, which began about 300 million years ago [according to the theory], *the trail fades completely.* Insect origins beyond that point are shrouded in mystery. It might almost seem that the insects had *suddenly appeared* on the scene, but this is not in agreement with accepted *ideas* of animal origins."[15]

If we are willing to accept the evidence, then all the facts indicate that insects appeared suddenly upon the earth. This may not coincide with evolutionary theory—but it does match up well with the alternative of creation.

The same is true of the appearance of animals with backbones, called vertebrates.

Vertebrate Fossils

The animals with backbones first appear in the geologic record in great diversity and complete with backbones already present. Earliest fossils show no transition from invertebrate to vertebrate.

Says the paleontologist Romer: "In sediments of late Silurian and early Devonian age, numerous fishlike vertebrates of varied types are present, and it is obvious that a long evolutionary history had taken place before that time. But of that history we are still mainly ignorant."

Continues Romer: "The appearance of the typical bony fishes in the geologic record is a *dramatically sudden one*. . . . In the Middle Devonian, however, *all the major types*—ray-finned forms, crossopterygians and lung fishes—appear *full fledged and diversified,* and at once dominate the scene."[16]

The sudden appearance of fish in the early fossil record is more strong evidence that the theory of evolution is a fraud.

Evolutionists of course feel that "*belief* in the descent of the later bony fishes from unknown forms closely related to the acanthodians is extremely *reasonable*." "But" they do admit, "this is, of course, *pure speculation*, for which at present there is *not the slightest scrap of fossil evidence.*"[17] But if this conclusion is admittedly "pure speculation," without a single scrap of supporting evidence, then isn't the theory of sudden Divine creation a better alternative?

What about the origin of whales? Surely the largest animal which has ever existed has left some record of its origin!

The whale's past is extremely obscure. Supposedly, sometime after 100 million years ago some smallish, four-footed land animals began a series of extraordinarily rapid evolutionary changes. In the span of 50 million years they learned to swim instead of walk, and reproduced offspring able to swim from the moment they were born.[18]

What were these smallish, four-footed land animals that evolved into whales? Geologists haven't the slightest idea! "No fossil remains of the land ancestors of the whale have been discovered as yet,"[19] says William Stokes.

Flying Reptiles and Birds

The origin of the flying reptiles, presents no less a problem for the evolutionist.

One of the earliest flying reptiles was Dimorphodon. It was a small, queer-looking reptile, with an enormous head and a long tail. The fourth finger of each hand was greatly elongated to support a wing membrane.

Dimorphodon was, in spite of its strange appearance, a highly specialized animal. Evolutionists believe it must have had a long evolutionary history bridging the gap from ground-living or dwelling reptiles to fully fledged flying types. But, remarkably, there is not the slightest trace of this history to be found in the geologic record![20]

Reptiles, of course, are supposed to have evolved into birds, giving rise to our fine-feathered aerial acrobats, ranging from the incredible hummingbird to the giant albatross.

Surely a great evolutionary leap such as this must be well documented in the geologic record. Or is it?

When we look into the subject e find the contrary is true: "In spite of the *patchiness* of the evidence it is clear that birds are closely related to the reptiles."[21] Patchy evidence! But this should be appalling to a died-in-the-wool evolutionist.

Furthermore, in our search for the documentary fossil evidence, we run across statements such as: "The origin of birds is largely a matter of deduction. There is *no fossil evidence* of the stages through which the remarkable change from reptile to bird was achieved."[22]

One fossil creature, the archaeopteryx, does have characteristics of both bird and reptile, and occurred during the time the transition was supposed to take place between reptiles and birds. But there are no other transitional fossils. There should be a graded, complete series. No creatures with partially developed wings are found in the fossil record!

Since evidence is lacking, why should we *assume* birds evolved from reptiles? Is that scientific?

The greatest alleged "proof" of evolution—the geologic record—seems to be crumbling to dust in our hands! When we examine it carefully—we find no proof at all. Rather, we run into strong evidence of a series of sudden, full-fledged creations!

Surprising as it may seem, we find that the geologic record seems to provide more evidence of creation than evolution!

The fossil record says nothing about any supposed evolutionary development of countless creatures. The evidence points to the sudden creation of insects, reptiles, birds, whales, fish and every other creature.

Perhaps a slower creature, the turtle, would substantiate the evolutionary concept? Again, the evidence is disappointing. Turtles *seemingly arose suddenly* in Triassic times!

The presence of snakes on the earth likewise cannot be accounted for by the theory of evolution. There are no fossils available of lizards which were in the process of losing their limbs. Snakes are assumed to be derived from the lizards, but there is no certainty as to the point of origin.[23]

Says another specialist: "Snakes are essentially highly modified lizards, but exactly when their divergence from lizard ancestors took place, we do not know."[24]

What about rabbits? Rodents and rabbits "appear fully developed at the close of the Paleocene."[25] Horses, rhinoceroses, cattle, sheep, pigs, goats, deer—all the odd-toed and even-toed hoofed animals—"appear *abruptly* at the beginning of the Eocene."[26]

Lions, elephants, monkeys, dogs, cats, bears, etc., all appear fully formed with no long evolutionary ancestry!

Where, then, is all the highly lauded proof of evolution in the geologic record?

Living "Fossils"

"Living fossils" also present a problem for evolutionists.

"Living fossils" are animals or plants which are alive today, yet have exact or almost exact counterparts in the fossil record that are supposed to be millions of years old. This would mean that such forms of life have reproduced generation after generation for millions of years withoug evolving.

An outstanding example of a "living fossil" is the *coelacanth* —a fish which was until recently thought extinct for millions of years. One was caught in 1938 and others have since been captured and kept alive briefly. From the time they first appear in the fossil record until their discovery alive in the 20th century, coelacanths have kept the same form and structure. "Here is one of the great mysteries of evolution" says Jacques Millot in *Scientific American.*[27]

No less a problem is found by investigating the fossil representatives of the cockroach, dragonfly or spider. These little creatures we are told have been around for 250,000,000 years. But like other insects, they look today much the same as they did in the beginning! An article in the November 1951 issue of *Scientific American* states: ". . . by and large the insect population of today remains remarkably similar to that of the earlier age." [28] The fossils of these insects have been beautifully

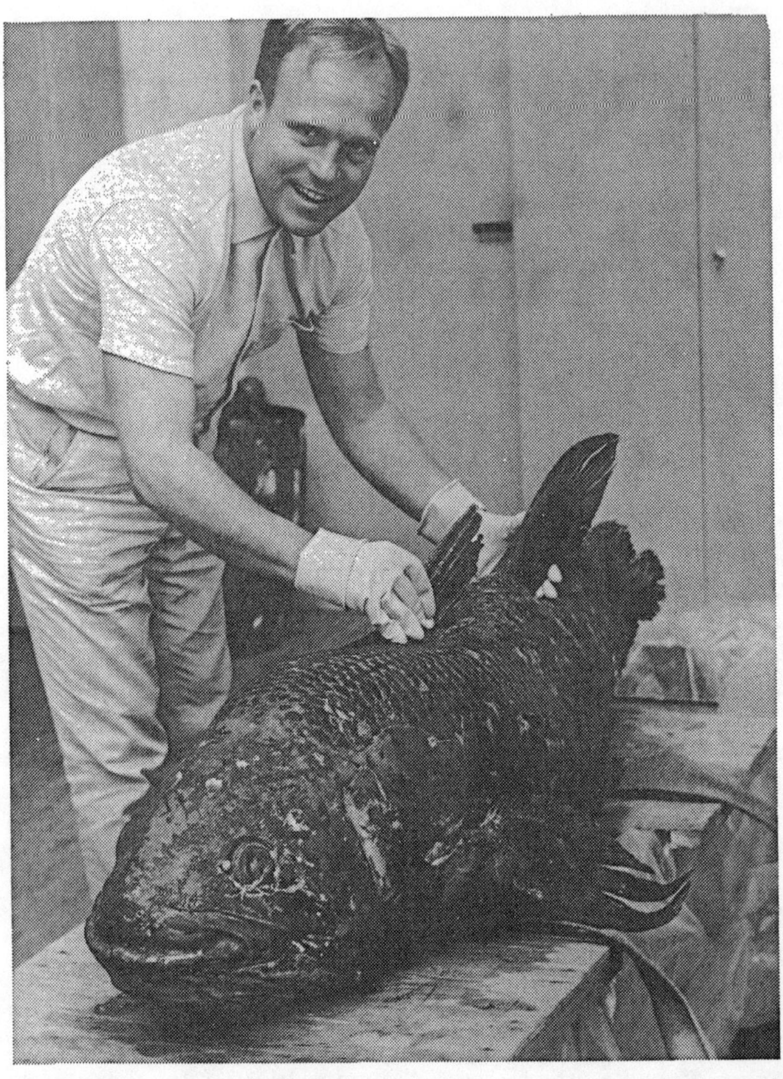

The primeval fish Latimeria, also called the coelacanth, a relic from the days of the dinosaurs, was believed to have disappeared 60 million years ago—until a living specimen was discovered in 1939, the "biological find of the century."—*Courtesy of the Ludwigsburg Museum of Natural History, Germany.*

preserved in amber. They are almost identical to those still alive today.

Says entomologist Ross E. Hutchins, "Strangely, many of these ancient insects resemble very closely those that live today. At least six different species of ants found in amber (where they are remarkably well preserved) are so closely related to modern types that they cannot be distinguished from them."[29]

The opossum, too, is a "living fossil." Modern opossums are virtually the same as opossum specimens found in Cretaceous and Tertiary rocks generally dated about 60 million years ago!

The existence of so many "living fossils" forces us to question the theory of evolution. Why didn't they evolve? If these fossils which match modern-day life forms are millions of years old, we find the theory of evolution straining to account for their continued *unchanged* existence!

No wonder evolutionists exclaim, "We marvel at these veterans of the struggle for existence and seek to understand why they have survived while their contemporaries have long ago vanished. The secrets of their success may be difficult to uncover or to understand, for there seems to be no common characteristics that account for their survival."[30]

The answer to this riddle, of course, is amazingly simple if we acknowledge that all life forms on earth—from insects to mammals—were the product of divine creation!

The existence of a divine Creator would help explain many of the perplexing riddles, unsolved mysteries, and unexplained enigmas of the geologic record.

He who will not reason, is a bigot; he who cannot is a fool; and he who dares not, is a slave.

William Drummond

Chapter Thirteen

The Fossil Record—Fact or Fiction?

How old is the earth and life upon it? Was life really created just 6,000 years ago as most creationists believe? Did God create fossils in the earth's strata merely to confuse, disturb, and annoy men—as a cosmic joke upon evolutionists?

Special creationists, by and large, interpret the biblical account of creation as stating the stars, the earth, and all life were created suddenly just six millenia ago. They reject almost all the scientific explanations of the geological column and hold that the entire column is primarily the result of Noah's flood.

Since they believe that all life on earth has only existed for about 6,000 years, and that the trilobites, brachiopods, dinosaurs and man were all created within a six-day span, or "creation week," creationists must conclude that all the paleontologic evidence in the earth has accumulated over a total span of 6,000 years. Most of the strata, they likewise tell us, was laid down violently, in the cataclysm known as "The Deluge."

But can these views be reconciled with the evidence in the rocks beneath our feet? If God is the Author of both holy writ and the cosmos, then it should be possible to harmonize the written record with the physical record in the earth. Does the Bible provide for the possibility of the earth, and life upon it, being perhaps millions of years in development?

Let's view both sides of the issue without favoritism.

The Ongoing Debate

The basic principles of the science of geology were laid down from the seventeenth century to the early 1900s. Nicolaus Steno in 1669 studied crystal growth and larger features, including layered sedimentary and volcanic rocks, and demonstrated that these phenomena result from sequential changes and require time to transpire.

In 1796 the Scottish naturalist James Hutton made another epochal discovery. He independently rediscovered Steno's method of sifting the evidence of the earth's past, and showed that gravity, erosion, sedimentation, heat and cold, volcanic eruptions and earthquakes are sufficient to explain the history of the earth. He believed, with Newton, that God has always worked through natural laws and that the works of nature glorify Him, and attest to His existence.

Hutton concluded that the known rates of change would mean that the earth had to be more than merely 6,000 years old, however. His contribution to the science of geology was the concept of uniformitarianism–the present is the key to the past.[1]

Charles Lyell, a contemporary of Charles Darwin, adopted Hutton's principle and elaborated upon it in his three volumn work *Principles of Geology*, which became the standard work on the subject.

Long before Darwin's evolutionary theory, William Smith discovered that changes of types of fossils found in rock could be used to determine the sequence and relative ages of the deposits in which they were found. In 1815 this English surveyor, engineer, and field geologist, published the first geologic map of England showing that each stratum contained organized fossils peculiar to itself.

Meanwhile, Georges Cuvier, a French naturalist, was organizing ancient shells and bones into a chronological succession of genera and species, many of which had become extinct. Wondering what events led to their demise in ages gone by, he speculated that a series of cataclysmic events had reshaped the earth, destroying former kinds of life. Cuvier embraced the concept of catastrophism and reconciled it with his belief in divine creation.

Baron Georges Cuvier, author of 12 large volumes on vertebrate fossils, was convinced that each different group of fossil animals was the result of a separate creation and had ultimately disappeared in a violent cataclysm. One of these catastrophes, of course, was Noah's flood.[2]

Cuvier, although lauded in his own day, and recognized as a genius, no longer merits the same respect among evolutionists who reject the concept of catastrophism.

Throughout the years of debate, the fundamentalist religious view, though dealt a severe blow by the growing discoveries regarding the age of the earth, maintained its conviction that these discoveries were in error.

Fossils, in particular, were a puzzle. Many of the ancients did not believe they were remains of living things at all. They were "jokes" or "sports" of nature, resulting from vapors, emanations, or spontaneous generation. Aristotle, for example, thought that fish fossils were fish that wandered into crevices looking for food, and were hardened into stone.[3]

The controversy about fossils was heated during the Middle Ages. Arguments raged fiercely for about 200 years, some arguing that the Creator had made several attempts at forming living things, producing many unsatisfactory forms, before succeeding. Others thought fossils were works of the devil created to deceive mankind. Some attributed fossils to Noah's flood. One fossil of a giant salamander in 1726 was declared the remains of a miserable sinner who had died in the Noachian deluge.[4]

Since those times of ignorance and superstition, however, the world of geology has come a long way. A vast amount of the earth's strata has now been carefully examined, scrutinized, sifted, analyzed, and investigated by thousands of geologists. Much has been discovered that bears heavily upon the question of the age of the earth, life, creation, and evolution.

What do these discoveries have to say? What do the *facts* of geology reveal about life on this planet? Does the evidence support instantaneous creation of all life forms simultaneously?

Or does it support long intervals of time in the geologic record?

Assumptions of Neo-Creationism

One popular book in conservative theological circles maintains that virtually all of the geologic column is the result of the Noachian deluge and associated catastrophism. Authors Morris and Whitcomb declare in *The Genesis Flood*:

> Any deposits formed before the Flood would almost certainly have been profoundly altered by the great complex of hydrodynamic and tectonic forces unleashed during the Deluge period. The fundamental principle of historical geology, that of uniformitarianism, however valid it may be for the study of deposits formed since the Deluge, can therefore not legitimately be applied before that time.[5]

These authors claim that the fossil sequence in the earth's strata rather often appears in the reverse order from that demanded by evolutionary theory. They maintain that the uniformitarian scheme of historical geology is basically fallacious. Whitcomb and Morris assert:

> Uniformitarianism, in other words, has simply been assumed, not proved. Catastrophism has simply been denied, not refuted.[6]

They add with conviction:

> But as a matter of fact it is not even true that uniformity is a possible explanation for most of the earth's geologic formations, as any candid examination of the facts ought to reveal.

Are these modern contentions of creationists really true? Can the preponderance of the geologic record be adequately explained in terms of one worldwide cataclysm such as the Biblical deluge during the time of man?

These are harsh, stinging indictments of modern geology, and paleontology, if true. But what are the facts?

Another creationist, Frank Lewis Marsh, in *Life, Man, and Time,* puts the problem this way:

> The Bible-believing scientist must face squarely the question, In the area of natural science which shall supersede, the clear assertions of God's inspired Book, or modern man's interpretation of what he

> thinks he sees in nature? . . . According to Bible chronology only a few thousand years have passed since the creation of the ancestors of our modern plants and animals . . . Contrariwise, if one accepts the assumption that the inorganic radioisotope clocks were reset wherever they became associated with fossil-bearing material, then apparently at least 600 million years have passed since plants and animals first appeared successively from that time over a duration of some 600 million years.[8]

Must the believer in the Bible choose between geological science and his faith in the Scriptures? Is there an insurmountable contradiction between the revelation of Genesis and the record beneath our feet?

First, let's take a look at precisely what the rocks tell us, and then examine what the Scriptures assert.

What is Geology?

Geology, defined, is the study of the earth. Historical geology is the study of the earth's *history.* Information about the past history of the earth accumulates at a rapid pace. The last decade has witnessed a remarkable growth in the knowledge of the geology of the earth, both above and under the seas.

What do the carefully collected and preserved facts of geology tell us?

Admits William Stokes, author of *Essentials of Earth History*, "At present, the accumulation of facts is well in advance of explanations and theories. We can ask more questions than we can answer, and be confident that most current theories will be thoroughly tested by new discoveries. . . . *Theories must be revised or abandoned as new facts invalidate them.*"[9]

This is the attitude scientists take, and it is a logical, sound approach. Hopefully, theologians will be willing to take the same approach, and not reject factual data because it conflicts with preconceived dogma.

No spot on earth has escaped geologic change. The history of previous eras lies exposed on the earth's surface, and lies buried in the rocks of the earth. Mountain-building, the shape of the continents, the size and the extent of the oceans, and the history of life on earth has been carefully preserved, if we have eyes willing to see it!

The prevailing theory of the earth's history in geological circles is the theory of uniformitarianism which tells us that the earth's strata has largely come about by *uniform, gradual processes.* According to this theory, "the present is the key to the past." In other words, what occurs on the earth today is a reliable guide to what occurred in previous times or eras. Since worldwise catastrophes are not occurring today, it follows that they have never occurred.

Says William Stokes: "Uniformitarianism rejects supernatural (miraculous or incomprehensible) effects as long as natural ones will suffice. It appeals to known laws or principles rather than to unproven or unprovable suppositions. It seeks explanations of the past, based on processes that can be observed in action at the present, and not those based on pure imagination."[10]

No thinking man denies that the same geologic processes in effect today also worked on the earth throughout its history. Eroding rivers have cut channels through rock; the seas have worn away coastlines; the winds have helped wear away mountains. These processes are interminable—and go on forever.

But can the earth's whole geologic history be accounted for by these common, everyday processes, occurring at the rates as they do now? Or can the geologic column, from trilobites to wooly mammoths, be best explained by the Noachian deluge?

Uniformitarianism became the geologic backbone of Darwin's theory of evolution. One of the originators of theory, Charles Lyell (1797-1875), greatly influenced Charles Darwin. They were close friends. Lyell's principle of geologic gradualism is the first essential element in Charles Darwin's theory of evolution.

Lyell laid the foundation of modern geology with his theory of uniformitarianism (previously advanced by James Hutton and John Playfair). In his *Principles of Geology* (1832) he paved the way for Darwin's *Origin of Species*, because his theory provided evolutionists with millions of years for life to have evolved. But remember, even if the basic principles of uniformitarianism are valid, this fact in *no* way proves the veracity of Darwin's theory!

THE GEOLOGIC TIME SCALE

ERA	PERIOD	EPOCH	AGE	DURATION
CENOZOIC	QUARTERNARY	RECENT PLEISTOCENE	0-1,000,000	1,000,000
		PLIOCENE	1-13,000,000	13,000,000
	TERTIARY	MIOCENE	13-25,000,000	12,000,000
		OLIGOCENE	25-36,000,000	11,000,000
		EOCENE	36-58,000,000	22,000,000
		PALEOCENE	58-63,000,000	6,000,000
MESOZOIC	CRETACEOUS		63-135,000,000	72,000,000
	JURASSIC		135-181,000,000	46,000,000
	TRIASSIC		181-230,000,000	49,000,000
PALEOZOIC	PERMIAN		230-280,000,000	50,000,000
	PENNSYLVANIAN		280-310,000,000	30,000,000
	MISSISSIPPIAN		310-345,000,000	35,000,000
	DEVONIAN		345-405,000,000	60,000,000
	SILURIAN		405-425,000,000	20,000,000
	ORDOVICIAN		425-500,000,000	75,000,000
	CAMBRIAN		500-600,000,000	100,000,000
PRECAMBRIAN	UPPER MIDDLE LOWER	The Precambrian lasted for at least 2½ billion years.		

The Geologic Column

If the record buried in the earth's rocks revealed that simple fossils were always underneath and complex fossils on top, and if the fossils were always found in the same order, then one might be justified in assuming the simple came first. Surprising as it may seem, this is what is found.

Around the world, in vast deposits, simpler organisms such as trilobites are *always* found in the lowest fossil-bearing strata and are *never* found in association with dinosaurs, or strata containing fossils of mammals.

Consider the extent of the geologic column:

"If a pile were to be made by using the greatest thickness of sedimentary beds of each geologic age, it would be at least 100 miles high.... It is, of course, impossible to have even a considerable fraction of this at one place. The Grand Canyon of the Colorado, for example, is only one mile deep."[11]

This column has been arduously pieced together on the basis of similarity of fossils and strata on a worldwide basis. William Smith (1769-1839), called "the Father of Stratigraphy," was the first to observe that different rock layers could be identified by the fossils they contained. Thus he was able to predict the location and properties of rocks below the surface on the basis of the fossils he found exposed in canals and quarries. For the first time it became possible to correlate deposits on a global scale.[12]

Now that a massive geological column has been pieced together, what does it show? Could the entire column be the result of one flood during the time of man? If so, then consider: That global flood had to account for sediment 100 miles deep! Could one deluge, lasting just one year, do the trick?

The Grand Canyon

The Grand Canyon is a classic study in stratigraphy and the geologic column. Almost two miles of sedimentary rocks are found in the Arizona-Utah area, ranging all the way from the Precambrian at the bottom of the Grand Canyon to the Eocene Wasatch deposit at Bryce Canyon in Utah. From the bottom of the Grand Canyon we can trace the geologic column upward, and as we go northward into Utah, the column continues

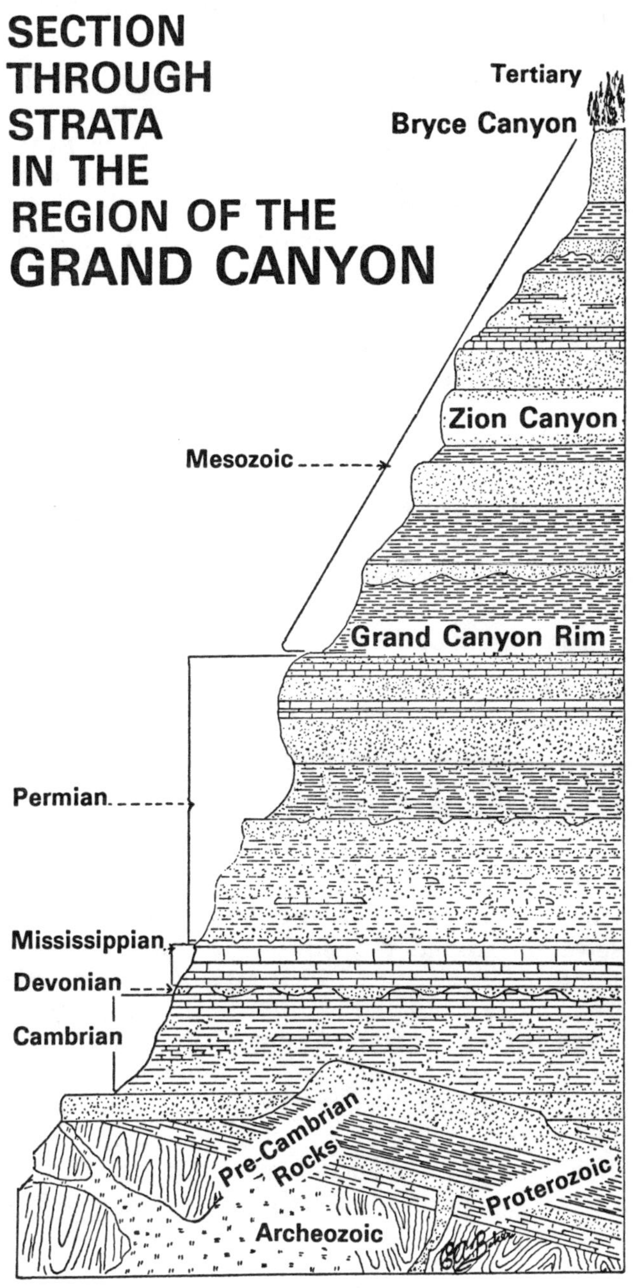
After McKee, Von Engeln and Caster
SECTION THROUGH STRATA IN THE REGION OF THE GRAND CANYON
Tertiary
Bryce Canyon
Zion Canyon
Mesozoic
Grand Canyon Rim
Permian
Mississippian
Devonian
Cambrian
Pre-Cambrian Rocks
Proterozoic
Archeozoic

through the Mesozoic, ending with the Eocene. All but two of the geologic periods are represented.

Robert Macdonald and Dick Burky, both of them experienced in practical geology, have examined these strata, one upon another, and found that the fossils do follow the sequence they are supposed to according to the principle of faunal succession. According to this principle, the fossils always occur in a certain definite order and no other. Their studies showed that there is a natural sequence of fossils. Mr. Burky relates:

> Local sequences such as the one in the Grand Canyon can be correlated worldwide. To a great extent, it is possible to make this correlation by physical criteria only. Where this fails, fossils are used. The use of fossils only is justified in such circumstances because where both kinds of evidence are available, there is never any contradiction between them.[13]

Neo-creationists accuse geologists of "reasoning in a circle" because they use fossils to date the rocks in which they are found when other dating methods are not available. Superficially, this may seem like circular reasoning. As an article in the 1956 edition of the *Encyclopedia Britannica* stated:

> It cannot be denied that from a strictly philosophical standpoint geologists are here arguing in a circle. The succession of organisms has been determined by a study of their remains buried in the rocks, and the relative ages of the rocks are determined by the remains of organisms that they contain.[14]

Though creationists like to quote the above statement, the author goes on to point out that this is only an apparent paradox. The order of the fossils is a matter of direct observation around the globe, and the fossils are used as an index to determine the rock strata only where other physical means cannot be used.

Examination of the Grand Canyon supports this fact. Starting at the bottom of the Canyon, in the upper Precambrian, we find fossil algae. In the Cambrian formations, trilobites and brachiopods are the first animal remains that are found. The first vertebrates appear in the Devonian Temple Butte Limestone in the form of fossil fish. The 550-foot-thick

Redwall Limestone of Mississippian age contains the shells of marine animals such as brachiopods, mollusks and sea lilies.

Creationists have suggested that the Coconino formation in the Paleozoic was water deposited and resulted from the Noachian deluge. Militating against this conclusion are several factors: The Coconino formation is a cross-bedded sandstone, and the cross bedding of this formation in the Grand Canyon is of the wind-deposited type. Wind-deposited sand has a characteristic frosted surface, and the grains in the Coconino sandstone show the frosting effect.

Further, the Coconino sandstone has tracks of land animals in it. Tracks would not have been preserved under water in the detail in which they have been found, nor would one expect to find land animals under water. Tracks of this kind are made in sand wet by rain and then covered by more sand.

Overlaying the Coconino in the Grand Canyon, is the Toroweap Formation. Here the fossils are water dwelling brachiopods and gastropods (snails) which are totally missing from the Coconino.

Was the Coconino formation rapidly deposited by water as neo-creationists assume for a Noachian deluge? The surface upon which the Coconino was deposited was a mud surface, and the contact line is very sharp. With rapid water deposition, turbulence there would have generated a broad, mixed boundary. Thus there is no evidence the Coconino was water-deposited.

Declares Robert Macdonald:

> The rest of the formations to the rim of the Canyon are all classified as Permian, the period closing the Paleozoic era. In the Supai Formation we find the fossil remains of the first land plants and animals. Similar fossils are preserved in the next formation, the Hermit Shale, which includes ferns and cone-bearing plants, insect wings and the tracks of salamander-like animals. The Coconino sand stone, which we discussed earlier, has within its layers of consolidated windblown sand the tracks of reptiles and amphibians. The Kaibab Limestone which rims the top of the Canyon has more marine fossils including brachiopods, coral, sea lilies, sponges and shark teeth.[15]

Evidence of Time in Utah

As we travel northward into Utah, we pass through a series of Mesozoic and Cenozoic formations more than a mile in thickness. Each one overlies the preceding formation. The Triassic Moenkopi Formation contains the trails of land animals in some places, and sea shells in other places. The Shinarump and Chinle formations contain the petrified wood of conifers. The petrified wood of the famous petrified forests of northern Arizona, preserved in the Chinle formation, includes tree trunks *standing* in the place they grew. Standing tree trunks are hardly the result one would expect if all the Grand Canyon formations were laid down by the Noachian deluge as neo-creationists assume.

After pointing out the evidence of faunal succession in this region, Macdonald asks:

> Can we account for this worldwide sequence by a universal flood? If during a flood one group of organisms were brought in from one area and deposited, then another assemblage from another area were deposited on top of that, and so on, we would have a local sequence. But the chances would be against the deposition of fossils in the same order in a local sequence in another area. What would be the chance that the same order would occur in all sequences worldwide? It would be nil![16]

A catastrophic flood, such as creationists envision, would tend to mix up sediments and fossils in a more random way than is actually found. Declares Macdonald:

> But instead, we find, for instance, the perfect separation of trilobites and dinosaurs. There is *never* any mixing of their remains as one might expect if they both died in the same cataclysm.
>
> The only explanation is that each geological horizon does indeed represent a definite time in the past during which the same assemblage of fossils was being deposited in many parts of the world. Slow deposition is therefore necessary to give time for the worldwide faunal changes from one stratum to another.[17]

Faunal succession as evidenced in the geologic column does not prove evolution. It merely shows that life forms have varied from one time to another through geologic history.

Algal Reefs

One major time indicator in the geologic column is a vertical series of algal reefs in the Eocene Green River formation in northwestern Colorado. Examining them on a field trip in the summer of 1971, Messrs. Robert Macdonald, Dick Burky and John Hopkinson found the following, as reported by Robert Macdonald:

> They obviously grew in the place they are found. The total thickness of the reefs was about 110 feet. Algal reefs have been studied in present day lakes, and based on present growth rates, these reefs would have taken 6,000 years to grow. Even if we double or triple the present growth rate, we are still in trouble if we try to account for them this side of Adam, especially when we consider the other occurrences during the Tertiary. Hundreds more feet of shales between the algal reefs require more time for deposition. Several other Eocene formations lie both above and below the Green River formation. The total thickness of these Eocene formations is more than a mile. The Green River formation itself, 2,600 feet thick in this area is mostly fine grained carbonaceous shales. The algal reefs as well as other environmental indicators show deposition in a fresh water lake. For instance associated with the algal reefs are abundant öolites indicating gentle wave action over a period of time.
>
> Not only a long period of time is required to account for the Tertiary deposits, but more time is needed to uplift and erode these formations to their present configurations. There is no way to account for the Tertiary here unless we assign it to the pre-Adamic period.[18]

Since fossil mammals are found in the Green River and the Eocene formations, it is apparent that mammals and angiosperms existed in that world before Adam.

Zonal Succession

Zones are the smallest recognized units within a geologic system such as the Cambrian, Ordovician, Silurian, etc. There is a definite sequence of zones within each system, even as there is a definite sequence of systems.

The fossil record contains hundreds of zones, each characterized by its own unique faunal assemblage. How could such worldwide sequences have been created, each in agreement with sequences in other areas, based on the sorting activity of water in a Noachian Deluge? The only logical way to account for faunal succession in the geologic column is *time*, not catastrophism. The matter is summed up best by Curt Teichert who says:

> It would be easy to repeat this investigation for almost every critical zone fossil or fauna throughout the geologic column for hundreds, perhaps thousands of test cases. The conclusions would be the same. In the words of Jeletzky (1956) we would have to "invoke a miracle," if for example, we were to assume anything but worldwide contemporaneous deposition for each of the 55 ammonite zones of the Jurassic. Not all of them occur everywhere, but wherever two or more are found in superposition they occur in the same order.[19]

Evidence for the passage of long periods of time is also provided by the studies of paleoecology, the study of ancient environments as indicated by fossil assemblages. Geologists can discern continuous changes in the environment with respect to time by means of such studies. A single catastrophe would not produce an orderly ecological succession of fossils, as the record reveals.

Coal Deposits

Coal deposits, for example, are commonly found in a sequence of beds, called a cyclothem. A cyclothem indicates a cycle of sedimentation and commonly has a sequence of up to ten beds, often including limestone. The coal beds of Kansas, Oklahoma, Illinois, Indiana, Kentucky, West Virginia and Pennsylvania were formed in the vast coastal swamps that existed during the Pennsylvanian period. Studies of coal beds reveal changes in the life forms and ecology from the bottom of the beds to the top, with intermittent burials followed by changing environments and new kinds of vegetation.[20]

Where, then, does this lead us?

The evidence for faunal succession and long periods of time

in which life existed on earth is overwhelming. How are these facts to be understood in the light of the Biblical record? Do they contradict it?

Not at all!

Progressive Creation

We cannot dogmatically proclaim that "the original creation" took place at a given hour, day, and year in the past. The Bible simply states, "In the beginning . . ."

The concept of progressive change, growth, and maturation, is distinctly Biblical. When God created a nation to obey and follow his laws, he began with one man—Abraham. And over centuries, Abraham's family grew into a great nation, and a company of nations. God promised Abraham, among other things, that his descendants would someday dominate the earth.[21] This was not fulfilled, even in type, until the time of David and Solomon, almost one thousand years later!

Too often, we forget the real meaning of the words of Peter, "But do not ignore this one fact, beloved, that with the Lord one day is as a thousand years, and a thousand years as one day."[22] We forget that God is very patient, careful, and wise, and does nothing without a purpose.

The precise processes of creation are not revealed in the pages of Scripture. However, God has given us minds with which to think, ponder, and contemplate life, and its beginnings. He has given us the tools with which to explore the remote time of "creation."

A Cosmic Joke?

Theodosious Dobzhansky, professor of genetics at the University of California, Davis, and professor emeritus at the Rockefeller University, New York, presented a paper at the National Association of Biology Teachers convention in San Francisco, in October, 1972. In it he pointed out that it is ludicrous to mistake the Bible for a primer of natural science. Stressing the importance of radiometric evidence in dating the earth, Dobzhansky said that contrary to Bishop Ussher's calculations, the earth did not appear in 4004 B.C.

If the radiometric evidence is wrong, and the duration of the geological and paleontological eras is grossly distorted, Dobzhansky concluded, the Creator must have seen fit to play deceitful tricks on geologists and biologists. If fossils were placed by the Creator where we find them now, deliberately giving the appearance of great antiquity, then God must be absurdly deceitful. Said Dobzhansky, "This is as revolting as it is uncalled for."[23]

Does it make sense that God created the universe to appear much older than it really is? The idea that God created the universe and the earth with "apparent age" is a common belief among creationists.

Sir Bertrand Russell, renowned British philosopher, said of this idea:

> The world [claim some fundamentalists] was created in 4004 B.C., complete with fossils, which were inserted to try our faith. The world was created suddenly, but was made such as it would have been if it had evolved. There is no logical impossibility about this view. And similarly, there is no logical impossibility in the view that the world was created five minutes ago, complete with memories and records.[24]

Would God go to the trouble of making the universe appear older than it really is? Why would He do this? Is such a "universal joke" in keeping with the character of a God "that cannot lie"?

God is not a great deceiver, or a cosmological practical joker. God had no reason to create a world which appears old, but in reality is only 6,000 years old. The great age of the earth, and life upon it, does not conflict with the Scriptures in any way.

When we take both the Biblical record, and the data amassed by scientists, and let the facts speak for themselves, then we must conclude that God indeed *created* the world, and life upon it. But much time passed in the process. The geologic record indicates that God created new forms of life at various stages of His Divine plan. Thus in the earliest strata of the earth containing abundant fossil remains, we find trilobites and brachiopods and other creatures of the sea predominate. At a much later era, we find that dinosaurs—huge reptilian creatures that cause us to stand in awe, today—suddenly appear. At a later time, deciduous trees, mammals, and finally man, take their place in the creation.

Too often we forget the admonition of Solomon, "It is the glory of God to conceal things, but the glory of kings (and scientists, biologists, astronomers, etc.) is to search things out. As the heavens for height, and the earth for depth, so the mind of kings is unsearchable."[25]

The organic diversity of the world and its geologic eras become understandable if we acknowledge that the Creator did not create the living world by "gratuitous caprice."[26]

Chapter Fourteen

The Day The Dinosaurs Died

Recently, I toured the Smithsonian Museum of Natural History in Washington, D.C. One section of the museum is devoted to the "Age of the Reptiles." The most striking fossil was that of a huge dinosaur standing in the middle of a vast room. The throngs of school children passing through and viewing the fossil were obviously awe-struck.

This fossil reminded me of one of the greatest unexplained riddles of paleontology—the extinction of the dinosaurs.

One of the greatest enigmas of paleontology is the mystery of the fate of the dinosaurs—the gigantic "thunder lizards" which once ruled the earth.

Equally mysterious, in the geologic record, are the evidences of similar destruction of other forms of life. The demise of vast numbers of species of creatures has occurred at various points in the geologic record. How does evolutionary theory attempt to explain not only the evolution but the *extinction* of huge numbers and types of animals?

Examination of the record of geology does not support the concept of slow evolution. The geologic record reveals periodic gigantic cataclysms in which sea life perished and land life was similarly entombed. Destructions of ancient life occurred long before the time of man.

Fossil Graveyards

The actual record of the Permian rocks records the destruction of many forms of life.

Says Norman D. Newell of the American Museum of Natural History: "Yet the fossil record of past life is not a simple chronology of uniformly evolving organisms. The record is prevailingly one of erratic, often abrupt changes in environment. . . . Mass extinction, rapid migration and consequent disruption of biological equilibrium on both a local and worldwide scale have accompanied continual environmental changes."[1]

The trilobites, according to geologists, finally perished during the Permian period, "one of the most violent in earth history."[2] This period "was one of the most inhospitable periods for life ever known, and the strain on many organisms was severe. . . . Many failed to survive."[3]

But why? Why did vast numbers, entire species and genera, both plant and animal, suddenly become extinct? Uniformitarian principles do not provide a reasonable answer.

The extinction of the trilobites and other animals was associated with great upheavals in nature.

The Permian, which closed the Paleozoic, was a time of great terrestrial and climatic change. At that time the Appalachian mountain chain along eastern North America uplifted. In South America, India, South Africa, Australia, and New Zealand there was extensive glaciation during the Permian period, apparently longer and more severe than the Pleistocene glaciation.

Many ancient plants and marine animals perished. Tree ferns and their giant relatives all but disappeared. The last of the trilobites also died.

Wholesale Destruction

Remember that under normal conditions comparatively few fossils are preserved. Here and there, remains of organisms now inhabiting the earth are being preserved as fossils. But some geologic formations contain uncounted *millions* of fossils!

Writing for the *Journal of Paleontology*, N.D. Newell points out that: "Robert Broom, the South African paleontologist, estimated that there are *eight hundred thousand million* skeletons of vertebrate animals in the Darroo formation."[4]

What could have suddenly buried so many multiple billions of animals?

Such fossil graveyards are found around the world.

In California, it has been estimated that remains of "more than a billion fish, averaging 6 to 8 inches in length, died on 4 square miles of bay bottom" in ancient times.

In Alberta, Canada, a rich bed of fossil dinosaurs has been found. Innumerable bones and many fine skeletons of dinosaurs and other reptiles have been quarried from a fifteen-mile stretch of a local river to the east of Steveville. This region is a veritable "dinosaurian graveyard."

Dinosaurs have also been found buried together in a coal-mine at Bernissart, Belgium. Bone diggers in the rich Morrison Formation in Wyoming found a tremendous source of dinosaur remains:

> In the Bone-Cabin Quarry . . . we came across a veritable Noah's-ark deposit, a perfect museum of all the animals of the period.
>
> Here are the largest of the giant dinosaurs closely mingled with the remains of the smaller but powerful carnivorous dinosaurs which preyed upon them, also those of the slow and heavy moving armored dinosaurs of the period, as well as the lightest and most bird-like of the dinosaurs.
>
> Finely rounded, complete limbs from eight to ten feet in length are found, especially those of the carnivorous dinosaurs, perfect even to the sharply pointed and recurved tips of their toes.[6]

For such perfect preservation, immediate burial was necessary. For so many to have been buried "closely mingled" together would have required extremely unusual circumstances.

Cretaceous Catastrophe

The mystery of the ultimate extinction of dinosaurs has puzzled millions. The most dramatic and most puzzling event in the history of life on the earth is the change from the Mesozoic Age of Reptiles, to the Age of Mammals. Writes Carl Dunbar: "It is as if the curtain were rung down suddenly on the stage where all the leading roles were taken by reptiles, especially dinosaurs, in great numbers and bewildering variety, and rose again immediately to reveal the same setting but an *entirely new cast*, a cast in which the dinosaurs do not appear at all, other reptiles are mere supernumeraries and the leading parts are all played by mammals. . . ."[7]

Great dinosaurs ruled the land; the pterosaurs and other flying reptiles ruled the sky. In the sea ichthyosaurs and mosasaurs reigned supreme.

Then, with bewildering suddenness, they all vanished. They all disappeared without a single survivor. They perished on all continents! Dinosaur graveyards are found around the world, in California, Colorado, Nebraska, Canada, Belgium, India, South Africa.

What caused this massive extinction around the world? Daniel Cohen points out the fact that "waves of extinction are a sticky problem for modern scientists. Most frankly admit that *mass extinction simply cannot be explained.*"[8]

Darwin himself admitted the extinction of species is a "gratuitous mystery." He confessed, "No one can have marvelled more than I have at the extinction of species."[9]

Darwin asked in astonishment:

> What then, has exterminated so many species and whole genera? The mind at first is irresistably hurried into the belief of some great catastrophe: but thus to destroy animals, both large and small, in South Patagonia, in Brazil, on the Cordillera of Peru, in North America up to Berring's Straits, we must shake the entire framework of the globe.[10]

Have such gigantic, earth-shaking catastrophes occurred before the time of man? If they did, they pose an awesome problem for the theory of evolution. How could life have "evolved" through gradual accumulations of mutations and natural selection under such inauspicious circumstances? Contrary to the expectations of evolutionists, violent environmental changes lead to extinction of life forms, but many new life forms appear in the geologic record at such times. Does life suddenly and rapidly *evolve* into new forms at such times of upheaval? Natural selection is not the sort of process which should be aided by catastrophe—such upheavals in nature should *slow down* evolutionary processes.

Yet, there were a number of startling changes near the end of the Mesozoic Era. Almost all fossiliferous areas indicate that large groups were being exterminated on the land and in the oceans. Dinosaurs and pterodactyls disappeared from the land. In the ocean the last plesiosaurs, mosasaurs, and ichthyosaurs vanished. Also, the ammonite cephalopods, the belemnites, the large rudistid pelecypods, and certain ancient lineages of oysterlike pelecypods became extinct.[11]

Some long lasting upheaval must have caused all these widely varying types of animal life to perish over a period of a few million years at the close of the Cretaceous period, at the end of the Mesozoic.

At this same general period distinct and sudden change took place in the vegetation of the earth.

Earlier, ferns, cone-bearing plants of various types, and cycads were most abundant on the earth. But after mid-Cretaceous times the chief plants were the great group known as the flowering plants, or angiosperms.

The Cretaceous finally ended in a massive upheaval called the Rocky Mountain Revolution. The Rockies, Alps, Himalayas and Andes were raised at that time and much volcanic activity occurred in western North America.

The borderlands of the Pacific became geologically active. Almost all the mountain ranges bordering the Pacific and the islands along its periphery date from the mid-Cretaceous. The great granitic masses of the Andes and Rockies are mostly of Cretaceous age.[12]

Climate was also affected. Large lava flows, igneous activity, erupting volcanoes and earthquake action were the rule rather than the exception.

Vast flooding also occurred. The Cretaceous period saw extensive marine invasions on all continents. "No obvious explanation for this unusual submergence has been discovered," writes William Stokes. "The degree to which *Cretaceous seas* rose and covered the African continent lends weight to the possibility that the rise in sea level was *world-wide* and not merely a matter of subsidence of individual continents."[13]

Cretaceous seas inundated broad areas. In some regions, vast deposits of sediment were laid down. The northern edge of the Gulf of Mexico received an estimated 10,700 feet of sediment.

Breakup of Continents

During this great upheaval, the earth's continents were largely separated from each other. A major breakup of land masses took place in the mid-Mesozoic. Very significant changes occurred between earlier and later parts of the era and the present ocean basins were in existence by the close of the Cretaceous. But the causes of this major breakup of land masses are not understood.

Says William Stokes:

> Evidence for a major redistribution of land and water areas comes chiefly from the Southern Hemisphere. There is no positive evidence for a South Atlantic Ocean until Cretacious time. . . . The oldest rocks of the Indian Ocean are of Cretaceous age, and this body of water may have had no earlier existence.[14]

The evidence, then, points to a rather long lasting period of upheaval which separated the continents, created new oceans, raised up towering mountain ranges, and destroyed much plant and animal life on the earth! During the same relative period, and at its termination, many new forms of life, including mammals, began to appear on the scene, each kind "full blown" as it were. How can evolutionary theory explain massive extinctions coinciding with the sudden appearance of new types of fauna and flora?

Where does this leave the theory of gradual evolution of life from simple to complex? Hard pressed to account for such tremendous changes in the biota of the earth!

For example, consider this classic statement by W.J. Arkell, about such incredible periods:

> Evolution is above all very uneven. Certain periods were outstand-

Dinosaurs ruled the world over 100 million years ago. But the world of the thunder-lizards ended abruptly, geologically speaking, in a global cataclysm. How they suddenly perished, and why, is still a matter of fierce debate.—*Courtesy of the American Museum of Natural History.*

ingly productive of new and virile forms *which often seem to have sprung into existence from nowhere*... and to have become dominant almost simultaneously over a large part of the world. These are the periods of paedomorphosis, macroevolution, saltative evolution, explosive radiation or evolutionary deployment, according to the terminology of various biologists and geneticists. *How such sudden multiple creations were brought about is a task for the future to determine.*[15]

Notice that this author speaks of "sudden multiple creations" that seemed to have "sprung into existence from nowhere." When many life forms were destroyed, new life forms emerged suddenly on the scene and dominate the earth. The best explanation for such events is the creation of new fauna and flora by the Creator to replace the old order which had served its purpose and was no longer necessary. This explanation is logical, rational, and consistent with the facts.

Mass Death

What are the major causes of extinctions of life? Three principal methods of extinction are catastrophes, or worldwide upheavals; mass destructions, or anastrophes, in limited regions; and slow, gradual replacements.

Mass destruction of sea life, involving millions of dead fish, can be caused by volcanic eruptions in or near the sea. In 1794 the eruption of Vesuvius "cooked" millions of fish in the Gulf of Naples. Earthquakes are another destroyer of sea life.

Other causes of far more devastating extinctions of life would include advances and retreats of seas across low-lying lands. Says William Stokes:

> During the extensive Cretaceous floodings, at least 30 percent of the continents were submerged, and many species disappeared or were greatly modified. As the waters retreat, sea-living organisms are forced toward deeper waters.

This author adds:

> The formation of vast ice sheets over continental areas is perhaps the most destructive of all natural events.... The advance of the

> Pleistocene glaciers across North America utterly depopulated half the continent. Although many animals retreated before the ice, there were widespread extinctions and replacements among groups.[16]

Great climatic changes, involving the oceans and glaciation, tectonic activity and the atmosphere, also is directly involved in the history of extinctions.

At the close of the Permian period, great numbers of animal species disappeared, chiefly marine invertebrates. Exterminated species included trilobites, eurypterids, productid brachiopods, fusilines and others. The severe and worldwide extinctions of the late Paleozoic have been attributed to climatic change on a worldwide scale.

The destruction of the dinosaurs, after ruling the earth for 140 million years, was probably much more colorful and awesome. Theories proposed to explain their extinction include the rise of egg-eating mammals, extremes of temperature, the rise of modern types of plants and their expanded release of oxygen. Other theories involve astronomical events, such as increased penetration of cosmic rays to the earth, causing harmful mutations to multiply and destroy the race. But, writes William Stokes:

> Even more spectacular is the theory that the impact effects of a tremendous meteor from space may have killed all dinosaurs simultaneously over the entire earth. Heat and shock waves, it is suggested, might wreak more destruction among large animals that could find no shelter than among smaller animals.[17]

"The Time of the Great Dying"

Theories abound. The close of the Cretaceous proved to be a great crisis in the history of life. Many animals declined markedly during the period, and others flourished until its end, only to become extinct. Not a single dinosaur is known to have lived to see the dawn of the Cenozoic era.

Declares Carl O. Dunbar:

> It is difficult to account for the simultaneous extinction of great

> tribes of animals so diverse in relationships and in habits of life. Perhaps no single cause was responsible. The great restriction and final disappearance of the epeiric seas at the end of the era, the rise of highlands from Alaska to Patagonia, a sharp drop in the temperature accompanying the Laramide uplift, the vanishing of the swampy lowlands, and the vastly changed plant world have all been invoked to account for the extinction, and the consequent rising of the weak and lowly into new kingdoms. Whatever the cause, the latest Mesozoic was a time of trial when many of the hosts were "tried in the balance and found wanting"—wanting in adaptiveness to the new environment. Walther has picturesquely called it "The time of the great dying."[18]

It is evident that science has not been able to adequately account for the tremendous periods of cataclysm and extinction of life forms during the earth's history.

Derek V. Ager confesses (if I may use that word):

> The greatest problems in the fossil records, however, are the sudden extinctions. . . . For any one ecological group, such as the dinosaurs, it is comparatively easy to find a possible cause. It is much less easy when one has to explain the simultaneous extinction of several unrelated groups, ranging from ammonites to pterodactyls, living in different habitats at the end of the Mesozoic.[19]

In seeking to explain such massive extinctions, almost all the theories advanced relate to climatic oscillations and the composition of the earth's atmosphere. These, in turn, seem to point to extraterrestrial phenomena. Ager declares: "We are always forced back on seeking some control *outside and greater than the earth.*"[20]

Professor Harold C. Urey, Nobel prize winning biochemist, strongly supports extraterrestrial causes for mass extinctions. Rare collisions between earth and comets, he has suggested, produced vast quanties of energy resulting in high temperatures and high humidities that may have had a disastrous effect on land and marine faunas.

Such massive extinctions are not occurring right now. Therefore they cannot be properly explained by uniformitarian geologic thought which says the present is the key to the past.

Catastrophism of some sort is the most reasonable explanation. Says Derek Ager: "I feel that we rely too much on the present state of affairs, too much on uniformitarianism, when interpreting the fossil record, especially in those groups that are now completely extinct or but a shadow of their former selves."[21]

How, then, can evidence for catastrophism be accounted for? Can theology help provide an answer?

Biblical Catastrophism

Does the awesome record of ancient catastrophism conform to the Biblical record?

It may come as a surprise, but the Bible does refer to awesome cataclysms before the time of man. The truth is revealed in a proper understanding of Genesis 1:1-2.

Verse one records the description of the original creation of heaven and earth. That creation *could* have occurred billions of years ago. It was a beautiful creation and all the angels shouted for joy (Job 38:4-9).

But verse two records something altogether different.

We read: "The earth was without form and void, and darkness was upon the face of the deep. . . ." The Hebrew word translated "was" could also be translated "became." In fact, in Genesis 19:16 it was translated "became"—in that verse it records that Lot's wife "became a pillar of salt."

The Hebrew words for "without form and void" are *tohu* and *bohu* and literally mean a desolation, desert, wilderness that is empty, uninhabited. The words strongly suggest some primeval cataclysm, or several such cataclysms, occurred. What was the cause?

In the New Testament the apostle Peter tells us that "God did not spare the angels when they sinned. . . ." (II Peter 2:4). The apostle John also refers to the punishment that befell the angels "that did not keep their own position but left their proper dwelling" (Jude 6).

The awesome destructions that occurred long before man existed may have been connected with the rebellion and activity of certain angels that followed Lucifer when he attempted to ascend to heaven and take over the throne of God (see Isaiah 14:12-15; Ezekiel 28:11-15).

A third of the angels followed Lucifer—who became known as Satan—in his rebellion, according to the Biblical account (Revelations 12:4). This celestial conflict may have contributed to the destructive upheavals that struck the earth in early geological history. The evidences of vast extinctions, tectonic upheavals and disasters in the geologic record could be mute testimony of that protracted ancient conflict.

Chapter Fifteen

Tohu and Bohu

The dinosaurs lasted upon earth, we are told, for over one hundred million years. And yet they perished from off the earth in less than one million years.

Writes Jacques Bergier: "Furthermore, it is impossible to pretend that they represented an evolutionary failure: any species that last a hundred million years must be considered fully adapted. Yet few species that were contemporaries of those reptiles survive—for example, certain crabs, which have not changed in three hundred million years. In fact, in less than one million years the giant reptiles entirely disappeared.

"How and why?"

"We can scarcely maintain that it was because of a change in climate; for even when the climate changes, the oceans hardly vary, and many of these reptiles lived in the oceans.

"It is impossible to believe that a higher form of life was able to exterminate them. This would have required a considerable army, whose traces we would certainly have found.

"One amusing hypothesis is that our ancestors, the mammals, might have fed on dinosaur eggs. But it is only that: an amusing hypothesis: the icthyosaurs deposited their eggs in the oceans, out of their adversaries' reach.

"It has been said that the grasses changed, and that the new grasses were too tough for the big reptiles. A completely unlikely hypothesis: large numbers of vegetation types survived, on which they could have fed perfectly well"[1].

None of these answers hold water. What then did happen?

Two Soviet scientists, V.I. Krasovkii and I.S. Chklovski, both of whom are eminent astrophysicists, explain the end of the dinosaurs by hypothesizing a star explosion occurred at a relatively small distance from our solar system—a supernova at five or ten parsecs from us that would have increased the density of radiations coming from space.

The English radio astronomer Hanbury Brown lends credence to this theory. He believes he has detected traces of the explosion of a supernova fifty thousand years ago at a distance of only forty parsecs from our solar system.

Two U.S. scientists have also studied the problem, K.D. Terry of the University of Kansas, and W.H. Tucker of Rice University. They have observed stars that actually produce such radiation bombardments when they explode. Says Bergier, "It is possible that seventy million years ago a violent bombardment may have coincided with a diminution in the earth's magnetic field, bringing about a wave of mutations in which the dinosaurs died . . ."[2]

In the opinion of Bergier, "The destruction of the dinosaurs certainly came from the cosmos and not from our solar system"[3]. He goes on to speculate that these explosions of supernova may have been controlled by superbeings. In 1957 in a broadcast on French television he asserted that the star explosion that killed the dinosaurs was deliberately induced, "designed to set off a slow process of evolution leading to intelligent life; that we were created by extremely powerful beings. Knowledgeable both of the laws of physics and of the laws of genetics, these beings—who could truly be called gods—set in motion a series of events that will not stop with man but will continue until this evolution results in other gods, beings equal to their creators"[4].

Needless to say, his hypothesis received an immense uproar. But perhaps he was closer to the truth than even he suspected. We will discuss this possibility in a subsequent chapter. There may be something in the hypothesis that a supernova close to the solar system exploded about the end of the Mesozoic and triggered the massive dying of the dinosaurs and other forms of life on earth.

The cause definitely seems to have been extraterrestrial. No terrestrial cause or agency would have been sufficient to kill off millions of dinosaurs, leaving not a trace, in a relatively short span of time.

So it seems that we are forced to look to astronomy—to the cosmos—for an answer. Is there any clue in the solar system itself, which might give us a hint of the answer?

In the Transvaal there exists an eroded granite dome 26 miles wide, called the Vredevoort Ring. It might be 250 million years old, according to scientists. "This must have been formed by an asteroid a mile in diameter, hitting with the explosive force of a million-megaton bomb" we are told.[5]

Astronomers believe major meteorites strike the earth once every 10,000 years. Such an encounter may explain the demise of the saurian kings 70,000,000 years ago.

Consider the following facts:

1. Hundreds of thousands of various sized asteroids orbit between the orbits of Mars and Jupiter.

2. These asteroids are irregular, fragment-like, with odd, unaccountable shapes.

3. Four irregular-shaped small asteroid like bodies now orbit Jupiter as satellites, apparently captured asteroids.

4. The planet Mars has numerous craters, or astroblemes ("star wounds").

5. Greek cosmology-mythology. The ancient Greeks mention a former planet, one of the sisters in the heavens, who fled the heavens, plucked out her hair, and was changed into a comet after an affair with Zeus (Jupiter).

6. The odd satellites of Mars, Deimos and Phobos.

Patten, Hatch and Steinhauer point out: "It is estimated there are 50,000 asteroids, battered fragments of a former planet. Orbits of 1,800 have been calculated, and 90 per cent of them have orbits with either their aphelion or, more often, their perihelion in the vicinity of 200,000,000 miles from the sun. These fragments are remains of a former planet, possibly one-half the size of our Moon, which fragmented when another, somewhat larger planet (we propose Mars) nearly collided with it."[6]

Many astronomers have speculated that the asteroids between Mars and Jupiter could be the cosmic debris of an ancient planet which was torn apart in some celestial cataclysm. Generally, the theory has been ignored, or put on the shelf, by most modern astronomers because it seems so difficult to explain an entire planet virtually blowing apart!

Nevertheless, when we realize the former planet, which some have called "Electra," may have been half the size of our moon, then perhaps an explanation is not so incredible. If such a planet had an eccentric orbit, and passed too close to another planet, gravitation forces could have created enormous stresses within the smaller body. Over a period of time, and perhaps several close encounters, these stresses and the unrelenting pull of gravity might cause such a planet to explode into fragments.

It is possible that the former planet Electra—or the fragments and debris left over from its destruction—could well have triggered the cosmic catastrophe which laid low the dinosaurs at the close of the Cretaceous period, 65 million years ago.

The former planet which disintegrated may have had a diameter of 1,000 miles—half the Moon's diameter, and one fourth the diameter of Mars. The largest asteroid's diameter is 480 miles. Iapetus, the second largest satellite of Saturn, interestingly has a diameter of 1,000 miles.

The fact that the four outermost satellites of Jupiter are small irregular shaped rocks, and orbit Jupiter in retrograde motion, suggests that they were once part of the former planet.

Deimos and Phobos, the two satellites of Mars, were probably fragments of this ancient planet. The four outer satellites of Jupiter, Andastea, Pan, Poseidon, and Hades, vary in size from about 10 to 25 miles in diameter, similar to Deimos and Phobos.

Phobos, about eight miles in diameter, is irregular in shape, fragment-like, changes magnitudes, and was very difficult for astronomers to detect. When Asaph Hall announced in 1877 that he had located two hitherto unreported moons on Mars, a genuine shock rocked astronomical circles. In naming the two moons, Hall chose the names of those two tiny mythical companions of Mars in Greek cosmology—Deimos ("Panic") and Phobos ("Fear").

Mars, being such a small planet, was thought too small to capture moons. But once they were seen, astronomers had to accept their existence. Astronomers point out that Jupiter, 3000 times the mass of Mars, only captured four asteroids. For Mars to have been able to capture two trabants seemed amazing.

But if Mars was indeed involved in a cosmic encounter with the former planet Electra, and Jupiter also, then the captured asteroids or planetary fragments makes very good sense.

Amazingly, Jonathan Swift who published *Gullivers' Travels* in 1726, one hundred and fifty years before Asaph Hall discovered the two moons of Mars, actually wrote of them in his book!

According to Swift the two Martian moons were well known to the astronomers of Laputa. Swift recounted:

". . . they have likewise discovered two lesser Stars or Satellites, which revolve about Mars, whereof the innermost is distant from the centre of the Primary Planet exactly three of his Diameters, and the outermost five; the former revolves in the Space of ten hours, and the latter in Twenty-one and a Half; so that the Squares of their periodical Times are very near in the same Proportion with the Cubes of their Distance from the Center of Mars, which evidently shews them to be governed by the same Law of Gravitation, that influences the other heavenly Bodies."[7]

For Swift to describe the distance of these two satellites from Mars in terms of Mars' diameter implies measurement and calculation. The Laputans said Phobos was three Mars diameters from the planet (12,420 miles). Modern instruments reveal it is actually 7,897 miles away. The Laputans said Phobos orbited Mars every 10 hours. Modern measurements show the actual time is 7 hours 39 minutes. The Laputans put the diameter of Deimos, orbit as five Mars diameters (20,700 miles). It is actually 16,670 miles. They put the revolution of Deimos at 21½ hours. It is actually 30 hours 18 minutes.

How did Jonathan Swift know? Was he merely guessing?

Isaac Asimov calls it "an amazing coincidence." He adds, "However, his guess that Phobos would rise in the west and set in the east because of its speed of revolution is uncanny. It is undoubtedly the luckiest guess in literature."

To ascribe Swift's detailed description to mere guesswork is, however, laughable. He must have been familiar with certain records which described the two satellites of Mars. Perhaps, as some have suggested, his friend and contemporary, William Whiston, a leading astronomer, historian, and catastrophist, helped Swift calculate these facts. But where did the records come from? Alas, no body knows where Jonathan Swift obtained his information. The information may have been developed from ancient Greek myths about Mars and its two companions, Deimos and Phobos.

Perhaps at some ancient time the planet Mars had a different orbit—or the earth did—or they both did—and they passed relatively close to each other. Viewers from the earth could at that time have detected the two small companions of Mars. Their ancient sightings gave rise to the mythology of the god Mars and his two tiny companions.

This may seem like science fiction—But science fiction often becomes science fact. It is usually only a matter of time.

Other evidence for ancient catastrophism in the solar system can be adduced from studies of the Moon and planet Mars. Close up photographs of Mars sent back to earth from Mariner spacecraft show the surface of Mars is crater-ridden. Huge craters, such exist on the moon, cover the surface of Mars. These craters are signs of massive meteoric impacts. The surface of Mars has been compared to an ancient battle field.

One tenth the mass of the earth, with a meteor ravaged surface, Mars seems to possess the scars of ancient conflicts. It seems amazing to astronomers, but Mars—unlike the other planets of the solar system—has a day almost equal to the earth's day. The time of axial rotation of Mars is 24 hours, 37 minutes and 23 seconds; the earth's day is 23 hours, 56 minutes, 4 seconds. No other two planets are so alike in the duration of their day.

Another striking resemblance between the two planets is the inclination of their axis of rotation. The equator of Mars is inclined 24 degrees to the plane of its orbit, whereas the equator of the earth is inclined 23½ degrees to the plane of its ecliptic. Such a similarity is unequalled among all the other planets of the solar system.

"Is it possible that the axis of rotation and the velocity of rotation of Mars, stabilized and supported in their present position and rate by certain forces, were influenced originally by the earth at the time of contact? Mars, being small as compared with the earth, influenced to a lesser degree the rotation of the earth and the position of its poles."[8]

The solar system's anomalies in many cases bear testimony to the fact that in ancient times there were great disruptions among the planets. Even the rings of Saturn—three rings composed of countless particles of ice or frost-covered gravel which circle the planet at different speeds—bespeak evidence of ancient catastrophism.

Saturn, the most remote planet known in antiquity, is the only planet which would float in water. Its low density is 13 percent of the earth's. One of its moons, Phoebe, like four of the moons of Jupiter, is retrograde in motion and may well be a captured asteroid.

The rings of Saturn, thousands of miles wide, are less than ten miles thick. They rotate exactly in the plane of the planet's equator. The center ring is opaque, the outer ring is nearly so, and the inner ring is semi-transparent. Each of the rings is composed of many individual particles, each one in its own orbit like a tiny satellite. Clerk Maxwell showed that a system of rings could be stable only if it consisted of discrete particles. Cecilia Payne-Gaposchkin suggests that the rings of Saturn may be the remains of an ancient satellite which was broken up within the tidal "danger zone" very near the planet's surface.[9]

The moon reveals evidence of bombardment from space. Most of the great craters were created by small asteroids—mountains of rock—hurtling in from space and colliding with the surface. So many asteroids have impacted on the moon that its entire surface was smashed into a new shape.

The crater of Tycho, nearly sixty miles across, is merely one of many lunar craters, by no means one of the largest. The far side of the moon, photographs from space and Apollo space shots show, was hammered so violently by meteors that the entire original crust was shattered and torn apart. The blasts of crashing asteroids and meteors released huge volcanic eruptions covering vast sections of the moon with flowing lava. The maria are actually huge lava seas.

Mars, also, and even Venus, we know to be covered with huge craters from twenty to hundreds of miles in diameter.

But the earth also shows evidence of ancient collisions with astral bodies. In addition to the 4,000 foot Barringer Crater in Arizona, and the Vredevoort Ring in South Africa, in Canada hundreds of craters exist, many of them several miles in diameter. Hudson's Bay was very probably formed by the impact of a comet, or asteroid, from outer space. Scientists are also convinced that the Sea of Japan was created in a similar fashion.

We now know, therefore, that interplanetary collisions have occurred in ancient times. The earth, Mars, Venus, and the moon all bear the scars of such ancient encounters. Very possibly a former planet, Electra, was involved in these ancient interplanetary encounters of a cataclysmic kind.

Such encounters are the most likely explanation for the worldwide upheavals, volcanic eruptions, and global cataclysms resulting in the extinction of the entire world of the dinosaurs, at the close of the Mesozoic Era, and the world of Pleistocene times. Sucn encounters also explain the global cataclysms recorded in the legends of ancient peoples and in the pages of Holy Scripture.

Nothing terrestrial could have accomplished such cataclysms. The cause must have been celestial. Could a wandering comet have triggered the cataclysms?

At one occasion D.F. Arago computed that there is one chance in 280 million that a comet will hit the earth. Nevertheless, huge objects from space have in historic times collided with the earth. The *Encyclopedia Britannica* states that the number of meteorites falling in the centuries before Christ was higher than today.

The metorite that fell in prehistoric times near Winslow, Arizona created a crater 4,500 feet across and 600 feet deep. It flung out masses of rock weighing up to 7,000 tons each, altogether displacing roughly 400 million tons of rock. The pressure of impact was greater than 1,000,000 pounds per square inch. In the blast, silica was changed into coesite and stishovite.

An even greater crater at Ries Kessel in Bavaria—16 miles across—was made by an enormous meteorite.

In *The Universe,* published by Life Nature Library, we read: "Asteroids sometimes come close enough to the earth to collide with it. Of the boulder-sized ones, which are called meteorites, about 1,500 strike each year. *Full-fledged flying mountains* are thought to strike much less frequently, perhaps once every 10,000 years on an average. When they do, the earth acts like so much soft mud and swallows them explosively into its surface. Geologists have only recently begun to recognize the 'astroblemes,' or star-wounds, which they inflict but it seems likely from the evidence unearthed so far that only the shield of the atmosphere and the healing power of vegetation, erosion and mountain-building have kept the earth from being as pockmarked as the moon."[10]

Out beyond the orbit of the planet Mars, over 3,000 odd asteroids—small chunks or islands of rock and metal—have been tracked by astronomers. Totalling less than 5 percent of the moon in mass, these wandering chunks of rock range in size from Ceres, discovered in 1800, with a diameter of 480 miles and surface area of 700,000 square miles; Pallas, 300 miles wide; Juno, 120 miles in diameter; and Vesta, 240 miles across; to the small flying mountains like Icarus, only one mile in diameter.

About 30,000 sizable asteroids are believed to exist, and uncounted billions of smaller asteroids, the size of pebbles, boulders, or grains of sand.

Since most of the asteroids move in a broad band between the orbits of Mars and Jupiter, the enormous planet Jupiter affects their motions. Some asteroids are called Trojans, named after Homeric heroes who fought in the Trojan war, and are held in captivity by Jupiter, much as satellites. Occasionally Jupiter's strong gravitation pull yanks one of the asteroids on a series of orbital trips toward the sun or the outer planets. Eventually such straying asteroids are likely to be hurled by Jupiter into new erratic paths, which may bring them uncomfortably close to the earth. Eros, a rock 15 miles long, tumbling end over end, can come within 14,000,000 miles of earth. Amor, Icarus, Apollo, Adonis can pass even closer to earth. The asteroid Hermes came so close to the earth in 1937 that astronomers compared it to the fly-by of a jet; it passed within 500,000 miles of earth, only twice as far away as the moon.

Comets, those odd denizens of the icy edges of the solar system, number in the 100 billions. They orbit not only in the flattened disc of the planets, but also in a spherical halo reaching out 10 trillion miles from the solar system. Those which have been studied by astronomers reveal they are an accumulation of frozen gases and grit, a few miles in diameter. When a comet approaches the sun, "solar energy vaporizes its outer layers to form a swollen head and then drives some of this material away to form a tail of incandescence pointing out toward space."[11]

The Great Comet of 1843 had a streaming tail 500 million miles long. Halley's comet, which returns approximately every 76 years, is so brilliant that records of its observation are complete for every time but once since 240 B.C. in the annals of the Chinese and Japanese. It may have been seen in 467 B.C.

What happens when a comet approaches too near the sun? Biela's comet, first noticed hurtling in from outer space in 1772, came close to the sun and began reappearing near the sun every six and one half years. In 1846 on its swing by the sun it became two comets; after 1852 it vanished. Twenty years later astronomers were still looking for it when the whole of Europe was suddenly treated to a wild pyrotechnic shower of meteors burning up as they entered the earth's atmosphere. Says *The Universe:* "The rain of cosmic sparks increased as it moved west. By the time it reached England, people could see a hundred blazing meteors a minute. Over the Atlantic, the display gradually diminished so that New Yorkers, at midnight, saw only a luminous drizzle. Careful calculations have since proved that the meteors were really the remnants of Biela's comet, crossing the earth's orbit just in time to meet the earth."

June 30, 1908 a comet smashed into the forests along the Tunguska River in Siberia, toppling trees, knocking people off their feet and blowing out window panes 100 miles away. The pressure of the blast affected barometers in England. The pall of smoke that shot into the air affected sunsets for a week.

Long a mystery, the Tunguska explosion was finally explained by the Committee on Meteorites of the Soviet Academy of Sciences in 1960. Chairman Vassily Fesenkov announced that the explosion had definitely been caused by the head of a comet with a diameter of several miles and weighing about a million tons. Other comets ranging over the solar system weigh a million times as much.

With these facts in mind, let us try to reconstruct what happened in the days of old.

Jesus told his disciples: "I beheld Satan as lightning fall from heaven" (Luke 10:18).

At some ancient time, some point in history, Satan fell from heaven. When did it happen?

A hint of the truth is given in the gospel according to John. Jesus said to the Pharisees of his day: "Ye are of your father the devil, and the lusts of your father ye will do. *He was a murderer from the beginning, and abode not in the truth,* because there is no truth in him. When he speaketh a lie, he speaketh of his own: for he is a liar, and the father of it" (John 8:44).

Long before becoming a human being, and partaking of human nature, Jesus had been with the Father from the beginning. He was the "Word," the second member of the Godhead. He said to the hypocritical Pharisees of his day: "Verily, verily, I say unto you, Before Abraham was, I am" (John 8:48). He was with God, and was God (John 1:1-3, 14).

At that ancient primordial time, Jesus saw Satan fall as lightning out of heaven. He saw him when he became a Murderer "from the beginning." He saw him when he first began to harbor thoughts of resentment, vanity, jealousy, greed, avarice, and gluttony. He saw him when he first began to stray from the truth, and began to become deceitful, tricky, clever, guilty of half-truths, slander, gossip, and falsehoods.

Jesus was there.

A much fuller account of the story is provided by the prophet Isaiah. Notice what the prophet was inspired to record:

"How art thou fallen from heaven, O Lucifer, son of the morning! How art thou cut down to the ground, which didst weaken the nations!

"For thou has said in thine heart, I will ascend into heaven, I will exalt my throne above the stars of God: I will sit also upon the mount of the congregation, in the sides of the north: I will ascend above the heights of the clouds; I will be like the most High. Yet thou shalt be brought down to hell, to the sides of the pit" (Isaiah 14:12-15).

Here the prophet Isaiah describes what happened aeons ago! An archangel by the name of Lucifer, which means "Day star," or "Shining star of the dawn," rebelled against the Almighty God. He attempted to ascend to heaven, to exalt his own throne or seat of authority above the other angels, called "stars of God." He attempted to ascend above the clouds (clouds are in the earth's atmosphere), to rise up and conquer space—to remove God from His Throne—to become "like the Most High." But his abortive attempt failed. He was cast back down to earth in a massive struggle.

Just how big was this cosmic battle for control of the Universe? Why did Lucifer want to be "like the most High?"

In his massive rebellion, Lucifer drew the allegiance of perhaps one third of all the angels. He was a very powerful personality, a mighty angel of God. But his angelic nature, consumed with greed and lust, became a loathsome thing, detestable, unclean, filthy, vile, putrid, ugly, distorted, misshapen, foul. He became characterized as a dragon.

In the book of Revelation, John tells us: "And there appeared another wonder in heaven; and behold a great red dragon, having seven heads and ten horns, and seven crowns upon his heads. *And his tail drew the third part of the stars of heaven,* and did cast them to the earth . . ." (Revelation 12:3-4). During this cosmic conflict it is probable that tens of thousands of meteorites in the solar system were also cast down upon the earth.

John describes this vision further: "And there was *WAR* in heaven: Michael and his angels fought against the dragon; and the dragon fought and his angels, and prevailed not; neither was their place found any more in heaven. And the great dragon was cast out, that old serpent, called the Devil, and Satan, which deceiveth the whole world: he was cast out into the earth, and his angels were cast out with him" (Rev. 12:7-9).

This "war in heaven" must have been catastrophic in nature. It must have been the greatest battle of all time! Armies of angels clashing with each other! The entire cosmos must have been shaken.

Peter speaks of the cataclysmic fall of Lucifer and his renegade angels this way: "For if God spared not the angels that sinned, but cast them down to hell (Greek, *tartaroo,* a "place of restraint"), and delivered them into chains of darkness, to be reserved unto judgment" (II Peter 2:4). These angels had "sinned." But what is "sin?" The Bible defines it as rebellion, lawlessness. "Sin is the transgression of the law," John wrote (I John 3:4). Further, Paul tells us, "whatsoever is not of faith is sin" (Romans 14:23).

One third of the angelic hosts, apparently, sinned–violated the laws of God–and acted wantonly. They attempted to overthrow the Government of the Creator God. They precipitated violence on a cosmic scale never before heard of or seen! They went astray from the paths of peace, goodness, faith, righteousness.

They looked upon God as a tyrant, a malevolent dictator, not fit for His office, not capable of running the Universe. They wanted *their* way. They wanted their ambitions–*right now!* They wanted to seize God's Throne and take over–He wasn't running things right, in their eyes. Perhaps they were jealous–they thought He was playing favorites and they didn't feel on the "inside group."

Lucifer may well have been jealous of the potential destiny and future of mankind. God very likely had made His plans known to the angelic world "from the foundation of the world," and they knew that ultimately, eventually, He intended for man to be over the angels (Hebrews 2:5-8; I Corinthians 6:3).

The thought of mankind ruling over him apparently did not sit too well with Lucifer. It was the "last straw." He couldn't—or wouldn't—take it any more.

Jude tells us: "And the angels which kept not their first estate, but left their own habitation, He hath reserved in everlasting chains under darkness unto the judgment of the great day" (Jude 6).

These rebellious angels were, Jude says, "Raging waves of the sea, foaming out their own shame; wandering stars, to whom is reserved the blackness of darkness for ever" (Jude 13).

The rebellious angels are largely confined to the earth today—in chains of darkness, reserved for judgment. The minions of the devil are known as "demons"—wicked spirits. They are disembodied spirits which roam the earth, trying to lead people into sin and rebellion against God. They are responsible for a great deal of the madness, lunacy, insanity and schizophrenia found in the earth among men and women.

The king of demons, or fallen angels, is Satan, formerly known as "Lucifer," or "Light bringer." But he exchanged light for darkness. Lucifer, or Satan, the "Adversary," is also known as *Abaddon,* or *Apollyon,* meaning "A destroyer." He is the "angel of the bottomless pit."

The apostle John, in a vision of the future ahead of us, said:

"And the fifth angel sounded, and I saw a star (angel) fall from heaven unto the earth: and to him was given the key of the bottomless pit [or, abyss]. And he opened the bottomless pit; and there arose a smoke out of the pit, as the smoke of a great furnace; and the sun and the air were darkened by reason of the smoke of the pit. And there came out of the smoke locusts upon the earth: and unto them was given power, as the scorpions of the earth have power . . . . And they had a king over them, which is the angel of the bottomless pit, whose name in the Hebrew tongue is Abaddon, but in the Greek tongue hath his name Apollyon" (Revelation 9:1-3, 11).

When did the original great Rebellion take place? Jesus said it was "from the beginning," that "from the beginning" Satan was a murderer and liar, and the father of such things. "In the beginning," we read, "God created the heavens and the earth" (Genesis 1:1). The angels were created before the earth was founded (Job 38:4-7). This ancient conflict, therefore, was probably millions of years ago—maybe even billions of years ago. Satan's Rebellion, with one third of the angels composing his aggressing army invading heaven, must have been responsible for the chaos and destruction which is recorded in Genesis 1:2—the *tohu* and *bohu* and darkness which covered the earth, long before the creation of Adam and Eve. The cataclysm in Genesis 1:2 is undoubtedly related to the cataclysmic fall of Lucifer from heaven.

How many times Satan's acts have led to destruction and cataclysm since that original rebellion we are not given to know at this time. His attempts to wage war upon God may have occurred many times over millions of years. The extinction of the dinosaurs may well be connected; the demise of the Pleistocene World may have been directly involved. Satan, as an agent of destruction, attempting to thwart God's Plan, has actually been a tool in God's hand. That is, everything he has done, God has caused to work out for mankind's ultimate good. Even the tests and trials that Satan brings upon us, God causes to work out for our eventual good (Romans 8:29).

Ezekiel tells us more about the ancient world. He tells us that Lucifer originally was one of the two cherubim that covered the throne of God.

In the days of the Exodus, God instructed Moses to make a replica of God's Throne—a sanctuary for God to dwell in. An ark was to be made, overlaid with pure gold (Exodus 25:3-11). A mercy seat of pure gold was to be placed in the ark, symbolizing God's Throne. And God said: "And thoushalt make two cherubims of gold, of beaten work shalt thou make them, in the two ends of the mercy seat. And make one cherub on the one end, and the other cherub on the other end; even of the mercy seat shall ye make the cherubims on the two ends thereof. And the cherubims shall stretch forth their wings on high, covering the mercy seat with their wings. and their faces shall look one to another; toward the mercy seat shall the faces of the cherubims be" (Exodus 25:18-20).

The prophet Ezekiel tells us what happened to one of these two cherubim. "Moreover the word of the Lord came unto me, saying, Son of man, take up a lamentation upon the king of Tyrus, and say unto him, Thus saith the Lord God; Thou sealest up the sum, full of wisdom, and perfect in beauty.

"Thou hast been in Eden the garden of God . . ." (Ezekiel 28:11-13).

Note that this could not be describing a literal king of the City of Tyre. The garden of Eden perished at the Noachian deluge, and Tyre did not become a city until much, much later. This king, as we shall see, was actually a spirit being—a cherubim!

Ezekiel continues:

"Thou hast been in Eden the garden of God; every precious stone was thy covering, the sardius, topaz, and the diamond, the beryl, the onyx, and the jasper, the saphire, the emerald, and the carbuncle, and gold: the workmanship of thy tabrets and of thy pipes was prepared in thee in the day that thou wast created.

"*Thou art the anointed cherub that covereth;* and I have set thee so: thou wast upon the holy mountain of God; thou has walked up and down in the midst of the stones of fire.

"Thou wast perfect in thy ways *from the day that thou was created,* till iniquity was found in thee" (Ezek. 28:13-15).

Consider, for a moment. Ezekiel is describing a beautiful, resplendent, angelic creature—one of the two anointed cherubim that covered God's Throne in heaven! This creature walked upon the holy mountain of God, in the garden of God in Eden. It was a created being—and it was a perfect creation!

But then something happened to change the beautiful nature and character of this brilliant, shining angelic being. "Iniquity" was found in him. A root of bitterness, a root of jealousy, of envy, of hatred, began to spring up (compare Hebrews 12:15).

Ezekiel continues the description of this ancient scene:

"By the multitude of thy merchandise they have filled the

midst of thee with *violence, and thou hast sinned:* therefore I will cast thee as profane out of the mountain of God: and I will destroy thee, O covering cherub, from the midst of the stones of fire.

"Thine heart was lifted up because of thy beauty, thou hast corrupted thy wisdom by reason of thy brightness: I will cast thee to the ground, I will lay thee before kings, that they may behold thee.

"Thou hast defiled thy sanctuaries by the multitude of thine iniquities, by the iniquity of thy traffick; therefore will I bring forth a fire from the midst of thee, it shall devour thee, and I will bring thee to ashes upon the earth in the sight of all them that behold thee. All they that know thee among the people shall be astonished at thee: thou shalt be a terror, and never shall thou be any more" (Ezekiel 28:16-19).

What happened eons ago?

Lucifer's heart was lifted up with pride. He became vain because of his beauty and brilliance. His wisdom became corrupted, and channeled into selfish, devious directions. God had said he "sealed up the sum, full of wisdom, and perfect in beauty" (Ezek. 28:12). But this beautiful creature became disloyal, disobedient, and destructive.

If we can reconstruct the scene, it would appear that in that ancient world there was much merchandise and traffic. Trade and commerce existed. The world was populated by millions of angels, and their king was Lucifer. His throne was on the earth. But he wasn't satisfied. He was a great king, and the greatest human king to compare with him was the king of Tyre, the mercantile city, in the days of Ezekiel.

But this angelic king grew restless. He said, "I will ascend into heaven." That shows he was located on the earth. "I will exalt *my throne* above the stars of God" (Isaiah 14:13). That shows he was a king, a ruler—he had a throne on the earth. But he wanted to reign upon the mountain of God, "in the sides of the north" (same verse).

Many verses of the Bible lend support to the theory that God's Throne is located in the northern heavens, in the general direction of the North Star. King David wrote: "Great is the Lord, and greatly to be praised in the city of our God, in the mountain of his holiness. Beautiful for situation, the joy of the whole earth, is Mount Zion, on the sides of the north, the city of the great King" (Psalm 48:1-2). The city of God, the heavenly Jerusalem, as we know, is now in heaven (Revelation 21:1-2).

Lucifer wasn't satisfied with kingship over this earth. He wasn't satisfied with being one of the two anointed cherubim that actually covered God's Throne—a position of great importance and supreme respect—very close to the throne itself. He wasn't even happy when God gave him his own throne upon the earth, over millions of angels. His heart seethed with discontent. He wanted what God had! He was created to be a ministering angel—but he wanted to be ministered to, not to minister to others. He didn't want to be a servant. He wanted to be served!

Very likely the straw which finally broke the camel's back was the fact that God intended to create man, and to give him eventual dominion over the earth and the angelic kingdom. This Lucifer could not stand!

He rebelled!

And God dealt severely with his rebellion. God's attitude toward rebellion is revealed in the first book of the prophet Samuel:

"And Samuel said, hath the Lord as great delight in burnt offerings and sacrifices, as in obeying the voice of the Lord? Behold, to obey is better than sacrifice, and to hearken than the fat of rams. For rebellion is as the sin of witchcraft, and stubbornness is as iniquity and idolatry. Because thou hast rejected the word of the Lord, he hath also rejected thee from being king" (I Samuel 15:22-23).

Lucifer was also rejected from being a king. He lost his throne, his kingdom, his power. But he still has limited authority upon the earth, and is the "god of this world," the "prince of the power of the air." He will remain in that position until God is through with him and replaces him.

Ever since that original rebellion, there has been a constant, ongoing, continual struggle between Satan, the "Adversary," and God. Lucifer's name, "Light bringer," was changed to "Satan," meaning "opponent."

Satan and his fallen angels, now disembodied spirits, roam the earth, in a condition of restraint. They have very little power compared to that which they used to exert. They cannot appear to men in strength and power, as the righteous angels can. They are vague shadows of their former selves. They have lost their intense brightness and brilliance. They are ghostly beings, like the wind, and are called "familiar spirits" that peep and mutter (Leviticus 19:31; 20:27; Isaiah 8:19-20).

In the pages of Genesis, as it relates to the original creation of the universe, we read the simple, matter-of-fact statement: "In the beginning, God created the heaven and the earth" (Genesis 1:1, *King James* Version). The *Amplified* Bible renders this verse: "In the beginning God (prepared, formed, fashioned) and created the heavens and the earth." The *Good News* Bible states: "In the beginning, when God created the universe . . ." The *Moffatt* Translation: "When God began to form the universe . . ." The *Goodspeed* Translation: "When God began to create the heavens and the earth . . ."

What exactly does the book of Genesis tell us? That God created the universe—the heavens and the earth—in a period of time called, simply, "the beginning." How long ago that primeval creation occurred we are not told anywhere in the Scripture. To determine that, God has given us brains and intellect!

That time of beginning could well have been six to ten billion years ago. Astronomers calculate that a "Big Bang" took place at that time, out of which the entire cosmos was created.

Verse two of Genesis, chapter one, continues:

"And the earth was without form, and void; and darkness was upon the face of the deep" (*King James* Version).

Is this verse describing the original creation as being formless and void? If so, it would seem a contradiction. Verse one tells us God created the heavens and the earth. When God creates something, it is beautiful, grand, and majestic. In the 38th chapter of the book of Job, we read:

"Where was thou when I laid the foundations of the earth? declare, if thou hast understanding. Who hath laid the measures thereof, if thou knowest? or who hath stretched the line upon it? Whereupon are the foundations thereof fastened? or who laid the corner stone thereof? When the morning stars sang together, and all the sons of God shouted for joy?" (vs. 4-7).

If the original earth had been created a chaotic ruin, formless and void, the angels would not have "sang together" or have "shouted for joy."

Isaiah 45:18 adds more light on this enigmatic passage. The prophet declares: "For thus saith the Lord that created the heavens; God himself that formed the earth and made it; he hath established it, he created it *not in vain,* he formed it to be inhabited: I am the Lord; and there is none else" (*King James* Version).

The Hebrew word translated "vain" here is *tohu* and means "to lie waste," "a desolation," "a desert." It can also be translated "confusion," "empty place," "without form," "nothing," "wilderness." It is the very same word used in Genesis 1:2, where we read the earth "was without form."

One place says God created the earth and it "was without form;" in another place we read God did *not* create the earth "without form." Is this a contradiction? Not at all!

The key to understanding this apparently complex problem lies in the little word "was." It can also be translated "became." In fact, in Genesis 19:16 it is translated "became." We read: "And Lot's wife *became* a pillar of salt."

What happened, then, is this: When God originally created the earth, it was indeed a lovely place. He created it with no waste, no wilderness, no desolation. It was inhabited. The angels leaped for joy, and shouted with admiration and enthusiasm when they beheld the primeval earth.

But then something happened. It *became* "tohu"—that is, waste, a ruin, a desolation. The original earth suffered a great cataclysm—a cosmic catastrophe. The Hebrew words translated "without form and void" in Genesis 1:2 literally mean a desolation, a wilderness, an empty, uninhabited ruin. These words, *tohu* and *bohu* are very strong words and denote catastrophe. They strongly suggest that some sort of primeval cataclysm, or several such cataclysms, occurred.

Destruction!

Paroxysm!

Chaos!

Scripture gives no data for determining how long ago the universe was created. And in the first chapter of Genesis, it only records three creative acts: 1) the heavens and the earth (verse 1); 2) new animal life (verses 20-21); and 3) human life, Adam and Eve (verses 26-27). The first creative act referred to the dateless past. The creation of new forms of animal life, and Adam and Eve, occurred approximately 6,000 years ago. Obviously, then, the first chapter of Genesis is not describing the original creation of the heavens and earth as occurring in seven consecutive days.

After the chaos and destruction which occurred, in verse two of Genesis one, God began a process of re-creation, reconstruction, if you please, which lasted for seven days. Verse 16 of Genesis one does not describe the sun and moon and stars being created on the fourth day. How could light have been created on the first day, but the sun and stars which impart light not till the fourth day? The original Hebrew for "made" in verse 16 actually means "made to appear, made visible." The sun and moon were created "in the beginning." The light came from the sun, of course, but the vapor in the earth's atmosphere diffused the light. After the great cataclysm, the earth was cut off from the light of the sun, moon and stars. Darkness prevailed everywhere. As verse two says: "And the earth was (became) without form and void (*tohu* and *bohu*); and *darkness* was upon the face of the deep. And the Spirit of God moved upon the face of the waters."

What do we see then? An earth destroyed, in pitch darkness, covered by water, the continents submerged, due to some great cataclysm.

During the process of reconstruction or re-creation, God first caused the light from the sun to penetrate the atmosphere once again, in a diffused manner (Genesis 1:3-5), allowing day and night to become discernible. He created order in the atmosphere (verses 6-8). He caused the dry land to appear once again (verse 10). He caused the earth to once again bring forth life, plants, vegetation, of all kinds. As the turgid clouds and atmospheric disturbances cleared away, He caused the sun, moon and stars to once again become visible from the earth's surface (verses 14-18).

Then, having refashioned the surface of the earth, and having prepared it, God created new living creatures—new animal life of all kinds, from great whales to small fish, from elephants to rodents, from flying birds to flying fish and insects—to repopulate the earth, and to replenish it (verses 20-25).

Something had happened to the Pre-Adamic earth. It had been overwhelmed in a mighty catastrophe, or a long series of catastrophes, which is briefly described in verse 2 of Genesis chapter 1.

Chapter Sixteen

The Riddle of Early Man

Today, we chuckle at the antics of "cave men" in syndicated comic strips. Hulking, hunkering beasts conk cave women over the head and drag them off. Stupid-looking dinosaurs are tied up to the cave hitching post and used for transportation.

The comic book concept about cave men, of course, is sheer fantasy. But the idea of ancient "cave men" is not a modern concept—it is as old as history!

Back in the days of Diodorus of Sicily, circa 50 B.C., men commonly believed their ancestors lived in caves.

The historian Diodorus wrote: "But the first men to be born, they say, led an undisciplined and bestial life setting out one by one to secure their sustenance and taking for their food both the tenderest herbs and the fruits of wild trees. Then, since they were attacked by the wild beasts, they came to each other's aid being instructed by expediency, and when gathered together in this way by reason of their fear, they gradually came to recognize their mutual characteristics."

How did these "cave men" learn language?

Diodorus continues: "And though the sounds which they made were at first unintelligible and indistinct, yet gradually they came to give articulation to their speech, and by agreeing with one another upon symbols for each thing which presented itself to them made known among themselves the significance which was to be attached to each term."[1]

What were the lives of these "first men" like? Again, Diodorus tells us: "Now the first men, since none of the things useful for life had yet been discovered, led a wretched existence, having no clothing to cover them, knowing not the use of dwelling and fire, and also being totally ignorant of cultivated food . . .

"Little by little, however, experience taught them both to take to the caves in winter and to store such fruits as could be preserved. And when they had become acquainted with fire, and other useful things, the arts also and whatever else is capable of furthering man's social life were gradually discovered."[2]

You could not find a more "modern" concept of "primitive man" in the latest textbooks of anthropology. But was Diodorus right? What does the fossil evidence reveal about early man? Has the "evolutionary tree" of mankind been discovered intact in the earth?

The Primate Tree

As with most branches of "evolutionary" science, the branch dealing with fossil man is fraught with disagreement. Anthropologists are divided about man's earliest beginnings.

Men and monkeys are generally classified as *primates*. All primates—including lemurs, tarsiers, monkeys, apes and man—possess relatively large brains, fingers, toes, a flexible arm, and a thumb that opposes the other fingers.

Naturalists have drawn up "genealogical trees" of the primates, according to their structural and chronological relationships. "We would mention in particular the attempts of Gregory, Keith, Pilgrim, Abel, Le Gros Clark, Schultz, Hooton, and R. Gates," says a volume entitled *Fossil Men*. It goes on: "A comparison of their diagrams is calculated to increase, if possible, our caution, for between the various diagrams there are great, sometimes even fundamental differences."[3]

This authoritative volume continues: "The human group is shown as having relationships so different that the wisest plan is to conclude that this group is still 'in the air,' and that we do not know exactly the place where the human branch should be inserted among the branches or twigs round about it."

The authors conclude, "the more authors, the more theories."[4]

The early lineage of man is a far from settled issue. Mankind just doesn't seem to fit the various theories.

The story of man's supposed animal ancestry is widely disputed in anthropology circles. Some believe a monkey-like creature called proconsul may be a direct ancestor of humans. Others think proconsul may be a common ancestor of man, the gorilla, and the chimpanzee.

Some anthropologists believe that a creature called *Oreopithecus cambolii*, dug up in 1958 in Tuscany, Italy, could have been an ancestor of man.

Other anthropologists, however, feel man split off from the apes at a later time. But, writes William Stokes: "The true lineage of man through the maze of the past is still so obscure that we can make no positive assertions about it."[5]

The subject of hominid evolution is fraught with dispute among anthropologists. Sherwood Washburn, whenever he talks about this subject, often begins his remarks, "My prejudice is . . ." and then continues with his own opinion.

Behavior-oriented anthropologists tend to wonder how much fossil men can really learn from a few scraps of bone. As one writer said, "Paleontologists are constantly making deductions from dental minutiae and just as constantly finding themselves disagreeing."[6]

Who split off from whom in the primate family tree is also a matter of dispute. Bjorn Kurten concluded that men are not descended from apes at all, having examined small-jawed 30-million-year old primate fossils. He traces mankind back through a fossil called Propliopithecus, a small-jawed primate, and says hominids split off from apes 30 to 40 million years ago.

Others put the split at 20 million years ago, and still others at 15 million.

On the other hand, measurements of the differences between the DNA of man and chimps, comparisons of the protein molecules in the blood, led Sarick and Wilson to conclude that the hominid-chimp split occurred less than four million years ago. This suggestion enraged those anthropologists working with fossils and who date various hominids four and five million years old. The entire field is very speculative.[7]

The Supposed Lineage of Man

The quest for evidence linking man to early primates continues.

One fascinating aspect of this search involves creatures which ostensibly lived 14 million years ago. Many kinds of apes existed, evolutionists say, 14,000,000 years ago. Some of them, they speculate, may have had certain hominid features.

In 1961 Louis S.B. Leakey, then director of the Center for Prehistory and Paleontology in Nairobi, Kenya, began digging on one of the hills in the region around Fort Ternan, in Kenya, about forty miles east of Lake Victoria.

The Fort Ternan fossils uncovered by Leakey were dated, using the potassium-argon method, to 14 million years ago.

Among the remains of pygmy giraffes, pygmy elephants, and antelopes, Leakey found an unusual primate, indicating a shortened face with a reduced snout. Leakey announced that the specimen exhibits enough hominid features to qualify as an entirely new variety than the normal run-of-the-mill primate. He claimed it helps fill "an enormous gap in the panorama of man's development." An upper jaw fragment and four teeth of the same sort of creature, a part of the collection at Yale's Peabody Museum, was found about sixty years earlier in the foothills of the Himalayas–the Siwalik Hills of the Punjab Province of northern India.

Another early fossil often claimed to be one of man's early ancestors, is *Ramapithecus punjabicus*. Not many specimens have been recovered–less than a dozen in all, generally only fragments and teeth–but anthropologists make interesting speculations from them. They believe that this ancient creature evolved into mankind, although there is no evidence that this is true.

Writes John E. Pfeiffer in *The Emergence of Man:* "Practically nothing is known about his development during the period between fourteen million and about five million years ago, the biggest gap in the story of human evolution." This distinguished scientist adds: "So the ten million years after Ramapithecus are still an almost *complete blank* as far as hominid traces are concerned."

But if the evidence the theory of evolution requires is missing for so vast a period of time, then why should we assume that evolution occurred? The likely explanation for the "big gap" and "almost complete blank" is the fact that evolution simply did not occur!

To fill such a huge gap, scores or hundreds of "missing links" in the chain of evolution would be required. Yet they simply have not been found!

Evolutionists by-pass the blank ten million years, till they come to the next hominid discovery.

Australopithecus

One day in 1924, Raymond Dart, professor of anatomy at the Medical School of the University of the Witwatersrand in Johannesburg, received two boxes of fossils from a miner at the village of Taung, near the Kalahari Desert. Dart found in the collection the cast of a large brain case and major parts of a skull and jaw of an infant. The creature was not a giant anthropoid, such as a gorilla.

Dart called the specimen "a manlike ape" and named him *Australopithecus africanus* or "southern ape of Africa." He believed that this creature later evolved into mankind.

But Elliot Smith at University College in London disagreed. He felt that the "Taung's baby" was an ape that more likely led to the chimpanzee or gorilla.

Australopithecus, with a brain weighing perhaps one pound—about a third the size of modern man's brain—did not fit in with prevailing theory. But gradually, the shifting sands of theory swung around to Dart's side. Other scientists gradually recognized his "southern apes" as actually full-fledged hominids.

Thirty miles west of Johannesburg, in the Transvaal, Robert Broom, in 1936, visited a farm known as Sterkfontein and examined fossils which had recently been unearthed. He found pieces of the skull of an adult *Australopithecus* within two weeks. Several dozen new specimens were eventually found at Sterkfontein and two nearby sites.

In 1967-68, Clark Howel of the University of Chicago examined fossil-bearing strata near the Omo River valley in southwestern Ethiopia and found Australopithecine fragments believed to be about four million years old.

But regardless of the excitement caused by these fragments, and others, most anthropologists now believe that Australopithecus was not the ancestor of modern men!

Homo Erectus

This dubious honor is now ascribed to *Homo erectus.* One specimen, found in 1963 and dubbed "Poor George," had a skull the size of a softball, consisting of some two hundred bits and pieces glued together by Mary Leakey over a period of eight months. This creature supposedly lived over one million years ago. Fragments of similar creatures have been found in Lantian County in northwest China, in 1963, and in a sandpit near Heidelberg, Germany, in 1907, and during the past ten years in Algeria, Chad, and in a village thirty miles from Budapest, Hungary.

Similar remains were found, of course, in 1892 by Eugene Dubois and later dubbed "Java man," and also in a stone cave in Dragon's Hill, about thirty miles from the city of Peking. Excavations were carried out from 1923 to 1936, and by the time diggers had excavated a depth of 160 feet, some fourteen skulls of "Peking man" and about 150 teeth and other fragments were discovered. Evidence of fire, and tools, were also found in the cave and signs of a struggle between Peking man and other cave dwellers.

But is *Homo erectus* a representative of true man? Or a bridge between man and ape? Or really an ape? Says John Pfieffer, "All investigators agree that they represent true man and belong to the widespread species known as *Homo erectus.*"

The evidence suggests that he was indeed unique. Whereas the

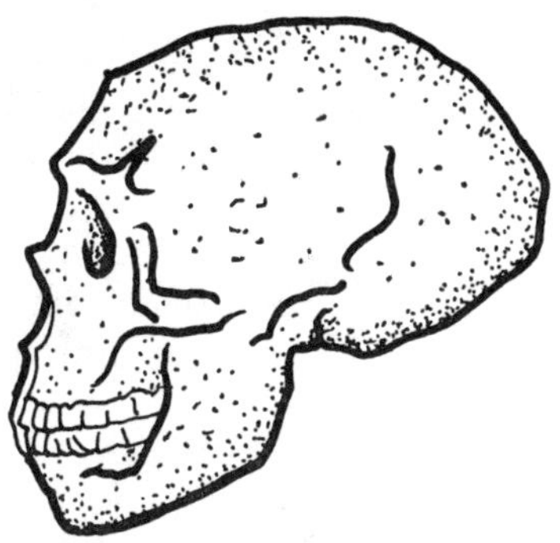

Australopithecus Africanus

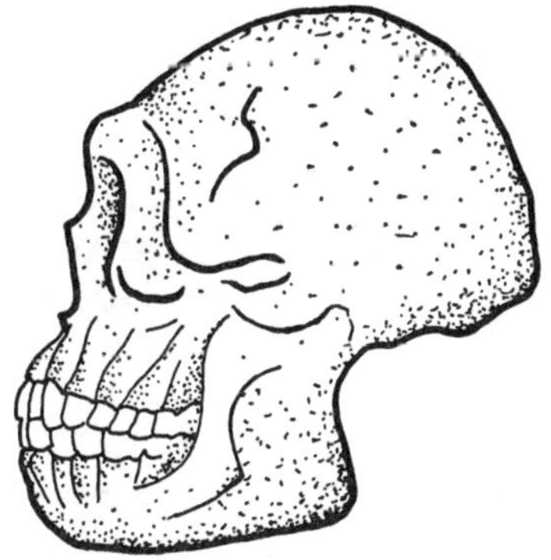

Homo Erectus

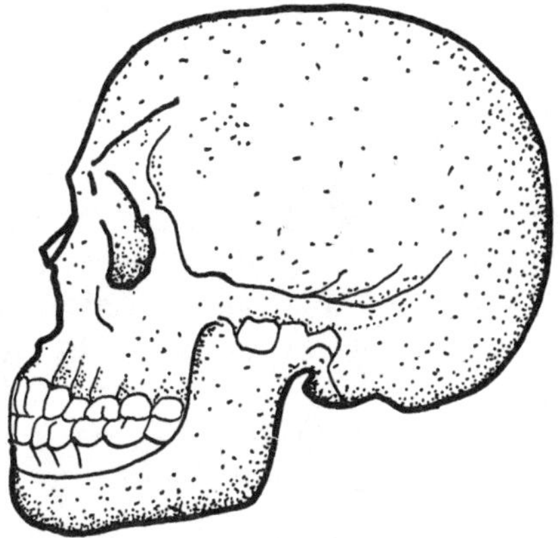

Homo Sapiens Sapiens

cranial capacity of *Australopithecus* varied from 435 to 600 cubic centimeters, *Homo erectus* had a capacity varying from 775 to nearly 1,300 cubic centimeters, with an average of almost 975. The upper range of the brain case of *Homo erectus* barely overlapped the range for modern man. Some members of *Homo erectus* had brains larger than some people living today. But what does this prove?

The Brain Gap

Anthropologists, when they compare the vast difference between the brains of *Homo erectus*, and *Australopithecus*, are amazed. How evolution could virtually double the size of the brain—is puzzling to paleontologists.

One theory speaks of "quantum evolution" as the key to the puzzle. But "quantum evolution" merely is a synonym for "rapid evolution." It doesn't explain anything. It is merely a descriptive term to explain what evolutionists assume must have happened.

The simple truth of the matter is that anthropologists don't know how to account for the size of the brain of *Homo erectus*. There is, at this point, no fossil evidence of a gradual change in cranial capacity—there are no solid, provable "links" between the ape-size brain of *Australopithecus* and the brain of *Homo erectus*.

How to account for the sudden doubling of brain size! It was to become an insurmountable problem. One suggestion is that when these creatures learned to "hunt" other animals for food, the hunt affected certain parts of the brain more than others. Says Pfieffer: "It must have brought about an increase in the size of the brain's integrating circuits, centers which help analyze the unceasing flow of messages coming in from the sense organs and trigger appropriate action on the basis of the analyses. It also led to an expansion of the frontal areas of the cortex which are concerned with planning . . ."

Such a statement is strikingly Lamarkian in nature, and surprisingly unscientific. Students of genetics now are well aware that animals do not evolve new organs or appendages because of "need." Therefore, it is with surprise and amusement that one reads in a current volume on anthropology that "hunting" in effect caused the brain to increase in size.

New Discoveries

Meanwhile, new discoveries in Africa are compelling anthropologists to completely rethink the pedigree of early man and his origins.

On a blistering hot day in August 1972, with the sun bathing the area of Lake Rudolph in Kenya, East Africa, in sweltering heat, a young worker, Bernard Ngeneo, was sweating it out digging in a wild, steep ravine. He was part of an anthropological expedition led by Richard Leakey, son of the famed late Dr. Louis S.B. Leakey.

As he was digging, Ngeneo noticed something rather unusual. He squinted his eyes, and brushed away the dirt, and there before him was a shattered cranium, surprisingly human and modern in appearance.

That same day more than thirty pieces of the jigsaw puzzle skull were dug up, many of them the size of a thumbnail or smaller.

The skull was shown to Richard Leakey, and he examined and scrutinized two of the fragments from the frontal section of the skull. He was amazed.

Instantly, Leakey knew that this hominid was different. It has a surprisingly large braincase!

Dating laboratories soon dated the find at about 2.8 million years of age, using potassium-argon dating methods on the rocks where the bone fragments were found.

But why is this skull so important? What is its real significance?

Richard Leakey himself put the fact bluntly: "Either we toss out this skull or we toss out our theories of early man," he charged.

The skull, indexed as "skull 1470," is the death knell of current evolutionary theories about the origin of man. Says

Leakey, this newly discovered fossil "leaves in ruins the sequence of evolutionary change." He adds, "It appears that there were several different kinds of early man, some of whom developed larger brains earlier than had been supposed."

Skull 1470 sent a violent shock wave throughout the anthropological world, exploding long-cherished theories.

The enormously significant fossil was obviously humanlike—*Homo.* But it contained remarkably advanced features for a hominid that supposedly lived roughly three million years ago.

Weeks of painstaking, diligent effort were required to fit the shattered pieces of the cranium together. This arduous task was assigned to Meave, the wife of Richard Leakey. After the pieces began to take shape, Leakey saw that it fit no previous model of early man. It was hard to see how such a modern form could be about three million years old. He writes: "Thus our past has now been pushed back at least 10,000 centuries—and *baffling new questions* have arisen concerning the human pedigree."[8]

How does this new "skull 1470" fit into the normally constructed pattern of human evolution? First of all, it is a complete misfit. The skull lacks the beetling brow of *Homo erectus* and the braincase, though much older, was nearly as large—estimated to be 800 cubic centimeters. The braincase of *Homo erectus* ranges between 750 and 1200 cubic centimeters. Modern man's cranium is about 1400 c.c.

Leg bones found in the same stratigraphic level were almost indistinguishable from those of *Homo sapiens*. The evidence suggests that this humanlike creature lived contemporaneously with smaller ape-like creatures, the *Australopithecines*, which at times have also been included in man's pedigree, though many anthropologists now consider them to have been an "evolutionary dead-end" and were not the progenitors of the human race.

The fossil beds of Lake Rudolph have yielded more than 40 specimens of *Australopithecus,* dated from one million to 2.9 million years. This ancient creature had a brain capacity of only 500 c.c. and was a strict vegetarian.

Also unearthed at Lake Rudolph were 300 simple stone cutting and chopping tools. It may prove to be that the type of man represented by "skull 1470" was the creator of these simple tool instruments.

Hominid Fossils

Further complicating the emerging picture are other fossil hominid finds. *Homo erectus*, as typified by Peking and Java man, has been found also at Olduvai. His dates range from 500,000 years to one million, based on radiometric dating techniques.

Homo habilis, also found at Olduvai by Louis S.B. Leakey, and which had a 650 c.c. braincase, dated to about two million years.

Which of these varied creatures, one might ask, reflect man—if any of them?

If we attempt to arrange them according to cranial capacity or brain size, we obtain the following:

Australopithecus—435 to 600 c.c., with a mean of 508 c.c.

Homo habilis—643 to 724, some 80 c.c. more than the largest Australopithecines.

Homo erectus (formerly called Pithecanthropus, Sinanthropus, Atlanthropus, etc.)—775 to 1225 c.c., with a mean of 978 c.c.

New discoveries in Africa have added to the disarray and confusion regarding "early man." Carl Johnson, a young American paleo-anthropologist, has discovered several leg bones and a skull fragment at Afar, a desolate region in northern Ethiopia. The layer of mudstone where the fossils were found is estimated to be more than 3 million years old.

Meanwhile, Richard B. Leakey, director of the Keny National Museum, has turned up more than 100 hominid fossils at his digging site on the eastern shore of Lake Rudolph. Leakey's group has found evidence of at least three types of man living side by side for almost 2 million years. Fragments of a skull which may have been bigger than 1470, and of similar age, have also been discovered.

One of the creatures, with a small brain and large jaw, may

have been a vegetarian. Another, with a small skull, has a jaw and teeth similar to modern man. Leakey, not knowing just what these ancient creatures were, calls them "Thing A, Thing B, and Thing C."

Standard Theory of Evolution

"Skull 1470" and similar finds pose an enigma to anthropologists. Since they appear somewhat modern in many respects, and since they are tentatively dated at about three million years old, they appear to destroy traditional evolutionary theory.

The standard, accepted theory, believed for several decades, holds that modern man descended from the Australopithecines, whose brain was about the size of most modern gorillas. He could walk upright, apparently, and his teeth were larger than modern man's, but he lacked the tusk-like canines and incisors of modern apes.

Australopithecus, states the theory, existed about two million years ago and gradually evolved into modern man. But since "skull 1470" is estimated at three million years and is substantially larger than that of the Australopithecines, and was found with modern-appearing thigh bones, it doesn't square with the standard theory at all.

Aside from this discovery, however, another equally staggering fossil was recently found in Border Cave, in southern Africa. Supposedly, according to traditional theory, the only true humans in existence in 100,000 B.C. were the hulking Neanderthal types, which eventually died out. *Homo sapiens*, theoretically, did not appear on the world scene until about 35,000 years ago.

But alarm and consternation struck when the fossils in Border Cave, on Bomvu Ridge in Swaziland, came to light. Actually, the cave was first explored in 1934 when scientists found pieces of fossilized human skulls and bone, and an infant skeleton. Then the cave remained undisturbed for 30 years, until 1964, when engineers opened an iron mine in the area and discovered curious stone implements.

In December 1970 Adrian Boshier of the Museum of Man and Science and Peter Beaumont began a thorough investigation. In fifty working days, they dug up some 300,000 artifacts and charred animal bones. Charcoal found in a level of ash above the artifacts was radiocarbon dated to in excess of 50,000 years.

Boshier and Beaumont found stone implements and ground ocher nine feet below the surface, leading them to the conclusion that the cave had been inhabited perhaps 100,000 years ago.

Astonished, the two men continued their search. They found stone arrowheads, indicating even the bow and arrow were known more than 50,000 years ago. Most archeologists had previously assumed the bow and arrow reached Europe only 15,000 B.C.

Boshier and Beaumont claim that the evidence proves that as early as 100,000 years ago men had learned to count, had developed a curiosity about the purpose of human life and human destiny, and sought answers to the causes and meaning of life.[9]

This discovery, added to the remarkable "skull 1470" found at Lake Rudolph, has contributed to a growing confusion about the real meaning and direction of humanity's pedigree. "Who begat whom?" is the question of the hour, and nobody has the definitive answer.

"What is the real cradle of mankind?" is another question that goes unanswered, unless we accept the Biblical record of Creation which tells us that the first true man and woman were created in the garden of Eden, in the Middle East.

As author Ronald Schiller has pointed out: "The descent of man is no longer regarded as a chain with some links missing, but rather as a tangled vine whose tendrils loop back and forth as species interbred to create new varieties, most of which died out."[12]

The Lord God is subtle, but
malicious he is not.

—Inscription in
Fine Hall, Princeton

Chapter Seventeen

In Search of Adam

In the book of Genesis we read the account of the creation of man. The chronicler relates: "Then God said, 'Let us make man in our image, after our likeness; and let them have dominion over the fish of the sea, and over the birds of the air, and over the cattle, and over all the earth, and over every creeping thing that creeps upon the earth.'

"So God created man in his own image, in the image of God he created him; male and female he created them" (Genesis 1:26-27, RSV).

More information is given in chapter 2, verse 7: "Then the Lord God formed man of dust from the ground, and breathed into his nostrils the breath of life; and man became a living being."

Is this creation account mere legend? ancient mythology? Or is it factual—literal—historical?

How does the evidence of paleontology relate to this question?

A person searching for truth must recognize that he must not prejudge an issue before he gets all the facts—before all the available evidence is in. And he must be willing to change his views if at any future time new evidence comes along which controverts his previous conclusions.

So it is with the field of anthropology and early man and dating techniques as they have been applied to fossil man. In past years, most if not all creationists have argued that radiometric dating methods, particularly radiocarbon dating, must be in absolute error because they would indicate that the earth is much older than 6,000 years. Also, potassium-argon dating, and radiocarbon dating, using this reasoning, must a priori be in error because they show that early man lived on the earth for anywhere from 40,000 years to three or four million years.

Potassium-argon dating methods have been used to date geologic material associated with remains of Homo erectus and Neanderthal man. If these creatures are true men, and if the dates are essentially accurate, then man has indeed been on the earth for many scores of thousands of years, as anthropologists insist on telling us. And they don't have any ax to grind; they are merely reporting what they find in the fossil fields of the earth. They are not striving to prove evolution. They did not invent these dating methods merely to embarrass creationists.

Even more embarrassing to creationists of the old school, however, is the perverse fact that more than one dating method reveals the same essential truth of the antiquity of fossil man. Creationists may continually assert that radiocarbon dating is a fraud; is unreliable because of the Noachian deluge; is based on false assumptions related to the influx of cosmic rays into the earth's atmosphere; and is therefore untrustworthy and must be categorically rejected.

As if that were not enough to disturb the quiescent theories dates for the last 8,000 years have been carefully examined and tested by comparison with tree-ring dating methods, or dendrochronology. And to the consternation of most creationists, the two methods are in general agreement as far back as they have been compared!

As if that were not enough to disturb the quiessent theories of creationists, and give them nightmares in their sleep, now a new dating method has entered the field—racemization, or the comparison of the proportion of D amino acids in fossil remains with L amino acids. This new, totally independent dating method, unfortunately, agrees with dendrochronology and radiocarbon 14 dating and potassium-argon dating, and provides an independent check on the other systems.

What does all this mean?

Pity the poor creationist who believes that the earth was just created by divine fiat 6,000 years ago because that is what he thinks, sincerely, the Bible says.

Such discoveries have rocked the faith of many erstwhile believers in the Bible and the inspiration of Scripture. But do such discoveries really conflict with revelation? Is there really a contradiction in the Biblical revelation and the well attested, authenticated discoveries of paleontology?

Not at all! The real conflict is between assumptions which students of the Bible have erroneously made, and the evidence of paleontology. It is time we re-examine some of the basic theological premises we have taken for granted and assumed to be true without adequately testing them by the Bible record itself.

Dating Methods

In 1963 two British scientists, Don Brothwell of the British Museum and Eric Higgs of Cambridge, took stock of the many methods developed up to that time to answer archaeological questions, including dating methods. Only twenty years before that time, nobody would have dreamed of such scientific discoveries relating to the dating of artifacts.

Of all the dating methods, C-14 or radiocarbon dating has created the greatest interest to date. Developed by Willard F. Libby of the University of Chicago—between 1941 and 1945 Libby participated in the development of the atomic bomb—this method of dating has become the touchstone of all fossil dating up to 40,000 years.

Libby postulated that cosmic ray-produced radiocarbon might be a key to age determination. Supposing that C-14 atoms produced by cosmic rays would be readily oxidized to carbon dioxide and would mix freely with the atmospheric carbon dioxide, and because of the rapid turnover of the earth's atmosphere, Libby assumed the radiocarbon portion of carbon dioxide would achieve uniform global distribution, and would logically be taken up in the same proportion by all plant life during photosynthesis. All animal life, which indirectly or directly lives off of plants and vegetation could also be expected to contain the same universal proportion of C-14. Similarly, even sea life would be thus affected, because carbon dioxide of the atmosphere is in exchange equilibrium with the oceans.

Adds E.H. Willis, "Upon the death of an organism, further uptake or exchange of radiocarbon would cease, leaving the trapped radiocarbon to decay exponentially with time."[1]

Simply explained, cosmic rays continually bombard our planet earth. Upon striking our atmosphere, neutrons are produced that react with atoms of nitrogen in our atmosphere, creating tiny quantities of C-14. This newly formed C-14 forms a chemical bond with oxygen as the polymer carbon dioxide. Plants cannot distinguish between carbon dioxide containing radiocarbon and the normal kind and absorb both into their tissues and convert them into food by photosynthesis. Animals and men eat the plants. Thus C-14 passes into the body of every living thing.

Since C-14 is radioactive, and radioactive substances decay at fixed rates, it is possible to determine that after a specified amount of time the amount of radioactivity in a substance will be reduced exactly one half, or one fourth, and so on. This is called the "half life" of the radioisotope.

The half life of C-14 was at first thought to be 5,567 years. Thus a tree cut down 5,568 years ago theoretically ought to produce only half as many Geiger counter ticks as one chopped down today, because it would have exactly half as much radiocarbon remaining in its tissues.

In January 9, 1948, the first conference took place to study the usefulness of Libby's method for archaeology. After that time, a flood of materials from the world over poured into Dr. Libby's lab to be analyzed. Bits of Egyptian mummies, charcoal from an ancient caveman's fire, the tooth of a mammoth, a piece of a beam of a Hittite temple, and hundreds of other objects, were tested.

Libby's theory was quickly confirmed. Comparisons of radiocarbon dates of material with dates derived archaeologically often turned out to be strikingly similar. Although Libby always estimated an uncertainty factor of about ten percent in his datings—thus a piece of wood 4,000 years old would be said to be 4,000 plus or minus about 400 years—Libby's method helped archaeologists pin down dates which could not otherwise be determined.

Carbon 14 testing, however, is not easy. The pure carbon must be extracted from the material, by burning the material. The carbon that separates out in gaseous compounds can easily be reduced to a solid. Not all the material would have to be burned, of course; for measuring wood, twenty grams of carbon was needed (or 65 grams of wood).

Early inaccuracies due to the interference of other radiation were eliminated as more was learned about the method. Sometimes when a particular object turned out to have a widely disparate date, further checking revealed that the archaeologist had sent a piece of wood from an older house which the builders of an ancient temple had later incorporated into that structure!

Another source of error is inherent in the material. Some aquatic animals have flesh that shows fewer traces of C-14 than their shell. Some plants do not take in as much C-14 as other plants in different environments. Only as enough evidence of these anomalies is accumulated can the errors be corrected.

Another problem is exhaust gases from automobiles. As vast quantities of carbon compounds are belched into the air, diluting the carbon compounds naturally found in the atmosphere, diminishing the percentage of C-14 found there, this makes certain plants and animals in such areas appear to have decayed much more than they have.

There are many more sources of minor error, but they are being scrutinized and eliminated one by one. Even the "half life" of C-14 has had to undergo revision, and it is now assumed to be 5,730 years. All the measurements taken before 1961, therefore, have had to be recalibrated. Nevertheless, radiocarbon dating has become an extremely useful tool in the hands of archaeologists. But another highly important tool, providing a cross check of C-14 dates, is the use of dendrochronology, or tree rings.

Tree Rings from the Past

The full benefit of tree-ring dating has only been realized during the past two decades. Tree ring analysis was proposed in 1837 by Charles Babbage. The real inventor of tree-ring dating, however, is Dr. Andrew Ellicott Douglass, physicist and astronomer, formerly director of the University of Arizona's Steward Observatory. In 1929 he wrote that by reading the story told by tree rings, the horizons of history in the United States had been pushed back nearly eight centuries before Columbus, establishing an accurate chronology for the southwestern United States.

Dr. Douglass died over twelve years ago. But his intensive investigations of tree rings has remarkably advanced the science of dating methods. He knew that trees add a new ring each year, and counting the rings can tell you the age of the tree. But he discovered that all rings are not of equal thickness—some are narrow, some wide, and often a series of narrow rings or broad rings would occur. Douglass reflected that the fat rings represented "fat years" and the lean rings "lean years"—or moist and dry years, respectively.

Further studies proved this to be the case. Douglass found also an unquestionable connection between sunspots and tree growth; every eleven years there had been a "fat period" of ample moisture.

Douglass pushed his research back further and further into the past, collecting cores and samples of wood from ancient trees used in old pueblos and Indian villages. He discovered that he could "cross-date" or "overlap" the tree rings of different trees of different ages, and gradually pushed the new chronometer back to before the birth of Christ.

Since that time, great new advances have been made, using the redwoods and giant sequoias of California, and the bristlecone pines, which are up to 4,500 years old—the oldest living organisms in the world.

By cross checking bristlecone pine dates with radiocarbon dates, the reliability of the method has been verified. Using dead wood, C.W. Ferguson of the University of Arizona has obtained an "unquestionably accurate back-dating to the year 5200 B.C."[2]

Although not all trees and climates are as favorable for dating purposes as the dry Southwestern United States, this absolute method of archaeological dating has been expanded to half the globe.

Potassium-Argon Dating

Another simple and essentially reliable method of dating appears to be the potassium-argon method, discovered in 1948. Potassium is the lightest element possessing a naturally occurring radioactive isotope, K-40, with a half life of 1,280 million years. K-40 transmutes to either calcium 40 or argon 40, a gas, about one atom of K-40 in seven becoming argon.

By measuring the amount of potassium and argon in a lava or rock specimen, the specimen can be accurately dated with very refined techniques. The method is based on two assumptions: that no argon was trapped within the specimen at the time of its formation; and that no potassium or argon was added or subtracted by external processes during the lifetime of the mineral.[3]

Potassium, a common mineral found in sedimentary and igneous rocks, offers great promise of dating many formations.

The potassium-argon dating method helps fill the gap between uranium dating and carbon 14 dating. It is useful for geological strata older than 40,000 years. Theoretically, it helps us establish the age of those near-human creatures which existed and roamed various parts of the earth during the Pleistocene age and before. This dating method has been crucial in establishing the dates of the Australopithecines, Homo erectus, Homo habilis and similar creatures dating from several hundred thousand years to a few million years in antiquity.

Use of this clock dated the Fort Ternan fossils found by Louis Leaky at about 14 million years, give or take a few hundred thousand years. Similarly the technique was useful in dating volcanic minerals at Olduvai, and the deposits containing the 1959 skull of Zinjanthropus turned out to be 1,750,000 years old, twice as old as had been estimated on the basis of geological studies.

The basis for these dates, by and large, appears to be irrefutable. Certainly, we must not reject out of hand, without due reason, these and many other established dates. The scientific evidence is substantial. In order to reconcile these findings with the biblical record of creation, we conclude that these creatures—Homo erectus, Homo habilis, Swanscombe man, and Steinheim man, all of them exceedingly primitive forms—were all pre-Adamic creatures.

Meanwhile, another useful dating technique has come into vogue.

Racemization

Two researchers at the University of California at San Diego report that men were living in the North American continent at least 50,000 years ago. Dr. Jeffrey L. Bada, an assistant professor of oceanography at the university's Scripps Institution of Oceanography, and Roy A. Schroeder, a graduate student, analyzed skeletal remains found between 1920 and 1935 around La Jolla, Del Mar, and ranging to Laguna Beach and the Baldwin Hills section of Los Angeles.

Using a technique called "racemization," which determines how much one form of an amino acid has changed into a slightly different form, they dated one skull found near Del Mar at 48,000 years old. Previously the oldest dated Amenzar skull was called Los Angeles Man, and was dated by UCLA scientists using carbon-14 at 23,600 years. A small sample of the same skull was analyzed by Bada and he arrived at an age of 26,000 years.

The Scripps team dated a fragment of another old skull found near La Jolla Shores at 44,000 years.

This discovery would indicate that early man came to the New World long before 20,000 years ago, the date most anthropologists have generally believed to be most accurate.

The findings have added a "new chapter in the story of man," the scientists claim.

Dr. Jeffrey Bada's new technique for dating bones can be used for dating purposes for fossils millions of years old. Bada measures the amount of the "D-form" of certain amino acids found in all fossils.

Bada's technique is based on the fact that the amino acid components of proteins can have two optical forms, or isomers—the D-form and the L-form. After an organism dies, the L-form gradually converts to the D-form. Modern amino acids consist almost totally of the L-form, but ancient bones and fossils have a progressively higher ratio of the D-form. Using his technique, Bada has dated a shark's vertebra at 8.7 million years and an ancient goat bone from the island of Majorca at 26,000 years.

Pre-Adamic Man?

If we accept the combined evidence of the various dating systems, then we must conclude that various hominid creatures lived 500,000 years ago, were familiar with fire, used stone tools such as had been made for hundreds of thousands of years—hand axes, notched and saw-toothed implements, scrapers, engravers—the basic Acheulian-type tools. These beings must have been pre-Adamic creatures, primitive hunters and cave dwellers. Everything about them speaks of a primitiveness and antiquity, a life style and mental ability that was distinctly not human.

Is such a thing possible?

Why not?

The answer is simple enough. First, not only do the geologic evidence and the dating techniques of modern science demonstrate the antiquity of these beings, but the biblical record clearly shows that Adam was *not* a brute or subhuman specimen. He was fully human in every respect. Adam was highly intelligent, articulate, sophisticated, knowledgeable. He was not only able to provide names for every creature God brought before him, but he was capable of language, and he was familiar with the art of cultivation and agriculture. To pinpoint when Adam was created, then, we must search the geologic and archaeological record for the beginning of animal husbandry and agriculture, as well as the beginning of civilization as such.

The scrapers, knives, hand axes, cleavers, and flint tools of the early and middle Pleistocene times were primitive, pre-human, pre-Adamic. The really astonishing thing, witnessed by geological evidence, archaeological discoveries, and radiometric dating, is the sudden flowering of civilization and truly human enterprise roughly 6,000 years ago!

Neanderthal Man

The strange breeds that arose during middle Pleistocene times and during the next to last glaciation had large brains, overlapping modern man, but their primitive features included lower cranial vaults, heavy bone ridges over the eyes and at the back of the neck, and sharply receding chins. Their bodies were stocky, short, and heavy limbed.

"These were the classic Neanderthal people, the people who come to mind whenever cavemen are mentioned and who almost invariably serve as models for artists depicting early man,"[4] says Pfeiffer.

Neanderthal man—a predecessor of modern man, but not necessarily directly related by lineage—was almost human in many respects. He was crude, dwelled in caves, hunted wild game to survive, and crudely buried his dead. His differences were more remarkable than his similarities to modern man. It has been said that if a Neanderthal man got on a subway in New York, dressed up in modern clothes, he could not be distinguished from certain others on the train. However, such a statement is merely discussing the physical appearance of Neanderthal. True, he didn't look too unlike certain of the more robust, physical specimens of mankind, today. However, the paleontological evidence shows that his society and living conditions were extremely primitive, created no lasting forms of art such as evidenced by Cro-Magnon man, and was not able to speak or articulate a true language.

How does Neanderthal fit into the biblical record then? One historian and geologist, Kenneth C. Hermann, a scientist located in Big Sandy, Texas, has come up with a remarkable theory. He suggests that Neanderthal man was truly pre-Adamic, but also co-existed with Adamic man. Adam, he suggests, was truly *modern man* in every respect—*Homo sapiens sapiens*—and was of the Cro-Magnon stock in antiquity.

Neanderthal man, if this theory is correct, may have been representative of the beings called in the biblical record *Nephilim.* These beings are barely alluded to in the Scriptures. But we read in Genesis 6:4 that during the pre-Flood world, when the descendants of Adam were multiplying on the face of the earth: "The Nephilim were on the earth in those days, and also afterward . . . " (RSV).

The Hebrew *nephil* means bully or tyrant. The *Nephilim* were the sons of Anak, a strong, powerful race. The King James Version refers to the *Nephilim* as "giants," though that may be a mistranslation. At any rate, they were a fearsome race of beings.

Were the *Nephilim* remnants of a pre-Adamic stock of men, whom anthropologists refer to as Neanderthal man? Is it possible?

Is it also possible that there was a certain amount of limited intermarriage between the two stocks, as appears to be evidenced at Carmel, in the Middle East, before Neanderthal man died out and became extinct?

The physiognomy of Neanderthal man would be enough to throw fear into more modern, gracile man. He was an excellent hunter. Short, stocky, with massive jaw, and evidently cannibalistic, there was good reason for modern man to view this competitor with alarm.

Neanderthal's remains have been found at Shanidar Cave in the Zagros Mountains of Iraq, excavated by Ralph Solecki of Columbia University. The deposits in the cave were up to 100,000 years and seven Neanderthal skeletons were found. Three had been crushed by falling rocks; one was recovering from a spear or knife wound in the ribs; one was a man buried deep in the cave with a special ceremony, attested to by the presence of fossil pollen collected from the burial site. The pollen was from the ancestors of present day grape hyacinths, bachelor's buttons, hollyhocks, and yellow-flowering groundsels.

Violence was common in Neanderthal times. Says John E. Pfeiffer:

> Some sort of mayhem took place in a sandstone-rock shelter overlooking a river in northern Yugoslavia, where at the turn of the century investigators recovered more than five hundred bones and bone fragments representing at least a dozen individuals. A number of the bones are charred, suggesting that cannibalism may have been practiced, while others show definite signs of having been cut (p. 172).

Extinction of Neanderthal Man

In most deposits in Europe, there is a definite interval between the last deposits of Neanderthal man and the earliest fossils of modern man, or what is called Cro-Magnon man.

The stone tools of Cro-Magnon were markedly more sophisticated than Neanderthal implements. When archaeologists dug through successive layers in European caves, they sometimes found toolless—sterile—layers between earlier Neanderthal deposits and later Cro-Magnon deposits.

But during the early 1930's an Anglo-American expedition searching for fossils in what was then called Palestine, struck it rich in two caves on the slopes of Mount Carmel, near Haifa. At Magharet et-Tabun a female Neanderthal skeleton was found; at Mugharet es-Skhul remains of ten individuals were uncovered, some resembling Neanderthals, and others approaching the appearance of modern man. Some anthropologists concluded the fossil men were hybrids—products of intermarriage between Neanderthals and true modern-type men. Louis Leakey even surmised that any marriage between the two races might well have produced sterile offspring. At any rate, the fossils uncovered at Mount Carmel possess a blend of Neanderthal and modern traits. But mysteries remain. For example, why did modern man suddenly seem to replace Neanderthal man? What led to the extinction of this formidable and widespread species of Homo? Why the sudden revolution in tool-making with the arrival of modern man? Why the sterile layers that often separate Neanderthal and Cro-Magnon periods of cave occupancy?

We don't know. But we can speculate. Was much of Neanderthal man wiped out in a pre-Adamic destruction associated with upheavals in climate and terrestrial cataclysms? Were the remaining remnants of Neanderthal, wiped out by Cro-Magnon man?

Neanderthal man, however, must have largely been pre-Adamic. This contention is supported by an investigation of the linguistic capabilities of Neanderthals by Philip Lieberman of the University of Connecticut and Edmund Crelin of Yale in 1971. Measuring the neck vertebrae and skull base of the fossil found at La Chapelle-aux-Saints, they concluded that Neanderthal man lacked a modern kind of pharynx. He was unable to utter the vowel sounds *ah, oo, ee, ou,* and could not form the consonants *g* and *k*. Thus European Neanderthal fossils give indication of only 10 percent the speaking ability of modern man.

The findings are hotly disputed, but if true, Neanderthal may have been very limited in verbal communication. Somehow, these creatures suddenly died out, replaced by modern man, the Cro-Magnons, who were accomplished artists who made marvelous cave paintings, engravings and statuary. The passing of Neanderthal man was the passing of an era.*

Says author George Constable:

> The disappearance of the Neanderthals seems to have the makings of a soul-stirring plan, with the world as a stage, and the happiest ending imaginable—the ascendancy of ourselves. The only trouble is that no one really knows what happened. . . . The twists and turns of the drama that brought about the replacement of the Neanderthals constitute the greatest of all prehistoric mysteries.[5]

---

*A few Russian anthropologists believe that the strange Asian beast-men variously called the Yetis or Abominable Snowmen, encountered in central Asian deserts and mountains, are the last surviving Neanderthals who managed to survive in the harsh climate of the Asian heartland which suits their adaptability.

Says this same author, discussing the various theories to account for what happened, "And still others—a minority nowadays—insist that all Neanderthals became extinct and were replaced by modern men who had evolved from an unknown genetic stock in an unlocated Eden."

Precisely!

Creation of Modern Man

The Neanderthal period of domination is classified by archaeologists as the Middle Paleolithic, or Middle Old Stone Age. The Cro-Magnon phase which followed it is termed the Upper Paleolithic. The tools of Neanderthal were very crude. The Upper Paleolithic tools, however, are more finely made, and include blades and burins or chisel-like tools.

Cro-Magnon man, which belongs to the same species as modern man, was generally smaller than we are, had straight limbs, and high foreheads. They wore animal skins as clothing, were hunters and fishermen and gatherers of fruits and berries. They had not learned to plant crops or domesticate cattle. Remains indicate that few men reached the age of 50, or few women the age of 35. They are believed to have been of superior intelligence and sensitivity, "if only on the basis of their cave art," writes Ronald Schiller.[6] They may have believed in life after death since they placed food and tools in graves to accompany the deceased on their journeys in the afterlife.

The most recent reliably dated Neanderthal fossil is dated as 40,000 years old, although some may have indeed come down closer. The oldest carbon-dated Cro-Magnon man lived about 26,000 years ago in Czechoslovakia. Between the two is a huge fossil gap that remains a mystery. How, when, where, and why human evolution crossed this gap cannot be explained by evolutionists.[7]

Western Europe is generally regarded as one place where this evolutionary record should be preserved. "Yet," declares Constable, "no fossil intermediate between the local Neanderthals and Cro-Magnons has ever been found there."[8]

The mystery remains. How hundreds of thousands of the

Neanderthal race could have suddenly perished, in Asia, Africa, and Europe where they are known to have existed, boggles the mind. Perhaps the only solution to the riddle is some ecological catastrophe, as some experts have speculated.

But if Neanderthal man can reliably be identified with the *Nephilim* of the Bible, then their extermination becomes apparent. Both ecological factors, climatic changes before and after the time of Adam, when the earth suffered *tohu* and *bohu*, may have been partially responsible for their demise; and the coup de grace may well have been administered by Cro-Magnon man, or modern man, thousands of years ago.

Who, Then, Was Adam?

If the radiometric and related dating systems are basically reliable, then how can we account for the Biblical epic of the creation of Adam? Who was Adam? When—and how—was he created?

Biblical evidence leads us to conclude that Adam—the first true man in whom God breathed the spirit of man—was created by God and endowed with fully human understanding and consciousness probably 4024 B.C.—if the generations of men, related in the book of Genesis, are complete and entire and omit none of the historical record.

Adam, then, actually was a fully modern man who was created after a period of pre-Adamic hominid existence. He was a relative late comer to the scene. He was apparently preceded by "Neanderthal."

But the time came when God chose to impart His unique gift to man—the spirit of man—to Adam, and created him in the garden of Eden.

Now He was ready for His supreme masterpiece—the first man created in His very own image and likeness, physically, mentally, and psychologically.

And this new creature—Adam—was the first true man, the forebear of the entire modern human race!

The biblical account reveals that Adam was highly intelligent; modern in every way; sophisticated in knowledge and language; and was definitely religious and knew God. The Scriptures also indicate that written history began in Adam's lifetime, and agriculture was practiced by Adam and his descendants. Does this fact square with the archaeological record?

Indeed it does. The earliest beginnings of true agriculture, according to anthropologists, are currently dated at the close of the last Ice Age.[9] The earliest signs of agriculture are in the "fertile crescent" along a 2,000 mile arc extending from Israel and Jordan up the eastern Mediterranean coast, swinging through Turkey and arcing to Iran and the Persian Gulf. Within this spot Adam was created and his descendants took up agriculture (compare Genesis 3:14-19). Adam's own son Cain, we read, was a tiller of the ground (Genesis 4:2). Abel was a herdsman (same verse).

Archaeologically, the first cities appear about this same time. "By 3500 B.C. cities were tightly organized, well governed and sophisticated, and by 2500 B.C. metropolises with the comforts and complexity of modern urban centers were in existence," says Dora Jane Hamblin.[10]

How are these dates arrived at? Says Hamblin:

> The refinement of scientific dating systems, such as those that measure the age of ancient relics by the radioactivity of carbon in charcoal or from the glow emitted by heated pottery, has taken much of the imaginative guesswork out of prehistoric chronology.

These dates, of course, may not be entirely correct. But they are at least in the right ballpark. Refinements in dating techniques, in the light of Scriptural evidence, should continually be made. Since the Noachian deluge may have affected dates of the pre-flood world, the accuracy of carbon-14 dating, prior to the disturbances caused by a global cataclysm, such as a dramatic deluge, may well have been jeopardized.

Before the Deluge

There is, of course, the possibility that dating techniques for early man are in error due to unknown factors. In particular, the dates assigned to Cro-Magnon man are still primarily based on C-14 dating. Is it possible that this particular dating method is invalid for the period before the Noachian deluge?

During the pre-diluvian world, we find described waters above the firmament as well as beneath (Genesis 1:7). At the time of the Deluge, the windows of heaven were opened like a mighty sluice, and the fountains of the great deep were broken up (Genesis 7:11). The waters which were above the firmament apparently cascaded down to the earth, altering the composition of the atmosphere. The waters above the firmament may have acted as a shield, absorbing much of the cosmic radiation, vastly reducing the formation of C-14 prior to the Deluge. The absence of cosmic radiation may be partly responsible for the long life spans of man before the Flood, as recorded in the book of Genesis. But after the Deluge, and the break up of the concentration of waters above the firmament, cosmic radiation would have increased in the atmosphere and on the earth, resulting in a rapid increase of C-14 until equilibrium was reached, and also in shortening the life span of man on the earth.

If this theory is true, then we can account for the apparent great age given Cro-Magnon man and Neanderthal man by the C-14 method. For example, if 4,000 years ago the C-14 in the atmosphere had reached equilibrium, it would now be dated close to 4,000 years by the C-14 method. However, if a sample was actually from the period of the Deluge, while the watery shield above the earth was being broken up, it might have received only one half the expected amount of C-14 in its tissues. Thus it would appear to have been 8,000 years old according to the C-14 method. If a sample started its decay curve with a level of C-14 content less than one eighth the strength of a fresh sample, today, it would appear to be 15,000 years old, when it might be only 5,000 years old. If originally there was very little or no C-14 content, a sample from the prediluvian world would appear to be extremely ancient—35,000 or 40,000 years old.

This is a very strong possibility which we should keep in mind. Several creationist schools of thought tend to think this is the proper explanation for early dates of man derived from the C-14 dating technique.

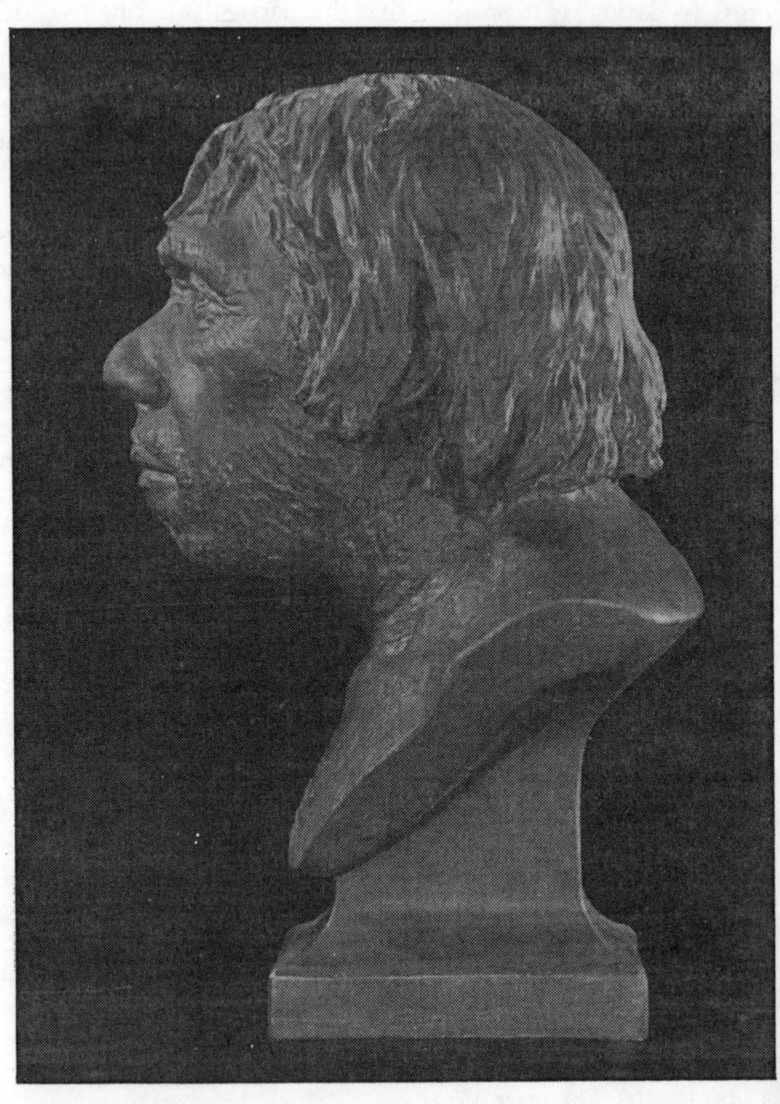

Was Neanderthal man really human? Was he a direct predecessor of modern man? Thus far no direct connection has been found.—*Photo courtesy of the American Museum of Natural History.*

Chapter Eighteen

The Incredible Cataclysm

If the frozen grey muck of the Alaskan Peninsula could but speak, what an eloquent, engrossing, spellbinding tale it could tell!

To the north of Mount McKinley, where the Tanana River joins the Yukon, prospectors have mined for gold out of the frozen Alaskan gravel and muck. This strange muck consists largely of the frozen bodies and bones of huge masses of prehistoric animals and trees.

Muck deposits have been found consisting of the dismembered remains of millions of animals, twisted, splintered, and torn apart by cyclonic forces. The frozen bones of extinct mammoths, mastodons, super-bisons, horses, have been found protruding from the miles and miles of muck.

Berezovka Mammoth

One seventh of the land surface of the earth is permanently frozen ground called "permafrost." Much of this ground is covered with a layer of soil called muck which thaws in the summer. It is composed of mud or silt, black organic matter, and ice.

The remains of animals taken out of this muck include extinct woolly mammoths, woolly rhinoceroses, wild horses, giant oxen, giant bison, huge wolves, mountain lions, and the giant saber-toothed cat.

How did these animals become quick frozen in Arctic soil? Various explanations have been offered, and each, in turn, rejected. Once it was postulated that the animals fell into rivers and were washed downstream and then covered over with silt. But the animal remains are not found in river deltas or estuaries, but in plateaus between river valleys, so this theory was shot down.

Russian scientists said that the animals may have sunk in certain kinds of clays found on the tundra, and a blizzard froze them in the goo. But alas, no such clay has ever been found holding any of the animals in question.

Ivan T. Sanderson, in "The Riddle of the Quick-Frozen Mammoths," points out that the Berezovka mammoth, found sticking headfirst out of a bank of the Berezovka River in northern Siberia, discovered about 60 years ago, was preserved in almost perfect condition except for portions eaten away by wolves. The lips, lining of the mouth, tongue were all preserved, and even portions of the animal's last meal was found stuck between its teeth—delicate sedges, grasses and buttercups which bloom in summer. Says Sanderson:

> Freezing meat is not quite so simple a process as one might think. To preserve it properly, it must·be frozen *very* rapidly. If it is frozen slowly, large crystals form in the liquids in its cells. These crystals burst the cells, and the meat begins to deteriorate.[1]

This means there had to be tremendous cold, especially in order for the center of the mammoth to freeze as well. The flesh of some of these quick frozen mammoths has been eaten by trail dogs and was sampled with no ill effects by Russian paleontologists. Mammoth steaks brought to London on ice were eaten by members of the Royal Society.

Vast herds of these enormous creatures, suddenly, inexplicably, died. The remains of one was radio-carbon dated to about 10,000 years in age. The Berezovka mammoth perished without any visible signs of violence—it simply froze to death.

What happened?

Was there a sudden climatic change in the ancient Arctic? There is evidence that at some time in the past the Arctic regions were much warmer than they are now.

Scientists agree that the earth's axis could not have shifted, thus, being responsible, as the earth is like a huge gyroscope. Resulting stresses from such a shift, they believe, would tear the planet apart.

Shifting continents, also, seem to be out of the question. Although continents do shift, the evidence from sea floor spreading is that the continents today shift only about 2 inches per year. Friction of the earth's crust would prevent any lightninglike sudden massive shift as would be required to suddenly change the climate of vast areas of the northern hemisphere.

Studies of paleoclimatology indicate that there are recurring cycles of climate every 50,000 to 100,000 years. The peak of the last cool cycle may have been 25,000 years ago, when continental glaciation advanced to cover much of Europe and North America. The ice sheets reached their maximum growth, scientists believe, about 15,000 years ago, and then a warming trend set in and the glaciers began retreating. The warm cycle peaked about 10,000 years ago and continued for 5,000 years during which the earth experienced a "climatic optimum," and the Arctic and Antarctic were both covered with lush vegetation. This would explain the present woolly mammoths in the region during this time. But we still haven't accounted for their sudden widespread destruction!

Sanderson suggests that the frozen mammoths may have walked over ice caves, and fallen in when the cave roof collapsed.[2] Subsequently, a shocking drop in temperature accompanying the first blizzard of the winter, during which the mercury drops almost 100 degrees, may have quick frozen the carcass. In the summer, as the soil over the permafrost melted, the whole gooey muck slid down from hills and accumulated at the bottom, forming marshes. Eventually more and more soil buried the trapped mammoth carcasses, and before their flesh could thaw out, the beasts were deeply buried in their frozen state.

This explanation could conceivably account for some of the remains of woolly mammoths which were frozen in perpetuity. But it hardly seems likely that it accounts for the sudden extinction of this creature, or of vast herds of mammoths.

Alaskan Chaos

The greatest harvest of the Alaskan gold mines has not been the yellowish priceless metal that men have industriously slaved after, but the tons and tons of smashed, ripped up and torn bodies and bones of millions of animals and trees. Bones of mammoths, mastodons, bison, horses, wolves, bears and lions have been found within the mass of fine, dark grey muck. Twisted parts of animals and trees have been discovered intermingled with lenses of ice and layers of peat and mosses.

"It looks as though the middle of *some cataclysmic catastrophe* of ten thousand years ago the *whole Alaskan world of living animals and plants was suddenly frozen in mid-motion in a grim charade*," writes archaeologist Frank C. Hibben in *The Lost Americans.*[3]

The frozen Alaskan muck presents a gripping, nightmarish scene of destruction and frozen death!

In the frozen bank of the Yukon River and its tributaries bones and tusks of animals have been exposed at all levels. "Whole gravel bars in the muddy river were formed of the jumbled fragments of animal remains," writes Hibben. And similar bone beds have been found in the frozen tundra of Siberia.

What caused the mysterious death of all these creatures? What cataclysm overwhelmed and buried the Siberian and the Alaskan mammoths?

How long ago did it occur?

The Alaskan muck is virtually a "gold mine" for fossils. Amazingly, the bones of ancient animals were found to be in a remarkable state of preservation. Says Hibben:

> The frozen muck had preserved, in a remarkable manner, tendons, ligaments, fragments of skin and hair, hooves, and even, in some cases, portions of the flesh and bone of these dead animals. In one place, at Cripple Creek, near Fairbanks, we found the shoulder of a mammoth with the flesh and skin yet preserved. We tasted the black and sand-impregnated meat. It was terrible-tasting and gritty. And yet an Eskimo dog wandered by and ate the stuff readily.[4]

Such a remarkable state of preservation argues forcefully for a comparatively recent date for the cataclysm that overwhelmed the mammoths.

At one location at Rosey Creek, north of Fairbanks, miners were using a bulldozer to shove the muck into a sluice box to extract gold. As the bulldozer blade pushed across the muck, it shoved aside huge piles of mammoth tusks and bones, and as the sun came up and blazed down from the summer sky, the stench became unbearable. Hundreds of tons of rotting mammoth flesh could be smelled for miles.

Hibben relates: "Apparently, a whole herd of mammoth had died in this place and *fallen together in a jumbled mass* of leg bones, tusks, and mighty skulls, to be frozen solid and preserved until this day. Only the greed of man for gold had opened up their long-frozen grave."[5]

Continues Hibben in his graphic description:

> Mammals there were in abundance, dumped in all attitudes of death. Most of them were pulled apart by *some unexplained prehistoric catastrophic disturbance.* Legs and torsos and heads and fragments were found together in piles or scattered separately. But nowhere could we find any definite evidence that humans had ever walked among these trumpeting herds or had ever seen their final end.[6]

The evidence for man's presence was not long in coming. As the remains of an Alaskan lion, somewhat reminiscent of a Bengal tiger, was unearthed from the frozen muck, the excavators stumbled across a flint point still frozen solid in silt.

Standard theory suggests that the Wisconsin glaciation (comparable in time to the Late Wurm glaciation in Europe) began about 50,000 years ago, or during the time of Neanderthal man. There were several advances and regressions, culminating in the Tazewell advance, dated generally 20,000-17,000 years ago. The maximum extension of the ice, says Dr. Charles Hapgood, "was not earlier than 17,000 years ago and may have been considerably later."[7]

Regardless of the precise time element, at the close of the Ice Age a vast ice cap covering half a continent and as deep as the Antarctic ice cap is today disappeared, in little more than one or two millenia. Hapgood says; "In any case it was, geologically speaking, a sort of miracle. There was nothing in this to suggest the painfully slow pace of usual geological history. To be blunt about it, it was a catastrophe, a cataclysm; it was a *revolution.*"[8]

Hapgood informs us that it is not popular in geological circles to speak of catastrophes, "because catastrophes, so to speak, went out with the Flood. Yet facts are facts, and come what may, we shall have to face some quite remarkable ones as we proceed."[9]

Can we clear our minds, for a while, and just allow the facts to speak their telltale story?

The evidence for catastrophism is found everywhere. Scientists have found places where animals of cold and warm climates, or animals and plants of different climates, are discovered jumbled together in caves or other places where they all suffered death under violent conditions. Hapgood cites a case reported from the Puy de Dome, France, where a peat bed contained fossils of warm-climate animals and cold-climate flora. Why the two types were found together was not explained in the report, because it was not understood.

In Japan, from Hanaizumi, from a conifer bed dated roughly 15,000 years ago, plant fossils implying a cold climate were accompanied by the remains of several extinct animal species including fossil elephant.

How extensive was the catastrophe? Was it global—worldwide in scope?

Geologist William Stokes reports that nearly half of Europe was submerged by a great sheet of ice radiating from the Scandinavian highlands and covering 1,650,000 square miles. Much of northern Asia was covered by another huge sheet of ice centering in northwestern Siberia, covering 1,600,000 square miles.[10]

In the western hemisphere, 4,500,000 square miles of North America were similarly submerged under tons of ice, covering almost all of Canada, much of northeastern United States, and ranging as far south as the Ohio and Missouri rivers. In the southern hemisphere, there is evidence that the Antarctic ice pack was once thicker. In New Zealand the ice descended below the present sea level, and Tasmania was covered with glaciers.

The higher Hawaiian and New Guinea mountains were once similarly glacier-covered. In South America glaciers of the Andes extended to sea level to the west and out on the Argentine pampas to the east. In east Africa, the glaciers of Mt. Kenya descended 5,400 feet below their present level.

Roughly, 15 million square miles, or 27 percent of the land surface of the earth, was submerged beneath the ice sheets during the last glacial stage!

As the glaciers retreated, huge lakes were left which slowly were drained out. One of these, the largest, was Lake Agassiz, covering 100,000 square miles in Ontario, Manitoba, Canada, and North Dakota in the United States.

Other remarkable evidence of the catastrophism of the Ice Age times is the discovery of several whale skeletons found in shore deposits of the ancestral Great Lakes. How these whales got there is not known, though some speculate they swam up the giant rivers of the time. One wonders, however, if they may not have been left high and dry as immense flood waters receded from the continent.

Other evidence of a possible deluge of vast dimensions accompanying the Ice Age, at its termination, is provided by ancient Lake Missoula which once covered several thousand square miles in western Montana. It may have been over a mile deep and contained 500 cubic miles of water, locked in a natural ice dam. Says Stokes:

> The catastrophic breaking of the ice dam during the Pleistocene released tremendous floods of water that rushed across a 15,000 square-mile tract of western Washington, now known as the 'channeled scabland.' The erosion and deposition resulting from this flood are so extensive that many geologists have had difficulty believing such a deluge was possible.[11]

Other mammoth lakes existed in North America at the close of Pleistocene times, giving evidence of gigantic disturbances that occurred at that time. Were many of these huge lakes the remains of an epochal flood or deluge that inundated vast portions of the earth at that time, accompanied by violent volcanic and telluric activity?

This explanation becomes even more meaningful when we consider that at the close of the Pleistocene, gigantic creatures were wiped out en masse. The great dire wolf, standing six feet high at the shoulders; the saber-toothed tiger; bears larger than today's grizzly; giant beavers, as big as a black bear; bison that had horns extending out over six feet; large camels, pygmy camels, huge pigs and dogs; a ground sloth as heavy as an elephant which could munch on leaves hanging 20 feet above the ground; the imperial mammoths and royal mastodons, the former with 13-foot tusks and a shoulder height of 14 feet; all these were suddenly wiped out.

It seems inconceivable that mere ice advances and retreats over many thousands of years could have accomplished such awesome extinction. But the action of catastrophism, accompanied by a tremendous deluge, is certainly a plausible explanation worth investigating.

Coinciding with the glaciation was a period of intense mountain building, folding, earthquakes, and volcanic activity. Edward Suess, the greatest geologist of the last century, described the earth's history this way:

> The earthquakes of today are but faint reminiscences of those telluric movements to which the structure of almost every mountain range bears witness. Numerous examples of great mountain chains suggest by their structure the possibility, and even in some cases the probability, of the occasional intervention in the course of great geological eras of processes of *episodal disturbances* of such indescribable and overwhelming violence, that the imagination refuses to follow the understanding and to complete the picture of which the outlines are furnished by observations of fact.[12]

Did this violence include massive flooding during the time of man?

The Biblical record, and corroborating traditions, legends, myths, and accounts of peoples around the world, from the Philippines to the Hawaiian islands, from the ancient Sumerians to the Chinese, from the Polynesians to the American Indians, from the Incas to the ancient Greeks, bear unanimous testimony that long, long ago there was a horrendous global catastrophe which included a tremendous deluge, where almost all life, human and animal, was direly affected.

For centuries, skeptics have held such stories in contempt. But as modern geology continues in its quest for the facts, the testimony of the rocks, fossils, and strata under our feet begins to corroborate in fascinating detail the ancient accounts of our ancestors.

Says Charles Hapgood, the sea has covered as much as 4,000,000 square miles of North America at one time, and that sedimentary beds composing the mountain ranges from the Alps to central Asia were laid down under the sea. Hapgood says that although geophysicists argue that such seas were shallow affairs, there is a fallacy in this argument. In fact, he states, the positive evidence against the assumption that all these seas were shallow is "enormously strong."

He quotes Umbgrove: "Not only have parts of the continents foundered below sea-level since pre-Cambrian times but they have done so *until quite recently*, and their subsidence occasionally attained *great depths!*"[13]

Was there indeed a universal deluge, such as the Bible describes? Is it really any harder to believe in such a phenomenon than the catastrophism of the Ice Age? Is it not likely that the two events were related aspects of a larger global cataclysm?

Paleo-Indians

Near the small town of Clovis in eastern New Mexico, some of the most astonishing ancient fossils have been found. Along the bed of an old river called the Blackwater Draw, evidence of animal bones of extinct species was found over a large area.

Dr. E.B. Howard of the University of Pennsylvania Museum began digging in 1932, and since then many archaeologists have exhumed bones from the banks of the ancient river. Evidence of early man, called "Clovis man," was unearthed, and huge piles of mammoth bones stretching for miles in all directions.

Also found at the site were remains of Folsom man, just above the Clovis layer, typified by the Folsom points. Whereas the earlier men had hunted mammoths with large lance points, fluted at the base, the Folsom men hunted bison with shorter fluted Folsom points. These men lived at the close of the Ice Age.

Folsom man was first discovered by Dr. J.D. Figgins, director of the Colorado Museum of Natural History in Denver in 1927 in an exciting indirect manner. A black cowboy noticed bones jutting from the bank of a dried stream bed in northeastern New Mexico, and found a curious flint projectile point unlike any he had seen before. J.D. Figgins learned of the discovery and determined that pieces of the bone which the cowboy sent to him had belonged to an extinct bison that lived 10,000 years ago.

When Figgins began his own excavation of the site, more projectile points were found. On September 2, a point was discovered still embedded between two ribs of the skeleton of an ancient bison!

Years later, high in the Sandia Mountains near Albuquerque, New Mexico, Dr. Frank C. Hibben was excavating and digging, looking for more evidence of early man in a cave where a few archaeological artifacts had come to light. While digging, he turned up the bony core of the claw of a giant ground sloth which became extinct at the end of the Ice Age, about the time the mammoths had died out.

As Hibben and his party continued digging, carefully searching for more fossils, they came upon a flint point of undoubted human origin—apparently older than the Folsom points found elsewhere. Eventually nineteen projectile points were found, evidence of Sandia man. The Sandia points were longer and more primitive in structure than the Folsom points.

During the Ice Age, these cultures had thrived, living on the vast teeming herds of animal life. Some archaeologists maintain that Clovis, Folsom, and Sandia cultures all overlapped in time. The radiocarbon dates for the Early Hunters generally range from 9,000 to 13,000 years before the present. But whatever happened to them?

They disappeared. As the Ice Age ended, something unique in the history of man happened. The big animals that roamed the plains by the millions suddenly were wiped out. And when the big game disappeared, so did the paleo-Indians!

According to radiocarbon dating, several thousand years passed before the next human cultures appear prominently on the scene—new cultures which knew agriculture, and which merged into the later Pueblo and Mound Builders of the American scene.

Unlike the Early Hunters, the new cultures seemed to live a more sedentary existence, picking berries and nuts. The big animals had gone—disappeared.

American horse, elephants and camels had died off. Mammoths, mastodons, saber-toothed tigers, and early bison had perished. And the early hunters disappeared from the scene.

But why?

Most scholars admit they don't really know the answers. As C.W. Ceram pointed out, "We may as well state at once that there are innumerable theories and no solution as yet."[14] There is a wide variety of opinions, and none has established itself. Why, for example, did small animals perish, too—including a variety of rabbit and three species of antelope?

One of the earliest and most attractive theories to account for the widespread extinction, was catastrophism. Partisans of this theory held that tremendous earthquake activity and volcanic eruptions accounted for the devastation and slaughter. These great convulsions that shook the continent took place about ten thousand years ago, according to this theory.

The catastrophic theory, for many reasons, is the most compelling theory, except for one drawback. If radiocarbon dating techniques are completely accurate for the period, then all the animals did not die out suddenly—some, like the mammoth, may have survived until 4,000 B.C. The *bison antiquus* roamed the prairies until 6000 to 5000 B.C.

The evidence, then, suggests that a series of catastrophes must have occurred at the close of the Pleistocene period. If the Biblical evidence is properly understood, these cataclysms culminated eventually, in the time of Noah. Many of these cataclysms may have begun prior to the time of Adam. Others may have been a result of his own rebellion against God. God warned Adam: "Cursed is the ground for thy sake; in sorrow shalt thou eat of it all the days of thy life . . ." (Genesis 3:17). Adam lived for 930 years. The curse lasted for all that time, until the Deluge.

Let's put aside dates for the moment, and just consider the facts.

The Pleistocene extinctions occurred. What was the cause?

Some have suggested that man was responsible—it was a case of "Pleistocene overkill." Fire may have been the agent of the destruction. But many animals would have fled from the fires. It is stretching the imagination and credulity to ask that one believe fire alone accounted for the massive extinction of many species of animals!

Perhaps a clue to the answer is contained in the words of Frank C. Hibben in *The Lost Americans:*

> With the occasional *torrential showers* of the closing phase of the glacial period, the bare earth of the Folsom landscape was *washed away by the millions of tons.* Many a Folsom point and mammoth tusk must have been sluiced away in the process. Other evidences were deeply covered. This washing process was the agent that changed the contours of the Lindenmeier valley and covered the original Folsom vale with *twenty feet of accumulated earth.* Many campsites and kill sites on high ground must have been *washed away entirely.* Those in the valleys and hollows were *covered so deeply* that many probably will never be discovered. *It was as though the cosmic forces of nature had, at the end of the age of extinct mammals and ancient hunters,* dragged a covering blanket over the landscape to hide all their traces. It has only been occasionally and by accident that corners of this blanket have been turned back or torn away to reveal the story of ancient man beneath.[15]

Notice the expressions and phrases that are in italics very carefully. Dr. Hibben is plainly talking about tremendous water action, flooding, and catastrophic storms at the end of the Ice Age, laying tremendous layers of sediment in some valleys and canyons, and eroding away other areas beyond recognition.

Does such flooding reflect at least in part the action of the

Noachian deluge, which occurred about 5,000 years ago? Or should we attribute the evidence to thousands of years of normal activity?

Near the town of Abilene, Texas, Dr. Cyrus Ray wandered along a local stream bed and examined the cutbank in 1929. He noticed charcoal lenses and fragments of chipped stone protruding from the sand. As he casually glanced upward, he was startled to see forty feet of layered sediments above him in the cutbank. Beneath all this sediment, he found evidence of early man—crude implements, charcoal, bits of bone, flint points, scrapers and knives.

The general opinion is that centuries must have been required to pile up the thickness of earth in the bank over the human relics. But sometimes a great depth of soil can be washed over a spot in a single torrential deluge. Could this sediment include that resulting from the Noachian Deluge?

Dating of the Abilene men indicates that they lived at the very end of the Ice Age. "Perfected techniques of collecting and identifying ancient pollen grains," says Frank Hibben, "show that the climate at Abilene was a cycle of increasing dryness interspersed with torrential rains. It was these that covered the evidence so deeply."[16] Could these have been a local aspect of a more general, widespread condition?

Lance points and bones were found fifty feet below the surface of Lime Creek, Nebraska. The points were again those of Ice Age hunters.

Evidence of paleo-Indians, or Ice Age hunters, has been uncovered in southern Mexico, Central America, South America, New Mexico, and in every corner of the eastern United States, besides southern Canada. Their fluted points have turned up in every state east of the Mississippi. From 1951 to 1957, some three thousand paleo-Indian tools were found beneath Wisconsin age sand at Ipswich, Massachusetts. Ecuador, Peru, Argentina, and Chile also bear testimony of Ice Age hunters.

Whatever happened to them?

The word Pleistocene is derived from Greek words that mean "most of the new," relates Frank C. Hibben. He points out that many new animals appeared—many new species and many millions of each species. It has been called the "Age of New Animals."

But most of them have died off—become extinct. Our landscape has lost a great deal since Pleistocene times. Imagine what it must have been like to hunt the sabre-tooth tiger, and the woolly mammoth, compared to hunting deer or elk. It was a hunter's paradise!

Dr. Hibben, in a chapter entitled fittingly enough "End of a Universe," describes the end of the Pleistocene thus:

> The Pleistocene period ended in death. This was no ordinary extinction of a vague geological period which fizzled to an uncertain end. This *death was catastrophic and all-inclusive* . . . The large animals that had given the name to the period became extinct. Their death marked the end of the era.
>
> But how did they die? What caused the extinction of forty million animals? This mystery forms one of the oldest detective stories in the world. A good detective story involves humans and death. Those conditions are met at the end of the Pleistocene. In this particular case, the death was of *such colossal proportions* as to be staggering to contemplate. The antiquity adds a rare relish to the tale. Who or what killed the Pleistocene animals is a query that has not yet been answered.[17]

The animals of the Pleistocene wandered into every corner of the New World not covered by ice. Their bones have been found in the sands of Florida and in the gravels of New Jersey, protruding from the dry terraces of Texas and from the sticky ooze of the tar pits of Los Angeles. These remains have been encountered by the thousands in Mexico and in South America.

How did these animals all die? Hibben, one of the leading anthropologists in the United States, declares:

> . . . where we can study these animals in some detail, such as in the great bone deposits in Nebraska, we find literally thousands of these remains together. The young lie with the old, foal with dam and calf with cow. Whole herds of animals were apparently killed together, overcome by some common power.
>
> We have already seen that the muck pits of Alaska are filled with evidences of *universal death.* Mingled in these frozen masses are the

> remains of many thousands of animals killed in their prime . . . We have gained from the muck pits of the Yukon Valley a picture of *quick extinction.* The evidences of violence there are as obvious as in the horror camps of Germany. Such piles of bodies of animals or men simply do not occur by any ordinary natural means.[18]

Pleistocene animals in Europe and Asia met similarly untimely deaths. The icy glaciations of Europe, Asia, and America occurred at the same time. The animal populations there met the same tragic fate. The mammoth herds of Siberia became extinct. At the same time, the European rhinoceros died out. The cave bear of Europe and the bison of Siberia perished. The American camels met their death at about the same time as Asiatic elephants.

Africa, alone, seems to have escaped. But did it? Perhaps the modern wildlife of Africa, which seems typical of the Pleistocene period, was saved from total destruction by the man, Noah, who built an Ark to save alive representatives of the animal world.

Hibben concludes, "the consuming mystery of the death of forty million Pleistocene animals still stands."[19] Hibben continues: "One of the most interesting of the theories of the Pleistocene end is that which explains this ancient tragedy by worldwide earth-shaking volcanic eruptions of catastrophic violence." In the Alaskan and Siberian regions, he says, this idea has considerable support because layers of volcanic ash are interspersed with the animal remains. Coincidental with the end of the Pleistocene animals, in Alaska, volcanic eruptions of tremendous proportions occurred.

Toxic clouds of gas from volcanic upheavals could have contributed to the gigantic death scale. But, adds Hibben:

> Throughout the Alaskan mucks, too, there is evidence of *atmospheric disturbances of unparalleled violence.* Mammoth and bison alike were torn and twisted *as though by a cosmic hand in godly rage.* In one place, we can find the foreleg and shoulder of a mammoth with portions of the flesh and the toenails and the hair still clinging to the blackened bones. Close by is the neck and skull of a bison with the vertebrae clinging together with tendons and ligaments and the chitinous covering of the horns intact. There is no

> mark of a knife or cutting implement. The animals were simply torn apart and scattered over the landscape like things of straw and string, *even though some of them weighed several tons.* Mixed with the piles of bones are trees, also twisted and torn and piled in tangled groups; and the whole is covered with the fine sifting muck, then frozen solid.
>
> *Storms, too,* accompany volcanic disturbances of the proportions indicated here. Differences in temperature and the influence of the cubic miles of ash and pumice thrown into the air by eruptions of this sort might well produce *winds and blasts of inconceivable violence.* If this is the explanation for the end of all this animal life, the Pleistocene period was terminated by a very exciting time, indeed.[20]

However, signs of volcanism are not found with the extinct remains of Pleistocene animals found in Colorado, Texas, and Florida, where extinction also occurred. Yet there the animals are just as dead. How did they die? What was the final agent of extinction?

Perhaps, after all, the best answer, was recorded long ago in that ancient chronicle of human history—the Bible.

The Pleistocene extinctions, themselves, may be alluded to in the first few verses of Genesis. Since the Pleistocene was a period of extinction, in which even Neanderthal man may have perished, along with many forms of animal life, it has been postulated that this period of worldwide trauma and extinction could tie up with the period of destruction, *tohu* and *bohu* mentioned in the second verse of the first chapter of Genesis.

If this is so, then the remains of early man, including Neanderthal man, would all appear to have been pre-Adamic. In this case, the vast overshelming continental destruction would have been in part attributable to the rebellion of Lucifer and his angels against the government of God over the earth. This would also imply that Adam was not created until after the close of the Pleistocene. This chronology would, of course, fit with the chronology of man presented in the Biblical record.

Another possibility is that this mind-bending destruction ties in with the curse God placed on the earth after the sin of Adam, and culminated in the Noachian deluge.

In the book of Genesis, we read this simple, poignant, gripping story: "In the six hundredth year of Noah's life, in the second month, on the seventeenth day of the month, on that day all the fountains of the great deep burst forth, and the windows of the heavens were opened. And rain fell upon the earth forty days and forty nights" (Genesis 7:11-12, RSV).

The "fountains of the great deep" are called "the subterranean waters" in the *Living Bible*. The *New English Bible* translates it this way: "all the springs of the *great abyss* broke through."

We read: "The flood continued forty days upon the earth; and the waters increased, and bore up the ark, and it rose high above the earth. The waters prevailed and increased greatly upon the earth; and the ark floated on the face of the waters. And the waters prevailed so mightily upon the earth that all the high mountains under the whole heaven were covered; the waters prevailed above the mountains, covering them fifteen cubits (roughly 22 feet) deep. And all flesh died that moved upon the earth, birds, cattle, beasts, all swarming creatures that swarm upon the earth, and every man; everything on the dry land in whose nostrils was the breath of life died. He blotted out every living thing that was upon the face of the ground, man and animals and creeping things and birds of the air; they were blotted out from the earth. Only Noah was left, and those that were with him in the ark. And the waters prevailed upon the earth a hundred and fifty days" (Genesis 7:11-24, RSV).

This is the simple, dramatic Biblical account, unembellished. Could it explain the final extinction of so many creatures at the close of the Ice Age? It is a direct, straightforward, dramatic story—eloquent and powerful in its utter simplicity.

Did it really happen? Was there a period of catastrophism commencing prior to the time of Adam and re-occurring until the time of Noah, culminating in a massive Deluge? Hopefully, the spade of the archaeologist and geologist will uncover more answers as excavation continues.

Chapter Nineteen

Will Noah's Ark Be Discovered?

An ancient tradition of the Incas says that the third age of man ended in a cosmic disaster—a flood.[1] One such legend states that a shepherd and his family were warned that the world would shortly be destroyed by a deluge. The shepherd collected his llamas and children and took them to the summit of the mountain Ancasmarca. At that moment the sea broke its bounds and rushed over the land, filling valleys, covering plains, lasting for five days. On the 5th day the waters began to subside and the stars to reappear.

A tradition from the Leeward islands declares that Ruahatu, the ocean god, was sleeping when a fisherman's hook became entangled in his hair. The roused god rose to the surface, upbraided the fisherman, and warned he was going to destroy the whole wicked land. When the fisherman repented of his deed, the angry god forgave him and directed him to proceed to a small island where he, his wife and child, would be safe. Thereupon the ocean rose, and the next morning only the tops of the mountains appeared above the sea. Soon these were covered and all the inhabitants of the land perished, with the sole exception of the fisherman and his family.

A tradition of the Fiji Islands mentions that a great rain took place, by which the islands were finally submerged, but before the highest places were covered, two large double canoes appeared. Rokova, the god of carpenters, and Rokola, his head workman, were in them, and picked up some of the people and rescued them from the flood waters. Those saved were eight in number.

The Papagos, and Indian tribe in northwestern Mexico, relate that there was a great flood from which Montezuma, a divine hero, escaped, having been warned of its coming by a coyote. Montezuma hollowed out a boat for himself, so he would be ready for the deluge.

Declared the native Mexican historian Ixtlilxochitl:

> It is found in the histories of the Toltecs that this age and the first world, as they call it, lasted 1,716 years; that men were destroyed by tremendous rains and lightning from the sky, and even all the land, without the exception of anything, and the highest mountains were covered by and submerged in water fifteen cubits (caxtolmolatli); and here they add other fables of how men came to multiply from the few who escaped from this destruction in a "toptlipetlocali," which nearly signifies a closed chest; and how, after men had multiplied, they erected a very high "zacuali," which is today a tower of great height, in order to take refuge in it should the second world (age) be destroyed.[2]

A very ancient Aztec flood legend, translated from the Codex Chimalpopoca, states that during the Sun Age all mankind was lost and drowned and turned to fishes.

> The waters and the sky drew near each other. . . . The very mountains were swallowed up in the flood. . . . But before the flood began, Titlachahuan had warned the man Nota and his wife Nena, saying, "Make no more pulque, but hollow a great cypress into which you shall enter in the month Tozoztli. The waters shall near the sky." They entered, and when Titlachahuan had shut them in he said to the man, "Thou shalt eat but a single ear of maize, and thy wife but one also." And when they had each eaten one ear of maize, they prepared to go forth, for the water was tranquil.

The oldest flood legend of India is found in the Rig Veda, a collection of ancient Hindu poems and hymns. A fish tells Manu if he protects the fish, and returns him to the ocean when of full size, he will protect Manu from a great deluge which will sweep away all creatures.[3]

Other deluge traditions come from the American Indians and Eskimos. The Kolushes of Alaska have a tradition that formerly the father of the Indian tribes lived toward the rising sun.

Warned in a dream that a deluge would desolate the earth, he built a raft and saved himself, family, and all animals, floating for several months on the water.

Another Eskimo tribe had this tradition: The water poured over the terrestrial disk, human dwellings disappeared. The wind carried them away. Men fastened several boats to one another. The waves traversed the Rocky Mountains. A great wind drove the boats. Presently the moon and the earth disappeared. Men died of a terrible heat. They also perished in the waves.

Amazing for its clarity is the Hawaiian tradition. The natives of Hawaii say that the earth became careless of worship and very wicked. Only one man was righteous, a man named Nu-u. He made a great canoe with a house on it and stored it with food, taking plants and animals on board. The flood waters came up and destroyed all mankind except Nu-u and his family.[4]

An ancient Chinese legend relates that Fuhi, the reputed founder of Chinese civilization, escaped the waters of a deluge and reappeared as the first man at the reproduction of a renovated world, with his wife, three sons and three daughters.

Other flood legends similar to the Noachian epic recounted in the Bible exist among the Voguls in the Ural Mountains of Russia, the Laplanders, Norwegians, the Welsh, Lithuanians, Assyrians and Babylonians. The Latin poet Ovid tells how Jupiter destroyed the impious race of men sprung from the blood of the Titans by a great flood. Manetho, Egyptian historian who lived about 250 B.C., states that there was a worldwide watery catastrophe in which one called Toth was saved.

The first mention of a Flood in Greek literature is found in the Odes of Pindar (522-433 B.C.). In the Greek traditions, Deucalion and Pyrrha, his wife, come down from Mt. Parnassus where the ark is supposed to have landed. Another Greek tradition relates that Ogyges, the oldest king of Boetia, escaped with companions in a boat from a deluge which reached to the sky.[5]

Many other fascinating legends, traditions and local beliefs relate similar stories of an ancient flood that occurred during the time of man.

Why do all the races of mankind have traditions of a vast deluge during the history of mankind if such an event did not occur?

Why did pagan writers such as Ovid, Pindar, Berosus, Appollodorus, Manetho, the scoffer Lucian, and others, all recount legends of a universal Deluge? They certainly had no desire to establish any biblical record or statement. Unless there was a tremendous Deluge, such as the Bible records, it would not make sense for scattered peoples all over the world to have remarkably similar flood traditions, each attributing the Deluge to the anger of their own local gods. But if there was such a Deluge, then the various flood traditions are just what we should expect to find!

The existence universally of stories and traditions of a great flood which destroyed all mankind is a remarkable confirmation of the truth of the Genesis account.

Search for Noah's Ark

In view of the impressive evidence that some sort of mighty Deluge must have occurred, several groups of scientists, theologians, and mountain climbers have attempted to organize expeditions to Mount Ararat in northeastern Turkey, a 17,000 foot mountain that lies at the borders of Turkey, the U.S.S.R., and Iran. A number of scholars and theologians believe that the ancient ship in which Noah survived the Deluge lies buried under thousands of tons of snow and ice somewhere between the 13,500 and 15,500 foot levels.

The most compelling evidence produced to date that the ark may be buried beneath glacial ice high up the mountains comes from intriguing planks of wood retrieved from the area by explorers in 1955 and 1969. Laboratory tests disagree on the probable age of the dark, almost fossilized fragments of wood.

In 1970, researchers at UCLA dated one beam found at 13,500 feet by French explorer Fernand Navarra in 1955 at about 1,250 years old. But labs in Madrid, Paris and Bordeaux, believing the radiocarbon dating technique invalid because of possible contamination of the samples, have asserted that the wood is of "great antiquity"—perhaps 5,000 years old.

If the ark should someday be found, it would be a monumental discovery and corroboration of the biblical Deluge.

The Biblical Record

A few facts about the size of the Ark, as mentioned in great detail in the Bible, might be in order. We read in Genesis, chapter 6: "Make thee an ark of gopher wood [many think this was cedar or cypress; cypress was anciently used in ship-building and abounded in Assyria; the exact meaning of "gopher wood," however, is not known—the word is nowhere else used in Scripture] ; rooms [nests or compartments] shalt thou make in the ark, and shalt pitch it within and without with pitch [bitumen] . And this is the fashion which thou shalt make it of: The length of the ark shall be three hundred cubits, the breadth of it fifty cubits, and the height of it thirty cubits" (Gen. 6:14-15).

How long is a cubit? The standard cubit—the length from the elbow to the tip of the middle finger—was about 18 inches. At this measurement, the Ark would have been 450 feet long, 75 feet wide and 45 feet high.

However, one ancient cubit was nearly 22 inches long. At this measurement, the Ark would have been 547 feet long, 91 feet wide and 54 feet high.

Another ancient Hebrew cubit would have been about 25 inches long, making the Ark possibly 600 feet long, 100 feet wide, and 60 feet high.

Just what cubit Noah used in making the Ark, is not definitely known. However, it was a huge vessel, even by modern-day standards of ship-building.

Using the smallest cubit, the Ark's volume would have been 1,396,000 cubit feet—a carrying capacity equal to 522 standard stock cars used by modern railroads—or eight freight trains with sixty-five cars in each one. However, if the 25 inch cubit was used, the volume of the Ark would have been 3,600,000 cubic feet—equal to 25 trains, each one 52 cars long. The three decks of the Ark (Gen. 6:16) would have contained an area of about 38 college basketball courts.

Some have calculated the tonnage of the Ark would have been between 40,000 and 50,000 tons. Stood on end, it would have been the height of a 45 story building.

Only in modern times have ships of such tremendous size and tonnage been built. The Queen Elizabeth II, built in 1968, is 58,000 tons. The S.S. United States, built in 1952, is 51,000 tons.

Was the Ark big enough to preserve animal life?

Consider: Noah did not have to carry any of the 18,000 species of fishes, or 88,000 species of mollusks or 15,000 species of protozoans, and others amounting to a total of 142,000 species of marine animals. Realistically, he probably carried no more than 35,000 individual vertebrate animals on the Ark. Even if the average size of the animals was the size of a sheep, there would have been ample room on the Ark. A standard two-decked stock car carries about 120 sheep per deck, or 240 total. To carry 35,000 animals, therefore, only 146 stock cars would have been necessary–yet even the minimal estimate for the size of the Ark gives it the capacity of 522 stock cars!

Undoubtedly, Noah had plenty of room to take care of the animals, and had room left over for food storage, grain, hay, and whatever he needed. There is no reason to assume he and his family were unnecessarily cramped or confined.

What History Reveals

In Genesis 8:4 we read: "And the ark rested in the seventh month, on the seventeenth day of the month, upon the *mountains of Ararat.*" One of the mountains of the range or group of mountains in this area is Mount Ararat itself, rising 16,946 feet into the sky.

That is the area where the Ark settled, when the flood waters receded. But does history tell us more?

History reveals the ancient Sumerians, who dwelt in the area of modern Arabia and Mesopotamia, had extensive legends and stories about a great flood which came upon the earth, in many respects paralleling the biblical account. The Sumerians, however, called Noah by the name Xisouthros. He was also called Ziusudra. The legend says God told him, ". . .a flood will sweep over the cult-centers; To destroy the seed of mankind. . . ." The story appears on the fragment of a Sumerian tablet found at Nippur.

Says the tablet: "All the windstorms, exceedingly powerful, attacked as one, At the same time, the flood sweeps over the cult-centers. After, for seven days and seven nights, The flood had swept over the land, And the huge boat had been tossed about by the windstorms on the great waters. . . ."

Old Babylonian traditions also relate the story of a great flood. However, they called Noah by the name Utnapishtim, which means "Day of Life." The Babylonian "Noah" was told by God, "Tear down this house, build a ship! . . .Aboard the ship take thou the seed of all living things. The ship that thou shalt build, Her dimensions shall be to measure. Equal shall be her width and her length."[6]

Obviously, the pagan traditions have been corrupted in the passage of time. There are relatively minor differences and changes in the overall story. Nevertheless, these traditions give outstanding corroboration of the biblical account of the Flood and Noah.

Ark's Whereabouts Known in Jesus' Day

There is much more evidence to substantiate biblical history and the account of the Flood than the legends and stories of scattered nations of mankind–though they themselves are impressive.

Even in Jesus' time the Ark and its whereabouts was known to the nations of the Middle East and Eastern Mediterranean region.

Flavius Josephus, a learned Jewish historian and general who fought the Romans in the conflict which raged in 67 A.D., but gave himself up to them when he saw the futility and hopelessness of the struggle, wrote a lengthy, detailed history of the Jews. In this history, he related the account of Noah building the Ark and the great flood. He declared that the Armenians call the place the Ark rested *The Place of Descent.*

The Ark came down, Josephus says, "on the top of a certain mountain in Armenia. . . ." A city was built at the foot of the mountain, with a name which signified "The first place of descent," and was a lasting monument to the preservation of Noah and the Ark.

Josephus tells us, "for the ark being saved in that place, *its remains are shown there* by the inhabitants *to this day.*"

This venerable historian adds:

> Now all the writers of barbarian histories make mention of this flood, and of this ark; among whom is Berosus the Chaldean. For when he is describing the circumstances of the flood, he goes on thus: "It is said there is still some part of this ship in Armenia, at the mountain of the Cordyaeans; and that some people carry off pieces of the bitumen, which they take away, and use chiefly as amulets for the averting of mischiefs." Hieronymus the Egyptian also, who wrote the Phoenician Antiquities, and Mnaseas, and a great many more, make mention of the same. Nay, Nicolaus of Damascus, in his ninety-sixth book, hath a particular relation about them; where he speaks thus: "There is a great mountain in Armenia, over Minyas, called Baris, upon which it is reported that many who fled at the time of the Deluge were saved; and that one who was carried in an ark came on shore upon the top of it; and that the remains of the timber were a great while preserved. This might be the man about whom Moses the legislator of the Jews wrote."[7]

Expeditions and Sightings

The history of attempts of men to go to Ararat, to scale the sides of the mountain, and to locate the remains of the Ark is intriguing.

There were quite a few expeditions up Mount Ararat during the nineteenth century. At least two of them, one Turkish and one Russian, may have found the Ark. There were reports that in 1883, an earthquake in the region of Ararat caused huge chunks of ice to be dislodged from the mountain. Subsequently a Turkish expedition found the wooden prow of an ancient ship protruding from a glacier.

Despite persistent reports of various sightings of parts of Noah's Ark, attempts to locate the Ark have been frustrated by bad weather, terrible snow storms, and Russian bears and perhaps acts of God. Said one explorer, "God has always been good to me, but I figured out that He does not wish me to find Noah's Ark." He had attempted to do so six different times.

In another case, an Associated Press dispatch from Istanbul, November 13, 1948, quoted a Kurdish landowner in the Ararat area as saying the petrified remains of what appeared to be a ship had been found in a canyon about two-thirds the way up the mountain. It came to light when unusually warm weather during the summer melted the covering of snow and ice.

In the early 1960's, a team of American archaeologists reported finding several pieces of wood, apparently part of a giant boat, 14,000 feet up the slopes of Ararat. The evidence suggested the wood came from a boat about two thirds the size of the Queen Mary (which is 1,019 feet long and 118 feet wide).[8]

But the search continues.

In the days before the Russian revolution, Vladimar Roskovitsky and other Russian aviators were stationed at a lonely air outpost about 20 miles northwest of Mount Ararat. On one day, he and a friend climbed to 14,000 feet and flew toward Ararat. Roskovitsky relates:

> As I looked down at the great stone battlements surrounding the lower part of this mountain, I remembered having heard that it had never been climbed since the year seven hundred before Christ, when some pilgrims were supposed to have gone up there to scrape tar off an old shipwreck to make good-luck emblems to wear around their necks, which they believed would keep their crops from being destroyed by excessive rainfall. The legend said that they had left in haste when a bolt of lightning had struck near them, and they never again returned. Silly ancients! Whoever heard of looking for a shipwreck on a mountain top?
>
> I made a couple of circles around the snow-capped dome, and then a long swift glide down the south side. We suddenly came upon

a perfect little gem of a lake; blue as an emerald, but still frozen over on the shady side. We circled around and returned for another look at it. Suddenly my companion whirled around and yelled something. He excitedly pointed down at the overflow of the lake. I looked and nearly fainted. A submarine! No, it wasn't, for it had stubby masts, but the top was founded over with only a flat cat walk about five feet across which ran down the length of it. What a strange craft, built as though the designer had expected the waves to roll over the top most of the time, and had engineered it to wallow in the sea like a log, with those stubby masts carrying only enough sail to keep it facing the waves. (Years later, in the Great Lakes, I saw the famous whaleback ore carriers with this same kind of round deck.)

We flew down as close as safety permitted, and took several circles around it. When we got close to it, we were surprised at the immense size of the thing. It was as long as a city block, and would compare very favorably in size to the modern battleships of today. It was grounded on the shore of the lake, with about one foot of the rear end still running out into the water. Its extreme rear was three-fourths under water. It had been partly dismantled on one side near the front, and on the other side there was a great door, nearly twenty feet square; but the door shutter was gone. This seemed quite out of proportion, as even today ships seldom have doors half that large.

Upon returning to base, the aviators were met with catcalls, hoots and jeers when they described their discovery. But their captain asked to see it himself, so they took him there. All this time, Roskovitsky says, he had no idea what the thing was. When the captain saw it, he told him, "This strange craft is Noah's ark. It has been sitting up there for nearly five thousand years. Being frozen up for nine or ten months of the years, it couldn't rot, and has been in cold storage, as it were, all this time. You have made the most amazing discovery of the age."

When the captain reported the find to the Russian government, the Czar sent two special companies of soldiers to climb the mountain. Nearly a month after starting up the mountain, chopping out a trail as they went, the ark was reached, complete measurements were taken, plans drawn of it, photographs were taken, and the information sent to the Czar, Roskovitsky relates.

> The ark was found to contain hundreds of small rooms, and some rooms very large with high ceilings. The large rooms usually had a fence of great timbers across them; some of which were two feet thick, as though designed to hold beasts ten times as large as an elephant. Other rooms were lined with tiers of cages, somewhat like one sees today at a poultry show. Only, instead of chicken wire, they had rows of tiny wrought iron bars along the front.
>
> Everything was heavily painted with wax-like paint resembling shellac. The workmanship of the craft showed all the signs of high type of civilization. The wood used throughout was oleander, which belongs to the cypress family and never rots. Together with the fact that it was painted and frozen almost the entire year, accounted for its perfect preservation.
>
> The expedition found on the peak of the mountain above the ship, the burned remains of the timber which were missing out of the one side of the ship. It seemed that these timbers had been hauled up to the top of the peak and used to build a tiny one-room shrine, inside of which was a rough stone hearth like the altars the Hebrews used for sacrifices. It has either caught fire from the altar or been struck by lightning, as the timbers were considerably burned and charred over, and the roof was completely burned off.

Roskovitsky concludes his remarkable testimonial:

> A few days after this expedition sent its report to the Czar, the government was overthrown and godless Bolshevism took over, so that the records were probably destroyed in the zeal of the Bolshevists to discredit all religion, and belief in the truth of the Bible.
>
> We White Russians of the air fleet escaped through Armenia, and four of us came to America, where we could be free to live according to the "Good Old Book," which we have seen for ourselves to be absolutely true, even as fantastic sounding a thing as a world flood.[9]

This eye-witness account of sighting the Ark high up on Mount Ararat has never been fully substantiated. Nevertheless, it is a remarkable story, and may very well be true.

In 1944 a Russian plane crew said they had seen "a monstrous boat" sticking out of the ice on the mountain.[10]

During World War II, Major Jasper Maskelyn, wartime chief of Russian camouflage, reported: "One of my men flew over Mt. Ararat in a reconnaissance aircraft in an attempt to check a story that the Ark had been sighted there by a Russian airman in the first World War. He reported that he saw a partly submerged vessel in an ice lake. Arctic climbers investigated the lake, which was partly thawed [again the weather element was favorable] and found the remains of an Ark, very rotted, over 400 feet long, composed of fossilized wood looking almost like coal."

Over the past 50 years, numerous Swiss and Austrian climbers have searched for the Ark on twin-peaked Mount Ararat. In 1951 and 1954 U.S. Supreme Court Justice William Douglas joined in.

In 1952, Fernand Navarra organized an expedition, reached the summit–but found nothing. The next year he returned and came within 100 yards of a glacier he had sighted previously. This time he was caught in an avalanche and had to leave when a snowstorm blew up suddenly. He tried again in 1954 and met with a degree of success. He and his 11-year-old son struggled across the glacier, saw something beneath the ice, chopped through it, and returned to civilization with a fifty pound piece of wood–wood which laboratories in France dated at about 5,000 years old–wood which Navarro was positive came from the Ark, hidden beneath the glacier!

According to reports, the wood–Greek oak–came from a beam or rafter some 8-10 inches thick, expertly cut and surprisingly heavy. Laboratory reports indicated the wood was cut from the heart of an oak, the trunk of which was probably about 25 inches thick.[11]

Through the years, Armenian villagers and inhabitants of the plateau near Mount Ararat have consistently claimed that the Ark lies submerged somewhere up on the mountain. From time to time reports have been made of sightings by local tribesmen. To local villagers, reports of the Ark are "old stuff." They have known about it for generations, they claim. But no one goes near it for fear of evil spirits!

Exploration of Ararat has been hampered by the fact that the area is very near the Russian border, in a militarily "sensitive" area. The Russians are vehemently against all such archaeological exploration for the Ark. They have protested expedi-

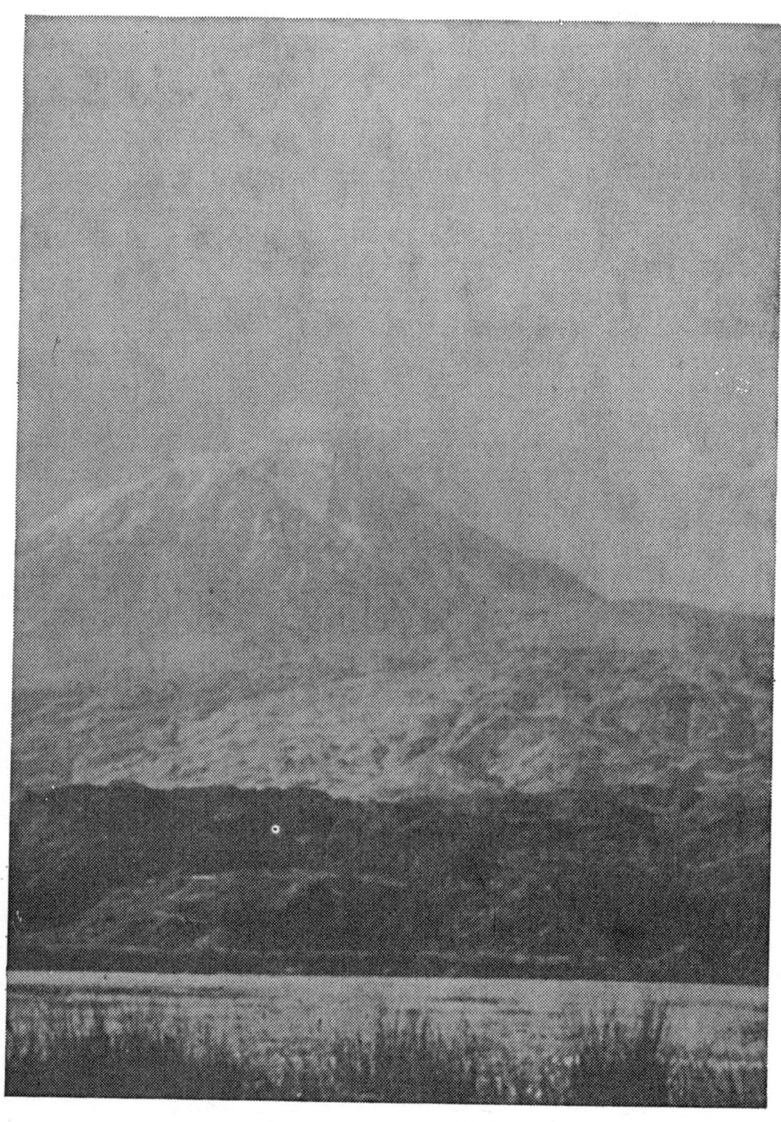

Does Noah's ark still lie hidden somewhere in the remote fastness of this strange mountain peak—Mount Ararat—in eastern Turkey? *UPI photo.*

tions to the area for years. Some observers claim that the Russians *know* the Ark is buried in a glacier on Ararat and don't want the world to discover it, as such a discovery would deal a severe blow to atheism!

Does Noah's Ark lie atop Mount Ararat? Only time and more research will provide the answer. The possibility is intriguing. It is doubtful that stories, accounts and claims that the Ark is there, stretching over at least 2,500 years, could be mere superstition. And wood brought back from the area adds spice to the enigma.

Chapter Twenty

The Awesome Human Brain

The most mysterious object in the universe is the brain. Three pounds of doughlike material, the human brain is presently the subject of the greatest scientific exploration in history.

Human beings, in scientific laboratories, are learning how to consciously control their brain waves through biofeedback. They are learning how to control perspiration, blood pressure and heart rate by sustaining alpha brainwaves. Rats have been taught similar tricks and rewarded by stimulation of the pleasure centers of the brain. Several became so proficient at controlling their heart beat that they died of cardiac arrest.

The human brain is indeed remarkable. Declares Marilyn Ferguson in the *Brain Revolution:*

> A computer sophisticated enough to handle the functions of a single brain's ten billion cells would more than cover the face of the earth. More mysterious than Mars, harder to plumb than the Mindanao deeps, the brain has been only tentatively charted.[1]

She adds:

> The human brain is sensitive to weak magnetic fields. It reacts to stimuli too faint to be registered in consciousness. It can literally hear light waves and experience visual effects from sound waves.[2]

R.L. Gregory, director of the perception laboratory at Cambridge University, points out that the receptors in the eye's retina are so sensitive that they can be stimulated by a single quantum, the smallest unit of measurement of light. Says

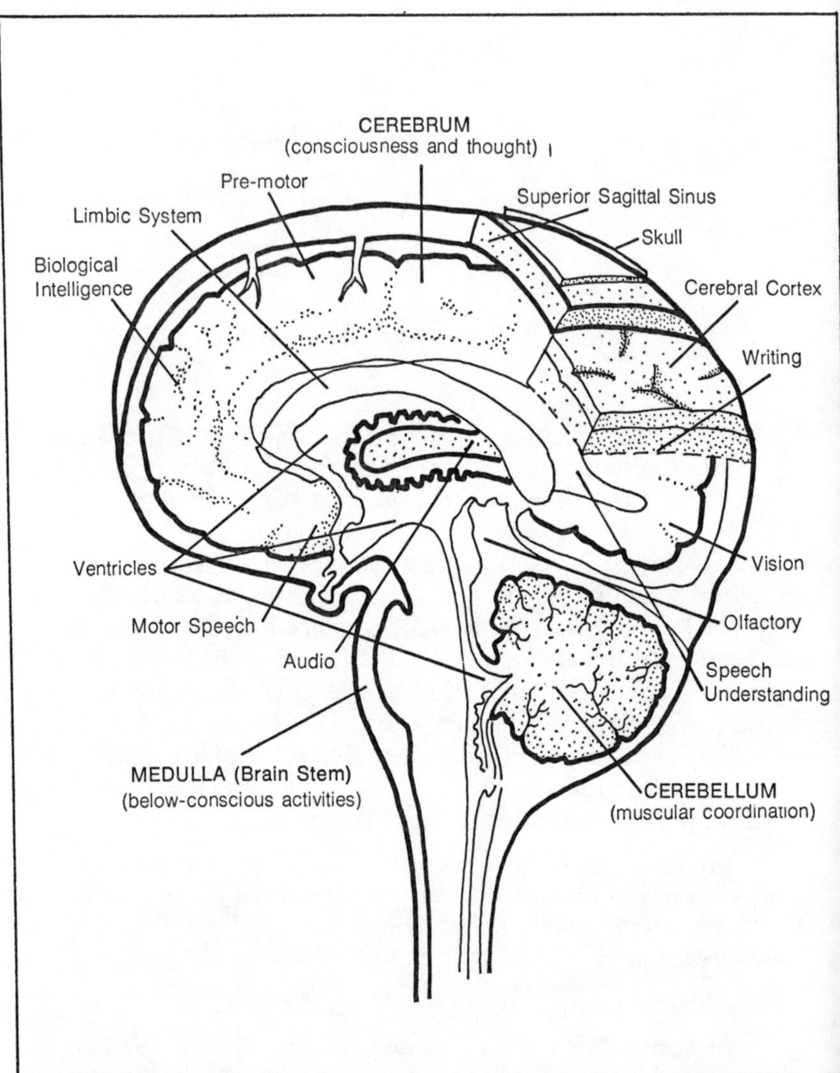

The human brain—the most complex organization of molecules in the entire universe—is truly a masterpiece of creative genius. No evolutionary theory has even begun to account for this marvelous and unique organ about the size of a grapefruit but which has the capacity for creative thought, memory, learning, love, hate, joy and even self-awareness. —*Illustration by Andy Voth.*

Gregory, "The brain is more complicated than a star and more mysterious." Very little is known about how the brain works—how we are able to hear, see, feel, taste, how the memory functions, how emotions are created, or what causes creativity or consciousness.

Says Maya Pines in *The Brain Changers*, "Even today, despite broad progress, researchers remain totally ignorant about how the brain performs its basic job: how it transforms 10 watts of electricity and some chemicals into our thoughts, feelings, dreams, memories—our awareness of being ourselves. It is beyond understanding."[3]

The cerebral cortex, the wrinkled and convoluted layer of gray matter on the surface of the brain, its surface area tripled by its corrugated convolutions, is where most of our thinking, planning, language, imagination, creativity and capacity for abstract thought occurs. But how? Why? No one knows.

The Mystery of Memory

Similarly, the study of memory is perhaps the most difficult and challenging field in the brain sciences. Its secret has so far eluded some of the top brains in the business, Nobel Prize winners, no less.

Controversial experiments performed by Professor James McConnell at the University of Michigan, were astonishing. Worms called planaria were taught to react to light, and then were cut up and fed to untrained planaria. The cannibals absorbed the light reaction knowledge of their predecessors! The experiment appeared to show that information could be transferred from one animal to another. Later, McConnell injected RNA extracts from the brains of trained rats into the brains of untrained rats, and noticed that the untrained rats thus injected seemed to learn the skills of the others at a faster rate than controls. But the whole area is hotly disputed, today. Many researchers vehemently oppose the conclusions that have been drawn.

The biggest problem of all may be how the brain codes events so they can be stored, compared and recalled. We simply do not understand the brain's filing system and how it works. We do not know how memories can survive nearly all brain injuries.

A new approach to get to the answers is based on the principle of the hologram. The hologram uses laser light, coherent light, and splits a beam into two parts, bouncing one ray back by an object, and interacting with the other beam. The interference pattern is recorded on film. Interestingly, if even a small corner of a hologram is then illuminated by the right input, the entire original scene reappears.

Says professor Karl Pribam, neuropsychologist at Stanford University, "Holograms can be layered one on top of the other and yet be separately reconstructed."[4] Could memory be stored in neural holograms caused by the interaction of different nerve impulses? It is a fascinating thought.

Pribam notes that several images can be superimposed on a single holographic plate; some ten billion bits of information can be stored in a cubic centimeter, and each image can be retrieved immediately and easily without disrupting the others.

Ironically, a memory's opposite condition–forgetting–is also "shrouded in mystery," says Maya Pines.[5] Researchers have found that this little gray box is more intricate, contains more secret codes hidden in devious nooks and crannies, possesses more incredible mysteries and tantalizing, sophisticated triggering and blocking mechanisms, than anything else ever studied. There are so many mysteries of the brain that no individual scientist could begin to grasp them all.

The elusive qualities of the brain, and memory, have fascinated and stumped the most distinguished researchers. For many years Karl Lashley attempted to locate the memory engram in the brain. He searched everywhere, and could not find it. For thirty years he explored the brain, experimenting with animals, selectively damaging certain areas, trying thus to abolish memory. He failed at every turn. At one point he wryly said that his research had proven that "learning just is not possible." He finally concluded there is no memory engram, but learning involves field activity.

D.S. Halacy, Jr. in *Man and Memory* writes:

> Not surprisingly, little or no agreement exists as to the actual

> mechanism of memory. There have been and continue to be various theories to account for the storate and recall of perceptions. Is memory a fixed "circuit" in the brain, linking neurons together much like a circuit in a computer? Or is memory instead the pattern of electrical or other activity, perhaps shared by all parts of the brain rather than resident in a single location?[6]

Researchers such as Hyden, Jacobson, McConnell, Rosenblatt and Ungar suggest that memory is stored in a molecule, something like the way DNA stores the blueprint of heredity for all living organisms.

The molecular theory of memory has gained great prominence, today. Swedish biologist Holger Hyden, at the University of Sweden, theorized that RNA might be the storehouse for memory, noting that the neurons and glial cells contain a considerable amount of RNA. Subsequent experiments showed that neurons, stimulated by learning situations, increased production of RNA. In study of rats, it was noticed that not only did the total amount of RNA increase when the rats were taught to balance on a wire to obtain food, but the proportion of adenine in RNA increased significantly and the proportion of uracil decreased, whereas the guanine and cytosine bases remained the same.

Would RNA molecules be capable of containing the memory code? Hyden points out that if some 25 bits of information are stored each second for ten hours a day over ten years, a tiny amount of RNA could code all this data. Others have mentioned that a single molecule has the storage capacity of a thousand books.

Another researcher, Peter Fong of the Physics Department of Emory University in Atlanta, in a paper presented in 1969, suggested that RNA in neurons functions something like a tape recorder storing information. Meanwhile, Dr. Samuel Barondes, Yeshiva University, New York, has demonstrated that protein synthesis in the neuron cell body accompanies the learning process. He feels this could be involved in long-term memory.

Just What is a Brain?

In the lower invertebrates, the brain consists of a group of nerve cell bodies. In lower vertebrates, it is tubular in form. But in higher vertebrates, the brain consists of a medulla, cerebellum, the two halves of which are connected by the pons, the mesencephalon or midbrain, the thalamus and the cerebrum. In man's brain, the cerebrum is greatly expanded and has grown over the rest of the brain, forming a convoluted layer of gray matter.

Interestingly, small animals generally have smooth brains, while large animals, such as the whale, elephant, dolphin and man have highly convoluted ones. The convolution pattern of the brain of a chimpanzee closely resembles that of a man. Man's brain is anatomically different from that of a higher ape's by its larger size, and greater development of the parietal regions. Mental differences include the faculty of speech, greater powers of concentration, reasoning, and appreciation.[7]

It is surprising perhaps, but the left half of the brain controls the right side of the body, and vice versa, because of a crossing of the nerve fibres in the spinal cord on the brain. Also, the top of the brain controls the lowest part of the body, and vice versa.

During the first three years of life, the brain grows rapidly, and approaches its full weight at about age seven. From this time forward the increase is very gradual, peaking by about age 20 for men and a little earlier for women.

Inside the Brain

The cells in the cerebral cortex are arranged in six layers. Going from the outside inward, they are: molecular, external granular, external pyramidal, internal grandular, internal pyramidal, and fusiform. The major functional regions of the cortex are the primary motor area, primary somethetic area, primary visual area, primary auditory area, and the association area.

The primary motor area controls the skeletal muscles of the body. Sensations from the skin, muscles, joints and tendons reach the cortex via the thalamus.

Association areas are especially dominant in man's brain. Association areas near primary sensory areas formulate sensory stimuli into images and enable us to comprehend their meaning.

Objects are associated with a constellation of past experiences or memories. Complex sensory and motor association mechanisms are important to the comprehension of language.

The prefrontal cortex, or frontal association area, is connected to the thalamus and also with association fibres from other regions of the cortex. This region of the brain is responsible for higher intellectual functions and emotional behaviour in man.

Another complex structure of the brain is the limbic system, consisting of the limbic lobe, parts of the temporal and frontal cortex, some thalmic and hypothalamic nuclei, and parts of the basal ganglia. The limbic system, through its connections with the cortex and hypothalamus is believed to perform a major role in emotional responses and seems to be involved in reactions of fear, rage, aggression and sexual behavior.

The thalamus, an oval mass of gray matter, receives fibres from the major sensory systems. It is a major sensory integration center and seems to be important in regulating the state of consciousness, alertness, and attention. The hypothalamus, lying below the thalamus, is small but has extensive and complex fibre connections. It plays a major role in temperature regulation, water balance, and glandular secretion, some of these functions being controlled through connections with the pituitary. Through its connections with the autonomic nervous system, it is a principal center of emotional expression.

In the brain cortex alone are perhaps 10,000,000,000 neurons. Throughout the entire nervous system, the human body has about 15,000,000,000 neurons, each with synaptic contacts with other neurons, and each one acting as an integrator, conductor, and transmitter of coded neural information in the form of electrical impulses.

A typical neuron has a cell body (soma), thin threadlike extensions called dendrites, and an axon, as well as a nucleus, essential to the life of the neuron, and other cytoplasmic substructures within the cell. The dendritic extensions receive and carry information into the cell body, and the axon conducts impulses away from the cell body to the terminal dendrites. These may chemically link and communicate (synapse) with the cell body of another neuron, with a gland cell or a muscle cell. The small neurons in the brain are a fraction of an inch long, but sensory neurons in a tall person may extend for several feet, from the big toe all the way to the central nervous system. They can be even longer in an elephant or a whale.

The cell body of the neuron also contains Golgi apparatus, mitochondria, neuroplasm, and Nissl substance, ranging from clumps of particles to dustlike bits, which functions in producing proteins needed to renew protoplasm. Neurons can replace one third of their protein content in a single day.

In the central nervous system, neurological cells outnumber neurons by five or ten to one. In the white matter of the central nervous system, glial cells produce the myelin sheaths of the axons. Astroglia are cells that lie between blood capillaries and neurons; extensions from them are in intimate contact with 85 percent of the capillary surface, and other extensions are in close synaptic contact with the cell bodies of neurons.

Chemical transmission between nerve cells occurs something like this: A specific chemical compound, called a transmitter, is synthesized in the nerve cell body and travels down the axon to be stored in structures called synaptic vesicles. When a nerve impulse arrives at the ending, it liberates the transmitter in packets called quanta. The released transmitter diffuses across the synaptic cleft, the tiny space (1/250,000,000th of an inch) between the two cells and combines with a substance called a receptor in the membrane of the next nerve cell or effector. This initiates a sequence of effects, resulting in a specific kind of ionic flow through the membrane accompanied by a change in electrical potential. The change spreads outward along the axon of a nerve cell. Or, the transmitter may be inhibitory, and prevent discharge or stop ongoing activity.

All "information" in your brain appears to be the presence or absence of these electrochemical sparks of electrical current. These tiny sparks, called "nerve impulses," are about one tenth of a volt in strength and one thousandth of a second in duration.

It may seem absurd that *everything* in your brain—all the

sights, sounds, smells, memory, and thoughts which we take for granted—is simply the product of these little sparks of electricity. Nevertheless, each one of the billions of neurons in your cerebral cortex alone is able to directly receive information from thousands of other neurons, send information directly to many other neurons, and indirectly communicate with *every* other neuron. It is an incredibly complicated network of interrelated parts.

The neurons take in information from the various senses and send out instructions to various parts of the body through the spinal cord and cranial nerves.

The 100 billion smaller non-nerve cells, called *glial* cells, appear to compose a supporting framework for the neurons. The glial cells account for about half the mass of the brain. They surround the blood capillaries that feed the brain, creating a selective barrier between the blood and neurons. Recent research indicates that they also may be intimately concerned with brain functions such as memory.

The brain is a living, active organ. It is never precisely the same at any two moments! Because of the different thoughts which occur, it is always in a state of change. According to the latest theories of brain operation, the number of possible "states of the brain" exceeds our power to express by any numerical notation. In fact, it can be *safely* stated that there are more possible "states of the brain" than there are *atoms in the entire universe!*

There is an extremely small space—called the *synapse*—separating the axon of one neuron from the dendrite of the next neuron. No electrical charge bridges this gap (if it did, your brain would simply be like one long curled-up wire, with little capacity). The only way for "information" to jump the synapse gap is for a *chemical* transmitter to diffuse across the gap and to generate a new nerve impulse in the next neuron.

Any single neuron may have tens of thousands of other neurons impinging upon it and feeding it "information." Therefore, there is obviously an enormously complex interaction pattern coming into each neuron. And so *each neuron must act as a miniature computer—analyzing, integrating, deciphering, creating.* In a sense, therefore, your brain is not "a computer"—rather it contains ten billion micro-computers!

Writes D.S. Halacy, Jr.:

> The human brain is obviously a thing of amazing complexity and fantastic ability. Packed into a volume no larger than a grapefruit are some 10 billion neurons, the nerve cells that seem to be the key to the operation of our minds. Hooked up like some ultra-complicated switchboard, the network of interconnections stores an estimated 200,000,000,000,000,000,000 bits of information during a lifetime! By comparison, today's most advanced computers do seem pathetically unimpressive.[8]

Says this same well-known computer specialist, "Packaging 10 billion parts in a volume the size of a grapefruit is a capability the computer designer admires wistfully. Since the brain has a volume of about 1,000 cubic centimeters, 10 million neurons fit into a space of one cubic centimeter! *A trillion would fit in one cubic foot, and man-made machines with even a million components per cubic foot are news today.*"[9]

Obviously, no computer made by man can begin to compare with the human brain!

Admitted Isaac Asimov in *Science Digest*:

> Even the most complicated computer man has yet built can't compare in intricacy with the brain. Computer switches and components number in the thousands rather than in the billions. What's more, the computer switch is just an on-off device, whereas the brain cell is itself possessed of a tremendously complex inner structure.[10]

How You Receive Knowledge

How does your brain receive new knowledge? Information from the outside world is transferred into nerve impulses by your sensory receptors—specialized cells which change a specific form of energy reaching them into electrical nervous impulses.

Your sensory receptors include those in your skin, eyes, nose, tongue, and ears. Certain cells in your skin are sensitive to pressure, others to heat or cold, others to pain.* But none respond to light. Certain cells in the retina of your eye generate nerve impulses when light falls on them, but they don't respond to heat or cold.

Nevertheless, all the sensory receptors of your body are amazingly sensitive. Olfactory cells in the upper reaches of your nasal cavity react when just a very few molecules contact them. They are so sensitive, in fact, that to "smell" something requires less than one twenty thousandth the amount of molecules necessary to taste something!

The retina cells in the human eye possess a tremendous range. The brightest object the normal eye can see in brilliant sunshine is 20 billion times brighter than the dimmest object it can see at night! Its sensitivity far exceeds any other physical instrument.[11]

The human eye is like a miniature camera which focuses itself automatically, snaps its "pictures" in a continuing stream, and transmits them as electrical charges to the "darkroom"—an area in the back of the brain which interprets the flood of electrical messages.

The *lens* of the eye adjusts itself and changes its curvature to focus on near or far objects. Likewise the *pupil* adjusts itself to take in just the right amount of light for optimum vision.

Aside from these and other marvels, the eye's key structure is the light-sensitive *retina*—the "screen" at the back of the eyeball which receives and records a constantly changing moving picture which comes in through the lens, and then transmits these "exposures" as electric charges to the brain. The retina is a ninefold layer of great complexity. The human eye has about 137,000,000 separate "seeing" elements located in the retina, with about 1,000,000 nerve lines leading from them to the brain.

The image transmitted to the brain has only two dimensions and is colorless. Astoundingly, it is the brain itself which adds

*Imbedded in your skin are some three to four million detectors sensitive to pain, half a million pressure or touch detectors, and more than 200,000 temperature detectors.

the third dimension when interpreting the two dimensional picture, and which also adds the color! The sensory organ of the eye is truly a wonder of wonders!

The ability of the human ears to "hear" is also incredible. The normal ear can hear a mid-range or normal tone (of 2,700 cycles per second) which involves a pressure variation of only one twelve thousandth dyne (a very weak force) per square centimeter. Says Philip Bard:

> This means that for sound to be heard, the tympanic membrane "ear drum" need only move 1,000,000,000th centimeter, a distance equal to one-tenth the diameter of a hydrogen molecule; and the energy thus required is close to the energy produced by collisions of air molecules in random brownian movement.[12]

How does light, sound, odor, touch, taste affect the various sensory receptors? All information is expressed by the *frequency* and *pattern* of the nerve impulses. This is called the "neuronal sensory code"—simpler than Morse Code since it only involves "dots and spaces" and not dashes.

Control of Movement

Have you ever stopped to think how fortunate you are that you don't have to stop and *think carefully* each time you take a bite of food, to insure that your mouth muscles work properly to chew the food? Or how wonderful it is you don't have to stop, think, and then meticulously flex and extend each and all of the multiple dozens of muscles your body uses when you take a walk?

If you did have to *think* about these things before you could do them, you might starve to death before you could eat enough food to carry on life. It would take hours just to walk a few steps.

Obviously, in order for you to chew food, sit, walk, drive a car, or run, requires a great degree of coordination and subconscious execution of learned muscular patterns.

A baby, of course, must gradually learn to flex and move its arms and legs. After several months it learns to crawl, and finally, to walk. Walking is not an unconscious activity. But how wonderful it is that we can "learn" to walk, and then we can essentially forget about it—we don't have to try to consciously coordinate each individual muscle each time we take a step!

The ability to coordinate muscular activity subconsciously is made possible by the cerebellum, a large structure with fine convolutions resting on the medulla at the back of the brain. The cerebellum is also responsible for ability to play the piano, violin, or other musical instruments.

A pianist plays dozens of notes every second; a violinist skips back and forth to incredibly precise positions on an unmarked string. How do they do it? Obviously, not by conscious thought. Yet, everything had to be consciously learned at one time. Then, after hundreds of hours of practice, different areas and mechanisms of the brain took over the control of the individual movements. As a result, the conscious thought of the performer could then be freed to concentrate on the emotional interpretation of the musical piece.

Consciousness and Thought

As you read these paragraphs, you are consciously receiving information and thinking about it. Your *cerebral cortex*, the center of consciousness, is functioning. But there are so many things to be aware of in the world that we would be hopelessly overwhelmed except for the "reticular activating system."

The reticular activating system is largely concerned with alertness and attention. It intensifies specific important sensations and inhibits general unimportant sensations. For example, it enables you to be immediately awakened by the smallest whimper of your child while completely ignoring the loud roar of a passing freight train.

The cerebral cortex not only contains man's "memory banks" and registers sensation, but it is also the center for decision making and the higher thought processes.

The posterior part of the cerebral cortex is involved in sensory associations and problem solving. The frontal cortex is involved in thinking, social awareness, and the "will." The frontal lobes of the brain are strongly involved in *inhibition*, including the inhibition of the emotions and inner drives. The frontal cortex was designed to override and control all emotions and drives. It provides human beings—from the scholar to the farmer—with the capacity of *free will* or choice.

Evolution and the Brain

Even firm believers in evolution often are deeply troubled by the existence of man's brain. They cannot explain it.

Evolutionists today are forced to admit: "Although much more is understood today about the mechanism of the human brain. . . there is still *no complete agreement* among anthropologists about the process that led to its present state of development. Research is proceeding along a number of separate lines, and the facts have *not yet* coalesced into a coherent theory."[13]

Haunting Problems

Could man's brain have evolved by natural selection? Many years ago Alfred Russel Wallace, an evolutionary contemporary of Charles Darwin, raised this question and answered it himself with a firm no, to the utter dismay and chagrin of his friend Darwin. Even today, evolutionists have no satisfactory answer to this question.

Wrote Loren Eiseley, "Today the question asked by Wallace and never satisfactorily answered by Darwin has returned to haunt us."[14]

Evolutionists simply cannot account for man's brain size. Two modern scientists, M.R.A. Chance and A.P. Mead, bluntly declared: "*No adequate explanation* has been put forward to account for so large a cerebrum as that found in man."[15]

Admits Eiseley, the evolution of man's brain has been "taken about as much for granted as the growth of a yellow pumpkin in the fall."[16]

Man's Brain Baffles Evolution

The brain of man is more than two to three *times* as large as that of the ape. The cranial capacity for chimpanzees and gorillas ranges from 325 to 650 cubit centimeters. Man's cranial capacity, however, ranges from 1000 to 2000 cubic centimeters!

How did man's brain grow so "fast"? *Why* is it so much larger than that of man's "nearest cousins"? Wouldn't an ape-sized brain have been sufficient for mere survival?

Evolutionists are perplexed—baffled. Ruth Moore declares: "Since 1950 the scientific evidence has pointed inescapably to one conclusion: *Man did not evolve in either the time or the way that Darwin and the modern evolutionists* thought most probable."[17]

Loren Eiseley, regarding the great size of man's brain compared to that of so-called "ape men" ancestors, commented: "Ironically enough, science, which can show us the flints and broken skulls of our dead fathers, has yet to explain how we have come so far so fast. . ."[18]

The theory of evolution is simply unable to account for the amazing brain of man. This paradox is explained by D.S. Halacy, Jr.:

> The evolution of the human brain is as intriguing as it is unexplained. Generally, it is thought that environment and natural selection provided the impetus for the brain to develop and improve. The erect walk of man, which freed his hands for the opposable thumb and for toolmaking, is often credited with evolutionary pressure. However, scientists have pointed out that there are a number of lesser animals that have the ability to walk erect and that have opposable thumbs but have not developed much of a brain. . . On the other hand, the dolphin and porpoise, with none of the environmental advantages of man, have developed large and apparently powerful brains whose accomplishments probably include speech.[19]

Clearly, here is another riddle for evolutionary theory to explain!

Viewing the stubborn enigma of the brain, David Hubel, a Harvard researcher, concludes that the way brain processes really work is often beyond the theorists' wildest imaginings.[20]

Often, in fact, brain research compels researchers to move beyond a mere materialistic view of the universe. Many brain scientists tend to become mystical in their outlook and appreciation of the marvels of the mind.

Growing scientific respect for the intelligence underlying all nature has led to a reappraisal of Darwin's theory of natural selection. Consider the ability of an embryonic tadpole brain, transplanted to another place, to cause the skin over the new area to dip down and form the lens of an eye. Contemplating this, Raynor Johnson declared, "We cannot have a plan without a planner. Mind is the only thing known to us with purpose, memory, and intelligence, and we may infer that it is the source and sustainer of the plans."[21]

Similarly, R.L. Gregory asserted:

> The problem of how eyes have developed has presented a major challenge to the Darwinian theory of evolution by natural selection. We can make many entirely useless experimental models when designing a new instrument, but this was impossible for natural selection, for each step must confer some advantage upon its owner, to be selected and transmitted through the generations. But what use is a half-made lens? What use is a lens giving an image if there is no nervous system to interpret the information? How could a visual nervous system come about before there was an eye to give it information?[22]

All these modifications would have to have arisen as a coordinated group. But for the brain, and its sensory organs, and the entire central, autonomic, and peripheral nervous systems to have arisen as a unit, by accidental simultaneous arrival, boggles the mind of the most ardent and sincere evolutionist!

Chapter Twenty One

Our Amazing Mind

George Leonard, author of *Education and Ecstasy*, was awed by the possibilities of the human brain. He declared: "A brain composed of such neurons obviously can never be 'filled up.' Perhaps the more it knows, the more it can know and create. Perhaps, in fact, we can now propose an incredible hypothesis: The ultimate creative capacity of the brain may be, for all practical purpose, infinite."[1]

This sounds shocking, incredible. But should it?

Man's Last Frontier

The brain may be man's last frontier—the greatest unexplored territory of them all. Said W. Grey Walter, "We need not yearn for greater masses of gray matter. We already dispose of enough nerve units to enumerate in their permutations every particle of Eddington's universe."[2]

How complex is the brain? Just to give you an insight into one of its functions, Arnold Trehub of the Veterans Administration Hospital in Northampton, Massachusetts, says his research indicates the brain performs complex mathematics in building up its picture of the world, computing on the basis of limited information and interpreting the remainder. It is "the most efficient stochastic signal detection scheme known," says Trehub. That is, it has an incredible ability to aim at a mark by estimating on the basis of known parameters and come very close to the bull's eye.

One facet of the brain's remarkable ability is appreciation of beauty. There are times of pure breathtaking, absorbing and exciting ecstasy, which overcome and engulf an individual. Sometimes a glorious ephemeral sunset with its deep rosy hues, or the smell of a beautiful rose, glistening with dew drops in a garden, can saturate a person's sense, leaving one with an eloquent and undying sensation of being at one with the universe. How is this possible?

Raynor Johnson, professor of physics at the University of Melbourne, puts it this way: "But we *do* see. . . cathedrals and primroses, works of art and works of steel—what a world the mind has constructed from the electrical storms in a few cubic centimeters of gray matter which it has interpreted!"[3]

The mind of man is unique—unmatched elsewhere in nature. The existence of a mind is reflected in sensations such as tickles, aches, mental images, sense perceptions, emotions, memory, expectations, hopes, dreams, desires, faith, inferring and other types of reasoning, motives, choices, actions and traits of character and personality.

Says the *Encyclopedia Britannica*, 1974 edition:

> One thing that sharply distinguishes man from the rest of nature is his highly developed capacity for thought, feeling, and deliberate action. Here and there in other animals, rudiments, approximations, and limited elements of this capacity may occasionally be found; but the full-blown development that is called a mind is unmatched elsewhere in nature.[4]

Just what is this thing called "mind," anyway?

Learning and Intelligence

Rats can learn to negotiate a simple maze. Chimpanzees can learn to do simple tasks. Animals can learn to adapt their behavior to some limited extent. But man's capacity for intelligent thinking far surpasses all animals. He learns all he needs to in order to survive, and then *keeps on learning.* His gift of language—which must be learned—gives him the ability to grasp and manipulate abstract ideas—to generate *new* concepts.

He is able to formulate new ideas, thoughts, to create new designs, patterns—such as the radio, television, telephone. He is able to invent contrivances for transportation.

Man's ability to think and to comprehend involves intelligence. But what exactly is intelligence? Intelligence covers a broad range of mental activities, from insight to logical thought, including the capacity for grasping intangible concepts. Intelligence involves our ability to find meaning and relationships in abstract symbols such as language, numbers, geometric figures.

One might be tempted to speculate that brain size must correlate with greater intelligence. This, however, is not necessarily the case. The brains of elephants and whales are larger than man's; but these creatures are not smarter. Also, in modern human populations, normally intelligent people may have brains ranging in size from 1000 cubic centimeters to 2000 cubic centimeters. Within this range, there is no convincing evidence that the larger is more intelligent than the smaller. Other factors than brain size are certainly involved in intelligence, such as the number of brain nerve cells and the complexity of their interconnections with each other.

But why are humans so vastly more intelligent than any animal?

More Than Animal Brain

Your mind is far more than a mere animal's brain. While animals can solve various kinds of problems, birds can build nests, beavers can build dams, these abilities are instinctive. They are passed on from one generation to the next. But each type of bird builds the same type nest that its species has always built. There is no originality. No bird or animal has the ability for rational thought; none of them has actual "intelligence"; none of them is able to *think* up new ideas, to imagine, to create.

Animals, in the technical sense of the word, may be "conscious." But they are surely not self-conscious! They are not able to consciously *think*, plan out actions, invent new ways of doing things. There is a vast difference between animal brain and the human mind.

John Lilly, a neurophysiologist and psychoanalyst, spent ten years of his life studying the brains of dolphins. He discovered that dolphins can communicate more information through the right and left blowholes in their noses than we can through our mouths in the same time span. They can carry on two conversations simultaneously, one in whistles and one in clicking sounds, with the two halves of their brains. Besides this, they have a built in echo-locating system.

Lilly arduously taught one dolphin to produce the sounds for the numbers one to ten. He then was amazed to see it teaching the dolphin in an adjacent tank to count from one to ten. Reviewing tapes of conversations between the two dolphins at night, he detected instances of systematic coaching.[5]

But despite these marvelous abilities, a dolphin doesn't have the unique characteristic of the human mind.

A dolphin, perhaps the smartest animal, cannot investigate itself. It doesn't wonder, "Who am I?" "What am I?" "What am I doing here?" "Where am I going?" "*Why* do I exist?" These questions are only asked by the human mind! *The human mind is utterly unique.*

Man's mind inquires about himself—his origin, his future, his purpose in life. Man's mind makes him aware of beauty and ugliness, order and chaos, ecstasy and sadness, love and hate, history and prophecy, humor and satire, kindness and cruelty, obedience and lawbreaking.

Man's mind makes him aware of the fact of life and the fact of death. A living man knows he is alive, and knows that someday he will *not* be alive. He wonders, "What *is* death?" "What happens after I die?" "Is there another life after death?"

Said Pierre Teilhard de Chardin in *The Phenomenon of Man:*

> Admittedly the animal knows. *But it cannot know that it knows...* In consequence it is denied access to a whole domain of reality in which we can move freely. *We are separated by a chasm*—or a threshold—*which it cannot cross.* Because we are reflective we are not only different but quite other. *It is not a matter of change of degree, but a change of nature, resulting from a change of state.*[6]

Man's mind is what supremely *sets him apart from* animal life. It makes man unique! Could your mind—your memory, intelligence, creativity, consciousness, have all evolved by blind chance?

Consider the Computer

In 1958 two scientists predicted that within ten years a computer would be the world's chess champion. The ten years have come and gone. Was their prophecy borne out?

The best programmed computer built to date, MacHac 6 has defeated one player in a human tournament, tied another, and has a rating of 1304 in a scale on which chess masters range around 2200 and champions around 2750. This is an immense gap!

But what does this mean? Simply this: There is a vast difference between the programmed "intelligence" of a computer and true human intelligence. Mankind has never succeeded in building a machine or computer which is more intelligent than man himself. All the evidence indicates that the ability of machines can only be brought along so far—and then they stop. Man cannot teach a machine to *think*!

Said Dr. Huston Smith, professor of philosophy at the Massachusetts Institute of Technology: "Machines are not going to be able to handle all the problems minds can handle—certainly not in the visible future and probably never."[7]

Although machines have been made that can "think" in the same sense that they can solve complex problems rapidly, write poor to mediocre poetry, music, or play a fair game of chess, there is still a vast qualitative difference between any computer yet devised and the human mind.

What computer has emotional feelings? What computer can know the joys of love, the ecstacies of passion, the bitterness of sorrow, the elation of accomplishment, the wrath of indignation, or peace of mind? What computer can experience the attitude of faith, or the feeling of humility? What computer can know the pangs of fear, the sorrow when a loved one dies?

Computers cannot "feel." They are not human. They don't

have any of the basic human emotions which play a vital role in human cognitive processes. Computers cannot know compassion for the suffering of others. They do not feel "pain." In a word, in order to operate, they must be given specialized instructions—they must be programmed—and they must be "plugged in." They are not *alive*!

There is an overwhelming gulf between the "intelligence" of a man-made computer of the most sophisticated type, and the human mind.

What does this imply?

Consider this: If the greatest scientists and computer engineers in the world, pooling their talents, cannot create a "machine" with anywhere near the intelligence of a man—do you think blind evolution could do it by sheer chance?

You have an intelligent mind. If you saw a modern computer system in operation, at the Manned Spacecraft Center in Houston, Texas; if you saw those computers rapidly solving complex mathematical problems dealing with Apollo flight trajectories, fuel consumption, oxygen consumption, and the orbits and velocities of the earth, moon, and spacecraft—you would logically infer that such a machine had a creator. You would consider anybody who believed such an incredible "electronic brain" evolved by sheer accident *absolutely dumb*!

But such marvelous modern computers, compared to the human mind with its billions of interconnected nerve cells and incredibly complex microcircuitry and its fantastic capacity for original thought, intelligence, decision-making and creativity, are only feeble tinker toys. Qualitatively, the human mind is in a totally different class than any computer!

You can easily see that a *computer* must have an intelligent builder and designer. What about your own mind? Doesn't its very existence also prove that it had to have a Creator?

Evolution of the MIND?

Evolutionists find it impossible to account for the evolution of the human brain—which they have never adequately done. But when it comes to the human mind—which is so much more than just a network of billions of nerve cells working together receiving and transmitting information—they are really "stuck"!

"Despite all the pioneering work done over the past 20 years in brain research, the mind is still very much a dark mystery locked in a bony box," declared an article in *Science News.*[8]

Continues the author: "The thing a man carries around under his hat is more complicated than anything known to science and at the moment there are no principles, physical or chemical, that will describe its action. . . .

"By now the action of an individual neuron is fairly well understood, but scientists have no concepts to deal with the brain's integrative functions or, simply, its capacity for consciousness. A common belief is that they never will."[9]

Renowned Nobel Prize winning neurophysiologist John C. Eccles has faith that evolution is true. But, says he:

> Yet I do not believe that his [Darwin's] theory provides a complete explanation of my origin. I can believe that, so far as the human body is concerned, the evolutionary theory gives a fairly adequate account, *but this theory fails completely to provide me with an explanation of my origin as the person I experience myself to be with my self-awareness and unique individuality.*[10]

The vast gap between man's mind and animal brain has never been satisfactorily bridged by evolutionary theory. Perhaps this is the reason Theodosius Dobzhansky says the majority of scientists consider the "mind" a "four-letter word which should not be uttered among well-bred scientists"![11]

Yet, Dobzhansky asserts: "This is, however, too easy a solution which *fails to solve problems too obtrusive to be ignored.* No matter how eloquently somebody may argue that my self-awareness is just an illusion, I know, with an assurance greater than I have about anything in the world, that my self-awareness is the most compelling of all realities."[12]

Sophisticated brain research has not revealed any physical-chemical explanation for the fact that man's *mind* is so vastly superior to the brain of any animal—whether that of the whale, dolphin, chimpanzee or great ape.

No animal has the ability to speak a language anywhere

nearly so sophisticated as that of the most "primitive" human tribe. No animal has anything remotely similar to an actual code of ethics or morality. No animal has concern for the dead.

Wrote Erich Fromm, a famed psychoanalyst: "Man has intelligence, like other animals, which permits him to use thought processes for the attainment of immediate, practical aims; but man has another mental quality which the animal lacks. He is aware of himself, of his past and of his future, which is death; of his smallness and powerlessness; he is aware of others—as friends, enemies, or as strangers. Man transcends all other life because he is, for the first time, life aware of itself. Man is in nature, subject to its dictates and accidents, yet he transcends nature because he lacks the unawareness which makes the animal a part of nature—as one with it."[13]

Says this renowned scientist: ". . .the theory of the evolution of the human mind is completely incompatible with man being anything but an ordinary 100% physical animal." And yet man's mind capacity is light years more than the brain of a 100% physical animal!

After surveying the vast differences between man's mind and the brains of animals, John C. Eccles reached this conclusion:

> *I believe that there is a fundamental mystery in my existence, transcending any biological account* of the development of my body (including my brain) with its genetic inheritance and its evolutionary origin; and, that being so, I must believe similarly for each one of you and for every human being. And just as I cannot give a scientific account of my origin—*I woke up in life, as it were, to find myself existing* as an embodied self with this body and brain—so I cannot believe that this wonderful divine gift of a conscious existence has no further future, no possibility of another existence under some other, unimaginable conditions.[14]

Eccles—although a believer in evolution—nevertheless states that for him evolution:

> . . .fails as a complete and satisfactory explanation of my own personal existence. For me there is a profound mystery in existence. We cannot even anticipate any fundamental breakthrough in understanding; but at least we should have a far-ranging vision of the marvellous adventure we cojointly find ourselves in—the adventure

> of life and in particular of the conscious life of the mind. This gives us all our civilization, our art as well as our science.

The existence of the human mind is a "mystery." The amazing human mind and brain baffle evolutionary theory. How could such a wondrous, complex, interconnected series of specialized parts and cells have *mindlessly* evolved by sheer chance and Darwinian "natural selection"?

The human mind stands as the greatest proof of God of them all. It did not evolve. It was designed by the greatest intelligence.

The brain and nervous system are obviously the result of masterful planning and purpose. There is a supreme Spiritual power behind the universe, responsible for the miracle of mind.

A cartoon in *Punch* sums up the current thinking of many researchers at the frontiers of knowledge. In it a scientist admonishes his colleague, "Don't laugh, Hartley—but every time I begin a new experiment, I wonder if this will be the one where I find religion."

W.H. Thorpe, of Cambridge University, one of the world's leading experts on animal behavior, has insisted on "the absolute necessity for belief in a spiritual world which is interpenetrating with and yet transcending what we see as the material world."[16]

Sir James Jeans put it this way:

> Mind no longer appears as an accidental intruder into the realm of matter; we are beginning to suspect that we ought rather to hail it as the creator and governor of the realm of matter.

Origin of Mind

How did the human mind originate? The Bible provides the answer: "Then God said, Let us make man in *our image and likeness* to rule the fish in the sea, the birds of heaven, the cattle, all wild animals on earth, and all reptiles that crawl upon the earth" (Genesis 1:26, NEB).

And further: "So God created man in His *own* image; in the image of God He created him; male and female He created them" (Gen. 1:27).

Man's unique mind is a reflection in flesh of the awesome mind of God. Man, like God, has creative, inventive powers. Man has intelligence, reasoning ability, powers of deduction and induction. He can theorize and formulate hypotheses concerning his own origin and the origin of the cosmos.

Ages ago, in the book of Genesis, we read that God made man *in His own image and likeness.* Doesn't it follow, then, that man has a mind like unto that of God?

Long ago, at the tower of Bable, God gave an insight into the awesome potential of the human mind. Observing mankind united in building a huge tower, God commented on their ability: "Behold, they are one people and they have all one language; and this is only the beginning of what they will do; *and nothing that they propose to do will now be impossible for them*" (Gen. 11:6, RSV).

Jesus Christ himself said to his hearers: "Is it not written in your law, 'I said, you are gods'? If he called them gods to whom the word of God came (and Scripture cannot be broken), do you say of him whom the Father consecrated and sent into the world, You are blaspheming, because I said, I am the Son of God?" (John 10:34-36, RSV).

Indeed, the Bible reveals that mankind is formed and fashioned like God Himself, only composed of clay. We are, as Jesus said, incipient gods–Gods in the chrysalis. We possess the potentiality of becoming someday on the God plane, as members of His divine family. Jesus Himself, very God, a member of the God head, calls us "co-heirs" of Jesus Christ. He is the "firstborn among *many brethren*" (Romans 8:17, 29).

Few have ever really understood the purpose for which God created mankind.

God ultimately intends for mankind, once he is perfected, and once true character is built within him, to become divine members of the God family and to assist him in ruling over the entire cosmos, the far-flung reaches of starry space. That is why we read in the book of Hebrews:

> What is man that thou art mindful of him, or the son of man, that thou carest for him? Thou didst make him *for a little while*

> *lower* than the angels. Thou hast crowned him with glory and honor, putting everything in subjection under his feet. Now in putting everything in subjection to him, he left nothing outside his control. As it is, we do not *yet* see everything in subjection to him (Hebrews 2:6-8, RSV).

Mankind is for a short time, lower than the angels. But God intends to crown him with glory and honor and will put everything—all the Creation and handiwork of God—under his control. Indeed, Paul says, God will leave "nothing outside his control"!

This, of course, has not happened "yet." But the time is coming, when the purpose of creation, the supreme plan of God, will be gloriously, majestically inimitably fulfilled! And then we will comprehend Him, even as He comprehends us, and "*we shall be like him*" (I John 3:2).

At that time we will become one with God.

The world embarrasses me,
and I cannot dream
That this watch exists and has
no watchmaker.
Voltaire

Chapter Twenty Two

Spaceship Earth—The Doubter's Dilemma

The night of December 6, 1972, I witnessed the last of the Apollos—Apollo 17—lift off the launching pad at Cape Kennedy, Florida, in a dazzling, majestic climb into the sky. As I watched, enthralled, the gleaming Saturn V rocket slowly agonizingly crawled into the night sky in front of a ferocious fiery blast which rivaled the sun in brilliance. The staccato rumble from the rocket engines swept over us at the reviewing stand. Vividly, I recall the newsmen shouting, "There she goes! Lift off, baby!"

It was awe-inspiring. Astronauts Eugene A. Cernan, mission commander, Harrison Schmitt, civilian geologist, and Ronald Evans, command ship pilot, rose into the dark sky on top of an inferno of fire, making man's last scheduled trip to the moon for this century. I couldn't help wondering if this was the beginning of the end of man's space flight—or merely the end of the beginning.

In the next few days, I toured the Skylab I mockup up at the Manned Spacecraft Center in Houston, Texas, and sat inside a simulator of the lunar lander and the Apollo command module. I was awestruck at the array of fascinating buttons, dials, scopes, gauges, and highly sophisticated gadgets, computers, and life-support equipment jammed into so incredibly small a space. To think that such a vehicle carried men 240,000 miles to the surface of the moon and back into lunar orbit to join up with the command ship!

The space odyssey of Apollo 17—the last of the Apollos—and

the incredible journey of the Skylab crews in orbit around the earth—serve as a vivid reminder that our own planet is actually a tremendous spaceship—a huge command ship orbiting the sun.

Spaceship Earth

The space laboratories of man can only orbit the earth for a few months before the food and oxygen supply runs out. Within months, a man-made space orbiter such as Skylab I becomes useless and unable to support life. And it is only able to support and sustain a few astronauts at a time.

Have you ever stopped to compare such an inconceivable achievement—which we marvel at—with the earth itself?

The earth can be compared to a spaceship. But it is of immense size—8,000 miles in diameter—and presently supports approximately four billion human beings. Besides three million other species of plants and animals.

The earth has been supporting life for a long time—and there is still plenty of food, water, and air available to eat, drink and breathe. The life-support systems of the earth are so ingenious that they are self-renewing.

But man now seems intent upon fouling his spaceship earth, polluting his planet, disrupting his life-support system, wreaking havoc upon many forms of life, depleting nonrenewable energy resources, ruining the landscape, contaminating his water supply, and belching noxious fumes into his air.

But consider the beautiful earth, with its rolling hills, jagged mountains, verdant valleys, tumbling and splashing mountain streams, magnificent rivers, trackless oceans. The earth is a veritable jewel among the planets.

The earth is uniquely designed to support life. Was it all a mere accident—a chance stroke of fate?

Astronauts have visited the moon, and found it to be devoid of life—barren, bleak, and unable to support life. Mariner spacecraft have flown by Mars, taking detailed close-up photographs and transmitted them thirty million miles back to the earth. Could life exist on Mars?

The Red Planet Mars

The entire atmosphere of Mars contains the equivalent of only three cubic miles of water. This water content is closely related to the seasonal fluctuations of the polar caps of frost or ice on Mars. Mars is an extremely arid planet, similar to the Moon.

The polar caps of Mars, which advance in the Martian autumn and winter to about halfway to the equator, and recede in the spring, were first recorded by Gian Domenico Cassini, about 1666. They are mostly frozen carbon dioxide and possibly contain some frozen water.

Does life exist on Mars? Scientists have long considered Mars a likely spot for life to be found. Small amounts of carbon monoxide and water have been detected, and perhaps nitrogen. Temperatures at noon on the Martian equator reach 85 degrees. Living on Mars would be like living at 100,000 feet up in the earth's atmosphere.

Experiments on earth, simulating the Martian environment, showed that certain micro-organisms could survive the martian conditions indefinitely. Nevertheless, at this point there is no direct evidence for life on Mars. While seasonal changes have been observed on the surface of the red planet, these may be attributable to raging dust storms rather than the growth of vegetation.

Militating against the existence of life on Mars is the fact that liquid water is deemed essential for development of life on earth, but water has been observed on Mars only in the vapor or frozen form and in extremely small quantities. Photographs taken by Mariner spacecraft show the present surface of Mars is extremely old, perhaps primordial. In all probability no oceans have existed on Mars for the last 4,000,000,000 years.

Also, the surface of Mars is exposed to ultraviolet radiation which is lethal to life. Astronomers agree completely that no intelligent life exists there.[1]

Venus

Venus, the second planet from the sun, was worshipped by the ancients as the goddess Aphrodite, Astarte, Easter, or Venus. The Venusian year is 225 earth days long. Gravity on the surface of Venus is about 88 percent that of the earth. Often viewed as earth's "sister planet," because it is roughly the same size, Venus is nonetheless strikingly different. Although Venus is 100 percent cloud covered, compared to the earth's 50 percent, scientists have been unable to detect the presence of water vapor in the Venusian atmosphere.

Strangely, Venus rotates in retrograde motion—that is, it revolves backwards on its axis, compared to the other planets. The time required for Venus to rotate once on its axis—a day on Venus—determined by radar reflection—is roughly 243 earth days in length!

The nature of the clouds of Venus remains shrouded in mystery. At the planet's equator, the heavy clouds move at speeds up to 200 miles per hour, and at the poles, twice that speed.[2]

Venus has almost no magnetic field. Thus it is not protected against bombardment by high-energy particles from the sun, and the "solar wind" dramatically interacts with the Venusian atmosphere.

Entry capsules of the Venera spacecraft revealed about 95 percent carbon dioxide and a few tenths of a percent of water vapor in the atmosphere below the clouds. It seems clear that the atmosphere of Venus is largely carbon dioxide.[3]

In 1956 it was discovered that Venus is a source of intense radiation at radio wavelengths, implying Venus is very hot. This would suggest Venus is uninhabitable. In 1970 Venera 7 reached the surface of Venus and radioed back to astronomers that the surface temperature is 900 degrees Fahrenheit or 482 degrees Centigrade—extremely hot.

Temperatures on Venus are prohibitive to life as we know it. Says one respected authority:

> Astonishingly hot, with an oppressively dense atmosphere

containing corrosive gases, with a surface glowing dimly by its own red heat and characterized by bizarre optical refraction effects, Venus (curiously identified in ancient literature with Lucifer) seems very much like the classical view of Hell.[4]

Mercury

Mercury is another strange planet, almost as much a mystery as far off Pluto. Half again as large as the moon and almost twice as dense, Mercury circles the sun once in 88 earth days. A day on Mercury, however, equals 176 earth days—a fact first discovered in 1965 by radar reflection.

Mercury has no appreciable atmosphere or magnetic field. This fiery planet has moonlike craters, rolling hills and valleys, and extreme surface temperatures. At noon temperatures may reach 940 degrees Fahrenheit, more than enough to melt lead. At night temperatures plummet to 350 degrees below zero. Nobody expects to find signs of life on this harsh, inhospitable planet.[5]

The Jovian Giant

Could life exist on Jupiter, the largest and most intriguing planet in the solar system?

Named after the ruler of the gods in the Greco-Roman pantheon, Jupiter is the most massive of the planets and has twelve known satellites, one of them larger than Mercury. It is the only planet besides the earth known to possess a magnetic field.

Its low density and large mass suggest that Jupiter is very different from the Earth. No solid surface of the planet has yet been observed.

Jupiter's Great Red Spot, long a total mystery to astronomers, was photographed by Pioneer 10 in December 1973, and appears to be a towering mass of clouds. Pioneer 10 passed within 81,000 miles of the clouds of Jupiter.

Dr. Tom Gehrels of the University of Arizona believes

sources of heat deep in the Jovian atmosphere cause gases to rise in columns just as they do on earth. As the gases rise, they condense, forming aerosols, giving them bright colors.

Curiously, infrared heat sensing instruments aboard Pioneer 10 indicate that Jupiter gives off twice as much energy as it receives from the sun. Also unexpectedly, astronomers found that Jupiter maintains nearly constant temperatures day and night, ranging between minus 215 and 230 degrees Fahrenheit. This may be due to the fact that Jupiter, eleven times the diameter of the earth, spins on its axis once in 10 earth hours.[6]

Pioneer 10 also discovered that Jupiter's radiation belts are different from those of the earth. They seem to be restricted to a swath around the plant's equator, rather than composing an invisible shield around the planet as the earth's Van Allen belts do, protecting earth life from harmful radiation.

The fantastic journey of Pioneer 10 shattered old theories about Jupiter. As Pioneer 10 sped through one radiation belt forming a ring 110,000 miles from the planet's surface, scientists were fearful its delicate instrumentation would be destroyed. The radiation bombardment was 1,000 times the amount needed to kill a human.[7]

Science News summarized the findings of Pioneer 10 this way:

> Adjacent bands of brilliant color move at violently different speeds around its massive girth and a vast red spot, more than twice the span of the entire earth, rages and screams at the listening ears of radio telescopes. Yet for all the miles of data gathered by its 11 sensitive scientific instruments, Pioneer 10 has but confirmed that the mighty world is indeed a planet of mystery.[8]

As the spacecraft reached a point 4.7 million miles from the planet, it encountered a shock wave where the solar wind collides with the planet's magnetic field. Once the spacecraft entered the magnetosphere, the expected magnetic field of Jupiter failed to materialize. For millions of miles Pioneer 10 shot forward, detecting particles that seemed to be aimlessly fluctuating. Finally, after being battered by the solar winds, and unexpected shocks, and surviving the planet's intense radiation zone, Jupiter's magnetic field was detected. Early signs indicated it is about eight times as strong as the earth's.

Astronomers now believe Jupiter's atmosphere consists of 15 percent helium, 84 percent hydrogen, 1 percent methane, ammonia and other molecules. The planet itself seems not to have a firm surface. It gradually begins to assume a pea-soup consistency, at greater depths, and thickens until a hard core of hydrogen is reached. Gravity on Jupiter is about two and half times stronger than earth's.

Despite speculation that ammonia or methane ponds, on certain of the moons of Jupiter or Saturn, may possibly be capable of hosting life and facilitating its development, there is no evidence, either direct or indirect, for life existing on these intriguing planets or their moons.

All of these facts should, of course, make us much more sensitive to the fact life exists on earth and our planet is capable of sustaining millions of forms of living organisms.

Prerequisites for Life

Why is the earth capable of supporting life, but none of the other planets in the solar system seem to be thus endowed?

In order for life to exist, a particular chemical environment must be present. Life on earth is structurally based on carbon. It needs water in liquid form as an interaction medium. Hydrogen and nitrogen are also necessary for structure. Phosphorus is vital for energy storage and transport, sulfur for three-dimensional configuration of proteins.

The earth is uniquely endowed with all of these vital prerequisites for life's existence.

Also, a planet, in order to sustain life, must have a suitable range of temperature, between the freezing and the boiling point of a liquid, such as water, serving as an interaction medium. The liquid must be an excellent solvent. It should be difficult to vaporize or freeze. It should be abundant.

A life-bearing planet should also have gases that can be used in biological cycles such as carbon dioxide, and oxygen. Therefore, it must have a suitable atmosphere.

The life-supporting surface of the planet must be shielded in some way from harmful ultraviolet radiation.

Thermodynamically, there must be a thermal difference between the planet's sun, or energy source, and potential plant life, so that photosynthesis can occur. Otherwise, this vital function would be impossible.

The earth appears to be ideally suited for the sustaining of life. It has a perfect interaction medium—water—which is an excellent solvent. Water is abundant on the earth, but not on other planets. The earth also is endowed with abundant carbon dioxide and oxygen. Ultraviolet radiation is shielded from the earth's surface by the Van Allen belts. Temperatures on earth are just right for proteins to exist. At temperatures above the boiling point of water, proteins become denatured. Hydrogen bonding and Van der Waals forces between water and protein disappear at those temperatures. Also, at high temperatures bonds within the protein molecule itself tend to break down, the proteins change their shapes, and lose their ability to take part in enzymatic reactions.

Furthermore, bonds which would be too weak at high temperatures are too strong at low temperatures, slowing the rates of chemical reactions.

In 1913, biochemist L.J. Henderson noted the biological advantages of carbon and water in terms of comparative chemistry. He was struck by the fact that those very atoms that are needed for life on earth are just those atoms which are around.[9] It is indeed a remarkable fact that the atoms most useful for life are abundant on the earth. Could this be mere coincidence?

The earth is truly unique.

What are some of the amazing relationships that make life on earth possible?

Climate

The earth's climate is just the right range to sustain life. Temperatures on the other planets are either too hot, or too cold. But the earth is just the right distance from the sun for the optimum use of the earth's surface for life. The sun is neither too big nor too small. As a result, the general climate and temperature of our earth is able to support life from the equator to the poles.

A life-bearing planet must have a general temperature range from freezing to the boiling point of water, the temperature range where water will freely exist as a liquid. At colder temperatures, chemical reactions would be too sluggish. At higher temperatures, the heat would rupture vital links between carbon and hydrogen atoms which are the basic units of living matter.

Was this sheer coincidence?

Atmosphere

The "good earth" has a truly remarkable atmosphere.

The earth has *enough* atmosphere, so that just enough helpful radiation from the sun reaches us. Thirty miles up in the atmosphere, a narrow band of ozone filters out harmful ultraviolet radiation which would make life impossible if it reached the earth. Was this layer of ozone a mere "accident" of evolution?

Writes Theo Loebsack in an article entitled "The Deep Realm of the Atmosphere":

> From humanity's perspective, this stratospheric ozone acts as a lifesaver: if the ultraviolet rays reached us at full strength, their powers of penetration and destruction would cause grave biological damage. The ozone layer, therefore, acts as an umbrella against the most dangerous of the Sun's rays.[10]

Ozone is a gas produced when ultraviolet radiation from the sun splits the normally occurring O_2 oxygen molecule into two atoms, which then unite with other atoms to make ozone, O_3.

The earth's atmosphere has just the right kinds of gases at the proper densities to filter out rays from the sun which would destroy life. On the other hand, fortunately for all of us, the atmosphere contains just the proper amount of oxygen and carbon dioxide. If it contained just 5 percent more oxygen, spontaneous combustion would occur much more readily, the fires would rage around the world, destroying plant and animal life. If there were too much carbon dioxide, it would absorb the redder wavelengths of light from the sun and reduce photosynthesis in plants.

The atmosphere is exactly balanced to support life in part because the earth itself is the right size. If the planet were too big, its atmosphere would be too dense and would filter out many healthful rays. If the earth were too small, like Mars, or Mercury, it would not be able to hold enough of an atmosphere to abundantly support life.

Were all these factors the resulf of mere "accident"?

Our atmosphere has 21 percent oxygen—just the right amount. Too little oxygen, and animal life could not survive. The atmosphere also contains 78 percent free nitrogen which is a vital ingredient in living tissue, used in building proteins, hormones, and enzymes.

Oxygen plays a very important part in our atmosphere, besides being necessary for respiratory processes. It filters out the very bands of ultraviolet light that are most devastating to nuclear acids and proteins, while at the same time allowing full penetration of the visible light needed for photosynthesis of plants. Thus the earth's atmosphere acts like a colossal membrane, shielding us from harmful forms of energy, but permitting useful forms to flow freely through.

Writes Lewis Thomas, M.D., former dean of the New York University School of Medicine, and current president of the Memorial Sloan-Kettering Cancer Center in New York City:

> All in all, the sky is a miraculous achievement. It works, and for what it is designed to accomplish, it is as infallible as anything in nature. I doubt whether any of us could think of a way to improve on it.

Thomas calls the sky "far and away the grandest product of collaboration in all of nature." He adds:

> It breathes for us, and it does another thing for our pleasure. Each day, millions of meteorites fall against the outer limits of the membrane and are burned to nothing by the friction. Without this

> carapace, the earth's surface would long since have become the pounded powder of the moon.[11]

Why are all these vital, beneficial gases abundant in the earth's atmosphere but poisonous gases exceedingly rare?

Was it merely another fluke of evolution? Or is the composition of our atmosphere evidence of *design*?

Water

No life could exist without water. Whereas the other planets have practically no water whatsoever—and so far as we know, none in its liquid state—the earth abounds in this precious commodity. Three fifths of the earth is covered with water—seas and oceans—to an average depth of two miles.

Water is prevalent all over the earth in oceans and lakes, rivers, and vast subterranean lakes, and scattered throughout the soil in the form of tiny droplets. These adhere so steadfastly to the soil that only the strong suction of a plant's root can dislodge them. Water simultaneously occurs on earth in the solid, liquid, and gaseous states as ice, water, and water vapor, respectively.

Water is a *necessary* constituent in the cells of all animals and vegetable tissues. Most people take this simple chemical compound and its unusual properties for granted.

Properties of Water

The most striking property of water is it expands about nine per cent when it freezes. Ice, therefore, is lighter than water and floats! This unusual characteristic is important of life.

In *General Zoology*, Storer and Usinger write: "The fact that ice floats, being lighter than water, is important to organisms. But for this, ice would form at the bottom of lakes and most large bodies of water would have permanent masses of ice in their depths."[12]

The lopsidedness of the water molecule—it is an isosceles triangle with an open angle of 150°—is what makes ice float. *By all the examples of physical behavior it should not!* Almost every substance, whether solid, liquid or gas, will *shrink* in volume as its temperature drops, becoming more dense. Thus its liquid form is heavier than its gaseous form, and its solid form is heavier than its liquid form.

Water obeys this rule faithfully as a gas. As a liquid, it obeys this law for 96 per cent of the way down the temperature range to its freezing point. But at 39 degrees Fahrenheit (3.98 degrees Centigrade) something strange occurs. As cooling continues the water begins to expand and becomes less dense. As it freezes into a solid at 32 degrees Fahrenheit (zero degrees Centigrade), it becomes still lighter, gaining about 9 per cent volume!

What does this mean? If water behaved like other liquids in freezing, ice would be heavier than water, and sink to the bottom and gradually build up. Lakes and Arctic seas which now are only superficially covered with ice would be frozen solid. The world's water supply would to a large extent become unusable for plants, animals and man.

The earth's climate, also, would be drastically affected. Since the world's climate is moderated by the ability of liquid water to absorb and store heat from the sun and to release it slowly, in such an ice-bound world the daily temperature would fluctuate hundreds of degrees and seasonal variations in temperature would be even more radical.

Are the peculiar properties of water a mere "accident"? Is the lopsided triangular shape of the water molecule, so vital for life, a product of blind chance?

The Moon, Tides, and Seasons

The tides of the oceans are principally due to the influence of the gravitational force of the moon. If our moon were only 50,000 miles from the earth, instead of approximately 240,000, the ocean tides would be enormous. They would roll over the continents twice a day with devastating effect. Mountains would be torn away under their relentless power! Life would be extremely hazardous, if not impossible.

Why is the moon at the proper distance from the earth so the tides are not damaging to life? Was this another "accident"?

Another factor indicating that the earth was *designed* for life is the tilt of the axis at 23½ degrees. If the earth rotated perpendicular to the plane of its orbit, with no tilt to its axis, there would be no seasonal changes in the weather. Weather patterns for the earth would be monotonously regular day after day. If such were the case, moist air from the equatorial regions would rise, and move toward the Arctic and Antarctic. The water vapor would fall as snow creating enormous continents of snow and ice.

Was this unique tilt of the earth's axis just happenstance?

Earth's Rotation

Consider another unique feature. The earth turns on its axis 1000 miles per hour at the equator. Since the circumference of the equator is 24,000 miles, this gives us a 24-hour day. If the earth rotated at the speed Venus does, each day and each night would be 121 days or 2904 hours long. During the day, the sun's rays would cause temperatures to climb drastically. At night, temperatures would drop to far below zero. What chance would there be for life?

None!

But if the earth rotated at the same angular speed Jupiter does, the day would be only 10 hours long. The earth's atmosphere would be exceedingly violent. Atmospheric storms would rage; oceans would be perpetually angry, hurling themselves against the continents. Can you imagine what living in the vortex of such violence and turbulence would be like? But the earth day is perfectly designed to make life possible—and enjoyable, too.[12]

Perfect Design

Our earth is in all respects perfectly designed for the habitation of life! It is a perfect spaceship equipped with all the essential life-support systems. It is perfectly constructed. It is rotating at just the right velocity. It is in orbit at just the right distance from the sun.

The odds against the chance evolution of such a perfectly designed planet are incalculable.

Do you think it is logical to believe Apollo 17—including the Saturn V rocket, the command ship, and the lunar module, with all systems and equipment—just evolved from the random collision of stray molecules? How much less sense does it make to believe that spaceship earth evolved!

Dr. Kirtley F. Mather, Professor Emeritus of Geology at Harvard University, has said: "We live in a universe, not of chance or caprice, but of law and order." He added, "The administration (of the universe) has certainly not been functioning in a blindly mechanical manner. Instead, it has proceeded in much the same way as would an intelligent, persevering and purposeful person."[13]

Dr. Edward W. Sinnott, Dean Emeritus of the Yale Graduate School, asserted: "If the universe were not an orderly and dependable place, science would be meaningless, for science is simply a persistent attempt to discover underlying regularities among the complex events in nature. The more we learn about these events, the more certain it becomes that they do not occur at random, but they follow definite laws."[14]

Asserted Dr. P. Dirac, professor of mathematics of the University of Cambridge: "It seems to be one of the fundamental features of nature that fundamental physical laws are described in terms of a mathematical theory of great beauty and power, needing quite a high standard of mathematics for one to understand it. . . . One could perhaps describe the situation by saying that God is a mathematician of a very high order, and He used very advanced mathematics in constructing the universe."

There is evidence of design throughout the universe. Everywhere in the cosmos we can behond the handiwork of a Supreme Architect or Designer. The earth and its atmosphere and seas, and its relationship to the sun and moon, is evidence of design.

From the splendor of a sunset to the beauty of the Oregon coast—there is evidence of the hand of God, the Master Builder. From the awesome majesty of the atmosphere to the fragile loveliness of a Chrysler Imperial rose we see the handiwork of God.

Wherever we look, we find the earth was designed to support life.

The existence of design in the earth is clear evidence of the existence of the original Designer. How could it be otherwise?

The solar system—beautiful, mysterious, majestic—no theory yet devised by man can account fully for all the properties of this arrangement of sun, planets, comets, moons and asteroids.

Who spread its canopy? Or curtains
spun?
Who in this bowling alley bowled the
sun?

Edward Taylor, *Poetical Works*

Chapter Twenty Three

The Majestic Universe

Thus far in this book, we have explored the mystery of life and its intriguing origin on this planet.

We have delved into the mysteries surrounding the living cell and the miracle of self-replication and reproduction. We have searched through the tantalizing corridors of the human mind, and the marvels of the brain.

As human beings, with the ability to think, reason, analyze, and wonder, as "curious" homo sapiens, then, let's now explore in our mind's eye the realm of the interstellar cosmos.

The incredible marvels of the universe around us stand as unimpeachable witnesses of the existence of a Creator God.

Let's take an imaginary "trip" through the universe, aboard the starship *Intrepid*, and behold the wonders of the universe. For the sake of our journey, let's imagine that our starship is capable of achieving velocities many times the speed of light.

We begin with our own neighbors in space.

Our Solar System

The solar system consists of one star, nine planets, thirty-two moons, about 100,000 asteroids circling the sun, most of them between the orbits of Mars and Jupiter, and another 100 billion or so comets, fleeting like fiery darts in and out of the planetary solar system, mere "ships passing in the night."

On our trip through the solar system, we first come to Mercury, the speediest planet. Mercury circles the sun once every 88 days, coming within 28 million miles of the sun at the closest point. A small planet with no atmosphere, Mercury is unbearably hot, so we pass on to the next planet.

Venus, almost the size of the earth, orbits the sun once every 224 days. Strangely, its day is as long as 243 earth days, and it rotates backwards in comparison to the other planets! Astronomers are at a loss to explain why. We are intrigued by the gaseous, thick atmosphere of Venus—but this planet is also as hot as an oven, so we pass on to Mars.

Mars, roughly 140 million miles from the sun, has a year of 687 days; it is one tenth the mass of the earth, but its day is just one half hour longer than an earth day. Mars, we notice as we fly by, is pocked with craters, has little atmosphere, and no signs of life.

Jupiter, the giant planet plowing through space 482 million miles from the sun, is our next stop-over. We are awestruck as we approach it. Swathed with an atmosphere hundreds of miles high, Jupiter is a great puzzle to astronomers. Its density, only one fourth of that of the earth, is belied by its enormous volume, 1,300 times that of the earth. Instead of solid rock and metals, Jupiter appears to be composed of mainly hydrogen, ammonia, helium, and methane. In its atmosphere hovers a huge red spot bigger than the earth in circumference. Some have wondered if Jupiter isn't really a young "star" struggling to be born!

Next on our journey is Saturn. Saturn, of course, is most famous for its mysterious rings, beginning about 6,000 miles from the planet's surface and extending to 48,000 miles. Saturn is 95 times the mass of the earth and has a day of only 10 hours duration; living there would be quite an experience for some would-be astronaut of the future!

One of Saturn's moons, Titan, is the size of the planet Mercury and has its own atmosphere—poisonous methane gas. The outermost satellite, Phoebe, is remarkable for another reason—it is one of six moons in the solar system which revolve in a direction opposite to the rotational direction of the planet they orbit. The cause of this retrograde motion is again unknown.

Since we still have much territory to traverse, and many miles to go, we continue our journey.

Out beyond Saturn we fly by the planets Uranus, Neptune, and tiny Pluto. Uranus requires 84 earth years to orbit the sun, and Neptune—about 2.8 billion miles from the sun—goes around the sun once in 166 years. Pluto, circling the sun once every 248 earth years, has a temperature about minus 370 degrees, Fahrenheit. All three of these planets, we note, are extremely cold and inhospitable to life.

Among the most interesting visitors to our solar system, sort of like wandering lost cousins, are the comets. On our journey, we pass close by Halley's comet. Named for Edmund Halley, a contemporary of Isaac Newton, Halley's comet returns to the sun about once every 75-76 years. The earliest record of its appearance was likely 467 B.C. It appeared during the year of the Norman conquest of England in 1066. Halley's comet has a retrograde motion around the sun, and goes out beyond the orbit of Neptune. It will return to the vicinity of the sun in 1986.

A rather unusual comet is Schwassmann-Wachmann 1 which has a nearly circular orbit, revolves around the sun once every 16 years. Occasionally it rapidly flares-up to an increase of 100 times normal brightness within less than a day.

Comets, composed of frozen material such as methane, ammonia, and water, also contain meteoric particles and dust. Generally, they have a nucleus no larger than one or two miles in diameter. The tails of comets may be gaseous, glowing with blue fluorescence and always opposite to the sun, or may be composed of dust, their radiance due to reflected sunlight. Some comets have tails consisting of meteoric particles which are released from the comet nucleus when the sun's heat melts the ice binding them together. The meteoric particles become scattered in the wake of the comet, along its orbit, as meteor streams.

Apparently, on June 30, 1908, a comet plunged into the Siberian wastes along the Tunguska River, impacting with a tremendous explosion that knocked people down over 100 miles away. The pressure of the blast affected barometers in

England. Sunsets over northern Europe were particularly beautiful for the next week, due to the dust which wafted into the upper reaches of the atmosphere. The fact that the explosion must have been a comet was not discovered until 1960 when a thorough investigation was undertaken, chaired by Vassily Fesenkov of the Soviet Academy of Sciences. He guessed the diameter of the comet at several miles and its weight at a million tons.

As we continue our journey, we pause to consider one feature of the solar system which no theory has explained: "Bode's Law." This observation deals with the distances of the planets from the sun. There seems to be a general rule—a mathematical relationship—between the orbits of most of the planets. If you write the numbers 0, 3, 6, 12, 24, 48, 96, 192, 384, and 768, add 4 to each number and divide by 10, the resultant numbers will be in relation to each other very close to the actual distance of the planets from the sun, including the asteroid belt between Mars and Jupiter. Neptune is the only exception to Bode's Law. But how can this relationship be explained?

Fritz Kahn states, ". . .it is difficult to see how it could be ascribed to chance. To think of it as an accident, as many astronomers do, is much like believing that a stuffed and properly labeled cockatoo in the British Museum flew there from Africa, hopped in through the window of the Tropical Birds Hall and alighted on a branch where the plaque had already been placed."[1]

We meditate on Bode's Law and muse: Could this be more evidence of the *design* of the universe by a Creator God?

The Milky Way

But our solar system is merely a tiny fraction of a larger celestial system known as the "Milky Way"—a galaxy of stars, 100,000 light-years across, with an estimated 100 billion starry children, like our sun. We rev up our starship to top speed and quickly flash outside the Milky Way to see it from a considerable distance.

The Milky Way galaxy, we note with fascination, is like a brilliant, sparkling pin wheel in space, with a central "hub" of stars 10,000 light years across.

We also notice flying through space as distant companions of the Milky Way are many other stars and star clusters.

About five hundred galactic clusters are located in our part of the Milky Way galaxy, ranging from about 24 stars to a thousand. These are also called open clusters because they are loosely put together. On the other hand, the globular clusters, consisting of spheroid groups of tens of thousands of stars, are much larger and compact. About 120 are in our vicinity of the galaxy.

One of these is the Hercules cluster, and we decide to fly through it. The striking Hercules cluster, an estimated 34,000 light years from earth, is estimated to contain more than 500,000 individual stars, most of them within its "core"—a scant 30 light years across. There are 10,000 times as many stars in the core of this fantastic cluster as in any comparable part of the sky probed by man's telescopes.

This breathtaking arrangement of stars is a marvelous celestial pendant hanging suspended in space.

Writes Fritz Kahn about globular clusters: "The similarity of globular clusters and crystals gives us a feeling of the unity of the universe, but we are completely at a loss to explain why stars form mathematically perfect globular groups, why these groups are found around galaxies everywhere, all of the same size and the same brilliance. Only on the wings of imagination can we fly toward these solitary worlds to learn how a man on a planet in the center of a globular cluster feels, beneath a sky filled with thousands of suns, one as bright as the other, sparkling like diamonds."[2]

Living on such a world would be an awesome experience. The Hercules cluster is estimated to have about half a million sparkling members in attendance. The stars in the central region are about 200 billion miles apart. A person living on a planet in the region would see a night sky a hundred times as star-spangled and glorious as the earth's night sky! The brightest stars would shine as brilliantly as our own moon!

The Family of Stars

We decide to visit several major stars on our trip. We quickly observe that stars come in many sizes, densities and brilliances.

There are double stars, or binaries, revolving around each other. We by-pass three-star combinations, four-star groupings, and so on. We circle big stars and zoom past little stars, hot stars, and cool stars.

The most massive, brilliant stars, known as "0" stars, are hot and blue, ranging up to 90,000 degrees in surface temperature. The coolest stars, called red giants, are from 6,000 to 3,000 degrees F. on the surface. Our sun, a yellow star, falls in the middling range between both extremes.

We decide to visit the blue supergiant Rigel in the constellation Orion. As we draw near, we notice it is consuming energy at the rate of 40,000 of our suns. Next we inspect the red supergiant Betelgeuse (sometimes referred to as "Beetle juice")—also in Orion. It is the ninth brightest star in the sky. Its surface is half as hot as the sun's, but Betelgeuse oddly equals 800 suns in diameter and 12,000 in brightness!

White dwarf stars, thought to be the remains of aged massive stars, are dim and small but incredibly compact, concentrated mass. Some white dwarfs contain as much mass as the sun, but are the size of Mercury! If a chunk of such "star stuff" were put on a scale on the earth, it would weigh in at 20 tons *per cubic inch!*

Beyond the Milky Way

But now it is time to continue our journey. Our next destination—the great galaxy in Andromeda, about two million light years away. Andromeda is a sister galaxy to our own Milky

Way. The galaxy in Andromeda, catalogued as Messier 31, in honor of Charles Messier, 18th century astronmer, is a veritable "island universe," a spiral galaxy shaped like an elongated pinwheel, with spiral arms or spokes, and a central hub, with a "halo" of star clusters about.

As we continue flashing through the far reaches of space, we encounter galaxies of all sizes, shapes and orientation. Eighty percent of them appear to be spectacular spiral galaxies, seventeen percent are elliptical, and three percent "irregular." The spirals look like celestial whirlpools, whereas irregular galaxies appear as ill-defined clouds with no clear-cut structure.

Mysteries of the Universe

As we continue our journey, we review some history. We read that in August 1967, Susan Jocelyn Bell noticed an intriguing and unusual wiggly line—the record of radio waves detected coming from outer space. Further investigation revealed that the strange marks were actually caused by "pulses of energy and were *incredibly regular*!"

This fact burst on the scientific world of the time like a bombshell. The pulses came at the rate of one every 1.3730113 seconds. The strange pulses rivaled in precision the best clocks on earth!

Applying scientific rules to the pulsating objects in outer space, scientists concluded that the pulses of energy came from pulsating stars which were very small—about midway in size between the earth and the moon. The first such "pulsar" was estimated to be 420 light years from the earth (about 2,500 trillion miles).

How could objects in outer space possibly pulsate with such precision? Our next destination—to visit one of these amazing pulsars.

As we approach one, we discover that it appears to be composed of dense neutrons, remnants of some stellar explosion. The pulsar is a "neutron star," consists of a mass of neutrons crammed together by gravity and weighing 10 billion tons per cubic inch! It is spinning rapidly, and sends bursts of radiation at each revolution, accounting for the pulses of energy regularly reaching earth.

The final size of a neutron star would be from one to ten miles diameter. Gravitational energy would raise the temperature to many millions of degrees, but the mile thick crust of the neutron star is an incredibly solid and rigid crystalline material 10^{15} times stiffer than steel.

Density of a neutron star is a "million billion times the density of water," writes Kenneth Weaver. "A teaspoon of neutron star material would weigh a billion tons"—the equivalent of 200 million elephants.[3]

If the entire earth were collapsed to the same density, its diameter would shrink from 8,000 miles to 328 feet! Such is the estimate of radio astronomer Frank Drake of Cornell University. On the other hand, Dr. Malvin Ruderman of Columbia says, "If you took all the human beings in the world and put them in one raindrop, you would have such density."[4]

Gravity on a neutron star would be one hundred billion times as strong as earth's gravity. If a quake occurred on such a star, which scientists believe they have detected, and the rigid crust cracked and the star shrunk a half an inch, the released energy of the "glitch" would equal the light of the sun for an entire earth year.

These fantastic celestial timepieces appear to be slowing down in rotation ever so slightly. As neutron stars use up energy, they slow down about 1 in 2,500 parts in a year. Today, over a hundred pulsars, or neutron stars, have been discovered.

Says astronomer Carl Sagan of this object:

> It is, in truth, a giant atomic nucleus a mile across. Neutron star matter is so dense that a speck of it—just barely visible—would weigh a million tons. The earth would not be able to support it. A piece of neutron star matter, if it could be transported to the earth without falling apart, would sink effortlessly through the crust, mantle and core of our planet like a razor blade through warm butter.[5]

As we continue our journey through space, we come to another remarkable object.

The Mystery of Quasars

Radio astronomy, born in the early 1950s, led to the detection of the first queer objects in the heavens, quasars. These brilliant starlike objects also broadcast radio waves. More than 250 of them have been catalogued, even as their nature has remained an ineluctible mystery.

Now Dr. James Gunn and J.B. Oke at the Hale Observatory in Pasadena have announced that quasars are really the exploding nucleus of distant galaxies. Using a specially designed disk to block out the fiery center of a quasar, they studied its diffuse halo and found that a quasar's corona came from a vast number of stars belonging to a galaxy which is in the process of evolving.

Dr. Gunn suggests that a quasar may be born as the result of a collision and combination of matter at the center of a spherical galaxy. It can be rekindled again, and reborn, after burning down, when more matter collides which it at the galactic center.

The new study also indicates that quasars are far more distant from earth than formerly believed. The quasar BL Lacertae is apparently a billion light years away.[6]

This finding indicates that some quasars are part and parcel of normal galaxies. Oke and Gunn concluded that BL Lacertae is perhaps only one light year in diameter, while the surrounding galaxy is over 100,000 light years across. Recognizing that extremely violent explosions must be occurring to generate the light and radiation that comes from the quasar, the Caltech scientists admitted the exact mechanism is still unclear. They suggested that material falling in toward the center could be producing the explosions. The brilliant light coming from a quasar could be due to electrons ejected from the object at extremely great speeds and spinning around strong magnetic fields—but what forces generate those fields and speeds is as unclear today as it was ten years ago when quasars were first discovered.

The most remote known object in the universe, and the oldest, is quasar OQ 172 discovered in 1973. This object plunges into space at 91 percent of the speed of light. It is an estimated ten billion light-years away from the earth.

Some of these intriguing objects produce as much energy as a hundred large galaxies totaling ten trillion stars. "In one second a typical quasar throws out enough energy to supply all earth's electrical needs for billions of years," writes Kenneth Weaver.

How can such stupendous amounts of energy be explained? Some scientists suggest massive gravitational collapse is the answer; others suggest that the energy results from the annihilation caused by the collision of matter and antimatter.

Theoretically, it is possible that such massive energy explosions themselves could account for the "red shift"* which otherwise would indicate the quasars are at cosmological distances. Maarten Schmidt thinks of the quasar as the brilliant central core of a much larger object, perhaps the nucleus of a galaxy about to be born.

First detected in 1960 by radio astronomers, these unfamiliar objects seemed to have very small dimensions and yet were sources of great radio and optical power output. Furthermore, a study of their "redshifts" seemed to indicate that they are very far away—some of them on the outskirts of the known or imagined universe!

One starlike quasar, estimated to be close to us, is probably from 1.5 to 2 billion light years away, but is a thousand times brighter than an entire galaxy would be at that distance. Another, 3C9, has a redshift of 0.8 times the velocity of light and would appear to be about as far away from earth as any known object.

---

*Most astronomers believe that since light waves travel through space, if the light from an object shifts toward the red end of the spectrum, that object must be receding. Although the speed of light does not depend on the speed of that light source, the *wavelength* of light does. This is known as the Doppler effect. The red shift is proportional to the speed of the source. If this speed is doubled, the red shift is doubled. A mundane example of this would be the change in pitch of a train whistle as it approaches you and then passes by on down the track.

Astronomers are still baffled by the nature of quasars. Arizona astronomers R.F. Carswell and P.A. Strittmater of Steward Observatory, have found a quasar travelling away from us at 177,000 miles per second, or 90 percent of the speed of light. The quasar, called OH471, has an unprecedented redshift of 3.5 units; since according to the theory, the greater the redshift the faster an object is moving, and since the fastest objects seem to be the most distant, this discovery lends support to the idea that the universe was created at one instant of time by a tremendous explosion of a central core of matter. Since that original "big bang," the universe has been continually expanding, and the objects moving outwards at the greatest speed must be on the very edges of the universe.

Some astronomers believe those quasars almost 10 billion light years away and approaching the speed of light provide evidence that the universe was created in a huge explosion about 10 billion years ago.

Rim of the Universe

Our journey aboard the *Intrepid*, to view the most distant quasars from close range, means we must travel about 10 billion light years. Since our spaceship is purely imaginary anyway, there is no reason we cannot attain a speed of infinity and be there right now!

This, of course, brings us to the apparent "edge" of the expanding universe!

When we reach that point, we check our files and find a report by Dr. John D. Kraus, director of Ohio State University's radio observatory and Dr. Beverley June Harris, an Australian astronomer. Completing a five-year survey of 8,100 sources of continuous radio noise scattered throughout the universe, Dr. Kraus reported that the radio signals and sources seemed to drop off sharply at a distance of between 9 and 10 billion light years from earth.

"This survey," Dr. Kraus asserted, "shows that something is happening out there; there is a feature that could be called an edge, although it might be better to describe it as the horizon of the expanding universe."

But now—the final leg of our trip—holds an exciting mystery unparalleled in astronomy. We are going to visit a "black hole" in space!

Black Holes in Space

The existence of "black holes"—to use popular phraseology—in space was first postulated in 1939 by J. Robert Oppenheimer and Hartland Snyder.

What do physicists mean by a "black hole" in space? They explain it this way: When a star consumes all its nuclear fuel, gravity causes it to contract and become compressed. As the star shrinks its inner gravitation attraction increases at a rate of two percent for every one percent of contraction. As the atoms of the star are pulled inward and crushed together the gravitational force of the star enormously increases.

Theoretically, when a star of huge mass exhausts its nuclear fuel the whole star will collapse due to the pressure of gravity. The star would no longer radiate light, thus appearing as a "black hole" in space!

One such black hole appears to be Cygnus X-1, a source of X rays discovered in the constellation Cygnus. A tiny orbiting space satellite, Explorer 47, picked up signals from deep within our own galaxy. As astronomers deciphered the data, they were astonished. An object smaller than the earth seemed to be exuding energy 1,000 times as powerful as the sun. It doubles its energy output within a tenth of a second and suddenly reduces it again.

Two independent teams of University of California astronomers have reported what they consider decisive evidence proving that "black holes" in space do exist.

In the Astrophysical Journal, the scientists reported finding compelling evidence for the presence of a black hole in the Cygnus X-1 binary star system.

Cygnus X-1 is a binary system within our own galaxy, one of its stars being a supergiant star called HDE 226868, the other an invisible and smaller companion. The companion star, in this case, is the black hole, the dense chunk remaining of a collapsed star that neither light nor radiation can escape from. The black hole appears to siphon off matter from the larger star, becomes agitated, and emits X rays.

Black holes in space would have an extremely smooth surface, astronomers believe—no gouges, craters, mountains, hills, valleys—smooth as a proverbial cue ball.

Theoretically, as gases are pulled toward a black hole, to be eternally trapped, they would compress, collide and become fiery hot, resulting in tremendous X rays.

Such intense X ray emission comes from Cygnus X-1, about 8,000 light years from the earth. The object is estimated to be three times or more the mass of the sun and revolves with a supergiant.

Dr. Kip Thorne of the California Institute of Technology says already one ten thousandth of the universe might have gone the way of black holes. Says he: "We would like to sweep this fact under the rug, but occasionally we drag it out and look it in the face and shudder."[8]

Such black holes may not be all that unusual, either. Princeton University physicist Remo Ruffini postulates that black holes may hide from view 90 percent of the matter of the universe. Ten miles from the black hole would be the "event horizon," the point of no return. All the matter of the black hole, however, would be concentrated at one point, and therefore would have an infinite density.

Clearly, modern astronomy has had its share of shocks. In fact, it appears to be in a state of continual shock! Whatever astronomers may predict, said Professor Philip Morrison, of the Massachusetts Institute of Technology, "the universe is incorrigibly otherwise."

But on our journey through space, we have come face to face with the deepest mysteries of the universe. We have seen, in our mind's eye, the awesome handiwork of the Creator God.

We have seen evidence of the glory of God.

We remember the words of the Psalmist of Israel: "The heavens tell out the glory of God, the vault of heaven reveals his handiwork. One day speaks to another, night with night shares its knowledge, and this without speech or language or sound of

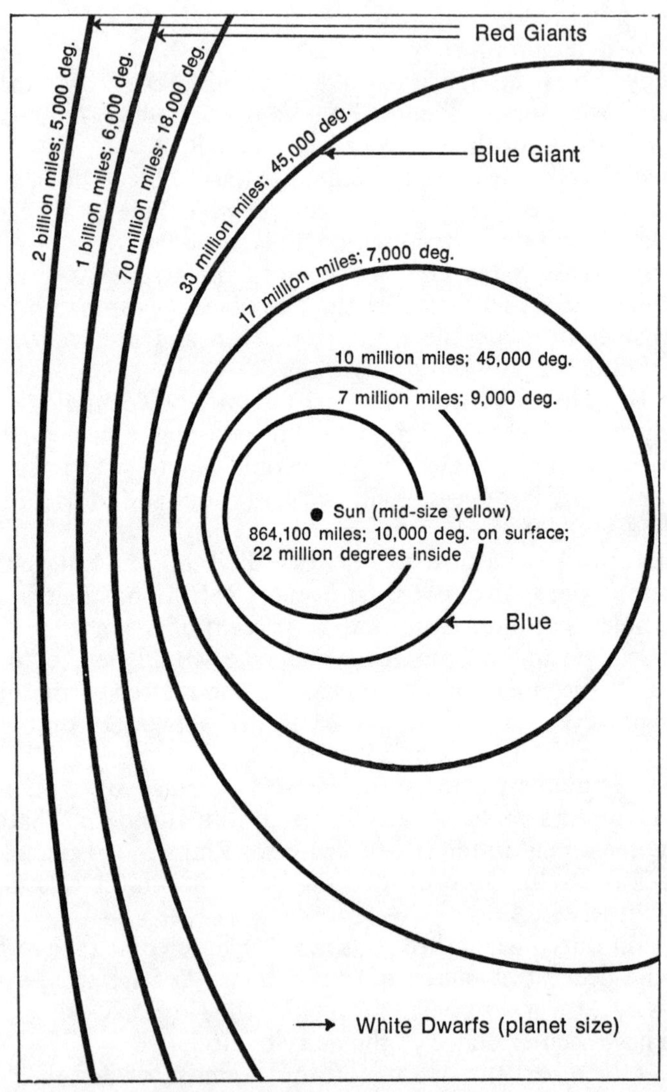

The incredible variation among the stars that inhabit our Milky Way galaxy, ranging from the planet size white dwarfs to the red supergiants, are depicted in this illustration by Andy Voth.

any voice. Their music goes out through all the earth, their words reach to the end of the world" (Psalm 19:1-4, *New English Bible*).

We open our Bible to the words of the prophet Isaiah: "Do you not know, have you not heard, were you not told long ago, have you not perceived ever since the world began, that God sits throned on the vaulted roof of earth, whose inhabitants are like grasshoppers? He stretches out the skies like a curtain, he spreads them out like a tent to live in; he reduces the great to nothing and makes all earth's princes less than nothing."

We read the words of God, quoted by the prophet: "To whom then will you liken me, whom set up as my equal? asks the Holy One. Lift up your eyes to the heavens; consider who created it all, led out their host one by one and called them all by their names; through his great might, his might and power, not one is missing" (Isaiah 40:21-26, *New English Bible*).

The heavens are a celestial tribute to the glory and power—and undeniable existence—of the Great Almighty Creator God!

By faith—by believing God—we know
that the world and the stars—in fact,
all things—were made at God's command;
and that they were all made from things
that can't be seen.

—Hebrews 11:3, *Living Bible*

Chapter Twenty Four

When Was "The Beginning"?

When did the universe begin?

Most astronomers admit that not much is known about the origin of the universe. Each of the major theories advanced has knotty, unsolvable problems. Because of these problems, as one scientist conceded, "It has taken nearly 40 years to get a hint of the answers."

The present state of knowledge of cosmology and cosmogony could be accurately described as almost completely "up in the air." There are a number of conflicting theories about the origin and fate of the universe. In an article which appeared in Reader's Digest, Earl Ubell cautioned: "But it should be remembered that no astronomer believes that *any current cosmology* adequately describes the universe. The theories are only *approximations*, too simple for the galactic complexities of space."

Dr. Philip Morrison of the Massachusetts Institute of Technology agrees. He asserted, "We have been *wrong too many times* in the past. We do not have enough measurements of distant galaxies to say ANYTHING *definite*. We're in the kindergarten state of cosmology."[1]

More recently, F.D. Kahn and H.P. Palmer in their book *Quasars* admitted: "We are almost completely ignorant about the early history of the universe."[2]

In the light of such admissions, we should be very cautious about assuming that any one theory is necessarily true.

The Big Bang

The most popular theory today to attempt to explain the origin of the universe is called the "Big Bang Theory." According to proponents of this belief, there once existed a huge primordial cloud composed of "matter". Atoms may have been nonexistent at this time. The cloud may have contained a "soup" of all the fundamental particles which exist within the atom. If you travelled backward in time, you would find the universe becoming hotter and denser. When the universe was about 100,000 years old, the background radiation had a temperature of 10,000° Kelvin. Earlier than this, the big bang theory implies, the universe was flooded with intense brilliant light, denser than matter. This was the "radiation era" of the early universe.

Further back still, you would come to a time when the universe was but one second old. At this ancient fireball stage, the temperature of the universe would have been 5,000,000,000 degrees Kelvin, the universe was filled with electrons, positrons, neutrinos, formed from the energetic photons of the high temperature radiation.

Still earlier, when the universe was only one ten thousandth of a second old, temperatures were thousands of times hotter still. The universe consisted mainly of strongly interacting particles and anti-particles. The ratio of the amounts of matter to anti-matter would have been one part in a billion.

As the universe expanded and cooled, matter and anti-matter annihilated each other, leaving a residue of ordinary matter. The energy released by this explosion and annihilation became the radiation of the radiation era, some of it surviving today as the 3° Kelvin background radiation detected in the universe in 1965. The residual matter became the present matter of the universe.

At the beginning of the radiation era, the universe was composed largely of photons, neutrinos, and a few protons, neutrons and electrons. Deuterium was formed by combinations of protons and neutrons, and about 25 percent of the mass of the universe was converted to helium, and 75 percent to hydrogen.

How the matter of this expanding universe then coagulated into galaxies is one of the "chief problems in cosmology." Most theories have invoked gravity as the cause.

Current theories suggest the first galaxies were born—or created—when the universe was about 10^8 years old, or 10^9 Figuring back by using the Hubble constant, we come to 10^{10} years, and the simplest big bang theories of the origin of the universe place the age of the universe slightly less than this figure. These series of results are consistent with a rational cosmology. They indicate that the structure of the universe originated and developed as a logical, ordered sequence of events.

As for galaxies themselves, this authority states: "At present, rapid progress is being made in the study of galactic structure and evolution, although a glance at the Atlas of Peculiar Galaxies (1966) by the U.S. astronomer Halton Arp reveals an amazing assortment of complex structures for which so far there is no explanation whatever."[3]

According to U.S. astronomers R. Bruce Partridge and Phillip J.E. Peebles, protogalaxies emerged from the radiation era with a density 1 percent greater than the average density in the universe. They expanded, but more slowly than the universe itself, and reached a size a few times their present radius, and then collapsed and attained their present size in a few hundred million years.

During this time, gas clouds within the protogalaxy became gravitationally bound and developed into globular clusters of stars. The first generation of what are called population II stars was also thus formed.

According to this theory, population I stars, such as our sun, developed later in the disk of a spiral galaxy, their arrival delayed due to turbulence, rotation, and the magnetic fields of the interstellar medium.

This model, however, does not explain the origin of galactic magnetic fields. Nor does it give a clue to the nature of galactic nuclei, or the phenomena of exploding galaxies, radio galaxies, and the existence of quasi-stellar objects, or quasars.

Birth of Stars

Where did stars first come from? As children, we all looked with awe into the night sky, and wondered.

Says the *Britannica*: "At present there is no general agreement concerning the formative stages of stars." It continues: "The protostellar or pre-main-sequence stages are by no means well understood. . . ."

The Soviet astronomer Viktor Amazaspovich Ambartsumian proposed in 1955 that stars formed from prestellar matter at high density in the early universe. But the more common theory is that stars form from the low-density interstellar medium. Available information suggests that stars have been forming for over 10,000,000,000 years and are still being born. Very luminous stars develop so rapidly that ages of only millions of years are possible for them. Adds the *Brittanica:*

> Stars apparently form in those regions where the interstellar medium is rich in gas and dust, and the presence of stars in these regions indicates that they are still young and have not had time to leave their birthplaces.[4]

Star formation itself is also obscure. The various stages are possibly: 1) the contraction of a cloud or region of enhanced density in the interstellar medium; 2) collapse of the cloud as gravitational forces become stronger; 3) eventual radiation failure to escape from the cloud causes temperatures to rise; the cloud becomes a cluster or protostars; 4) pressures inside the protostars build up to halt collapse, but contraction slowly continues; 5) a second stage of rapid collapse followed by slow contraction occurs; 6) central temperature in the contracting protostars rises to several million degrees Kelvin and fusion results; nuclear energy converts hydrogen into helium, causing the protostar to become an actual star, its candle now "lit" and shining brilliantly for the entire universe to behold.

Evidence tends to show that all the galaxies in any cluster are of about the same age. But how the raw material was gathered together originally, in appropriate quantities, is still a major unsolved problem.

Age of the Universe

Hubble's law implies a start to the expansion of the universe at a time on the order of 10,000,000,000 years ago. Totally different evidence suggests that the age of the Milky Way galaxy is of the same order.

The age of the earth's oldest surface rocks is estimated from the decay processes of radioactive elements they contain. Uranium and thorium decay slowly at a known rate. From measuring the abundance of the radioactive elements, and their decay products, radium and lead, and others, the age of the rocks can be determined. The oldest surface rocks have a calculated age of 3.5×10^9 years.

From the abundance of lead isotopes, it is estimated that the earth, the moon, and meteorites have an age of 4.7×10^9 years.

The age of the solar system is supposed to be no more than 5×10^9 years. From the chemical composition of stars of various ages, it is known that the heavy elements were produced mainly during the early history of our galaxy, between 7 to 8×10^9 years.

The determination of the age of the elements from the cosmic abundances depends on the theory of nucleogenesis in highly evolved stars and supernovae. The best estimates at the present time give an age of 6.2 to 7.7×10^9 years. Stars in globular clusters seem to be the oldest stars in the galaxy. For globular clusters, U.S. astronomer Allan R. Sandage finds an age of 10,000,000,000 years.

All this evidence, then, tends to point to the conclusion that the universe is very, very old.

The Universe and Entropy

But even if the universe is tremendously old, that fact would not provide evidence for the theory of evolution. Because the fact is, evolutionary theory runs counter to an established law of science.

One of the pivotal laws of physics is called the Second Law of Thermodynamics—or the law of entropy. This law states, briefly, "In a closed system, there is a tendency for organization to change into disorganization. . ."[5]

This tendency is called entropy. Rothman explains: "Every time we burn fuel for heat, every day that the stars shine and emit heat, *the universe runs downhill toward greater entropy.*"[6]

In simple language, this means that the universe—a "closed system"—is running down. The universe is irretrievably running out of usable energy. It is becoming more *dis*organized, *less* complex. Stars are burning out and "dying". Given enough time, the universe eventually will—according to the second law of thermodynamics—cease to function.

But what does this have to do with evolution?

Lincoln Barnett points out, "If the universe is running down and nature's processes are proceeding in just one direction, the inescapable inference is that everything had a beginning: somehow and sometime the cosmic processes were started. . .

"Most of the clues, moreover, that have been discovered at the inner and outer frontier of scientific cognition suggest a definite time of CREATION. . .

"Every theory rests ultimately on the prior assumption that something was already in existence."[7]

Entropy

Take a hot skillet off the stove, and gradually it will cool off. Take a hot poker from the fireplace, and gradually it will lose its heat. All things tend to radiate or absorb heat until the entire universe becomes an even, uniform temperature and all processes in the universe come to a halt. This is referred to as the "heat death" of the universe.

In other words, most of the energy processes in the universe are made possible only because there is such a tremendous range of temperature between the different objects, bodies, and particles in the universe. Flaming stars radiate their tremendous energy through all of known space.

Given enough time, all the stars would burn themselves out—just like millions of exhausted light bulbs. And when they "died," there would be nothing to "turn them on" again. Their energy would have been totally dissipated. It would have been irretrievably lost as useless heat energy into space.

What does all this really mean?

First of all, if all this physical energy existed for eternity, usable energy would have long since been totally dissipated—the universe would have long since run down aeons ago! Therefore, somewhere, at some particular time in the past—all this tremendous supply of usable energy had to come into existence. The Second Law of Thermodynamics clearly proves there has been no past eternity of organized matter and usable energy! Somehow, the universe had to be wound up like a gigantic clock, and set in motion.

Thus there had to be a distinct time when matter and energy were created. There had to be a time of creation. But—can your mind envision such an awesome creation. . . without an intelligent, super-powerful Creator? I think not.

Avoiding Theological Answers

An open-minded, honest inquiry of the origin of the universe brings us right back to a time of creation. And a magnificent creation logically demands a great Creator—an intelligent Being who designed the universe and who created intelligent life.

But many men don't want to face that reality. They wish to steer clear of any explanation that smacks of the theological or mystical.

In discussing the origin of the earth, one author declared: "As we must use something as a starting point and as we want to *avoid* stepping into the realm of theology and philosophy we shall use as our beginning, the time in the history of the earth when it may have consisted only of a gigantic turbulent cloud of gas with no particular shape and certainly no solid form."[8]

Thus the author side-steps the big problem of the earth's origin and begins with matter already in existence.

Evolutionist George Gaylord Simpson, after outlining a theory of evolution, admits the theory does "not yet answer all questions or plumb all mysteries. . . . It casts no light on the ultimate mystery—the origin of the universe and the source of the laws or physical properties of matter, energy, space, and time.

"*Nevertheless, once these properties are given*. . .," he continues, skirting the real issue (*This View of Life*, p. 21).

Astronomer Fred Hoyle also dismissed the questions concerning origin. He said: "There is an impulse to ask where originated material comes from. But such a question is entirely meaningless within the terms of reference of science. Why is there gravitation? Why do electric fields exist? Why is the Universe? These queries. . . are just as meaningless and unprofitable" (*Frontiers of Astronomy*, p. 342).

But are these questions really "meaningless and unprofitable"? Or don't they strike right at the heart of the issue?

"In The Beginning"–Hydrogen Gas?

Another theory, called the "steady state" theory, holds that creation is always going on in the universe. Old stars die, and new stars gradually form. Hydrogen gas is spontaneously "created" in space and continually forms into stars and galaxies, while old stars and galaxies disappear.

The Harvard astronomer Harlow Shapley put it this way: "*In the beginning* was the word, it was piously recorded, and I might venture that modern astrophysics suggests that the word was *hydrogen gas.*"[11]

In his book *View From a Distant Star*, Shapley wrote: "In the very beginning, we say, were hydrogen atoms. . . .

"Whence came these atoms of hydrogen. . . what preceded their appearance, if anything?

"That is perhaps a question for metaphysics. *The origin is beyond* astronomy. It is perhaps beyond philosophy, in the realm of the to us *Unknowable.*"[12]

Hydrogen is the most abundant element in the universe. To ignore the question of where it came from is actually to confess ignorance to the origin of the universe itself.

Where did this original matter come from?

English astronomer Fred Hoyle suggested: "It does not come from anywhere.

"Material appears—it is created. At one time the various atoms composing the material do not exist, and at a later time they do. This may seem like a very strange idea, and I agree that it is, but in science it does not matter how strange an idea may seem so long as it works. . ."[13]

The steady state theory has been abandoned by many astronomers. Most now regard it as dead. One of the significant nails in its coffin was driven home when astronomers Arno Penzias and Robert Wilson at the Bell Laboratories at Holmdel, New Jersey, detected just the kind of radiation that would exist in space at a temperature of 2.7 degrees Kelvin if a big bang had occurred some thirteen billion years or so ago. Says Kenneth Weaver, "The microwave background whisper found by Penzias and Wilson may be the dying echo of the big bang."[14]

Perhaps the greatest evidence in favor of the big bang theory of the origin of the universe comes from the observation of the expansion of the universe.

Astronomers, by studying the red shifts of receding galaxies, have determined that the galaxies are being spread out like a massive balloon. David Bergamini put it this way:

> No other explanation of the red shift has ever been lab-demonstrated. Moreover, relativity shows that the universe cannot remain static—unless forces beyond man's ken are at work in it.
>
> The universe, therefore, is undoubtedly expanding. And it is expanding uniformly. A galaxy one billion light-years away recedes half as fast as one two billion light-years away. In a given time every galaxy increases its distance from every other by the same percentage.[15]

Can this expansion be traced back to a single gargantuan explosion of a huge "atom"? Perhaps. Such a conclusion does not contradict the implications of the Biblical record.

But just where this mammoth atom could have come from is a mystery as great as the creation of the universe! For a single atom to be created from nothing is just as inconceivable as a universe being created!

Speaking very candidly, in a frank mood, the late English astrophysicist Arthur Eddington admitted, "The theory of the exploding universe is in some respects so *preposterous* that we naturally hesitate to commit ourselves to it. It contains elements apparently so incredible that I feel almost indignation that anyone should believe it—except myself."[16]

Overwhelming Ignorance

A college textbook on astronomy admits, "The problem of stellar evolution has never been satisfactorily solved. For half a century, theory has succeeded theory, and an account of the changes of thought would have the qualities of a kaleidoscope."[17]

Thus it should be clear that evolutionary theory has not yet relegated the concept of a Creator God to the junk pile of old, outworn, dilapidated antiques.

Man actually knows very little about the stars, or the planets, or even the earth. The problems and perplexities of the science of astronomy are so vast that one astronomer confessed, "We shall often find in astronomy that the most thoroughly observed phenomena present the most puzzles; the more we know, the less do we find that we understand."[18]

A world-famous astronomer, after spending a lifetime studying the mysteries of the Milky Way, confided with real candor, "Obviously the most interesting feature of this science, astronomy, is our eager ignorance."[19]

Origin of the Solar System

The same ignorance is found when it comes to understanding the origin of the solar system. The German philosopher Immanuel Kant in 1755 suggested that a nebula in slow rotation gradually pulled together by its own gravitational force, flattened into a spinning disk and gave rise to the sun and solar system.

In 1796, the French astronomer and mathematician Pierre-Simon Laplace proposed a similar model, but had the planets being formed before the sun.

In the late 19th century, British physicist James Clerk

Maxwell criticized these views, showing that if all the matter contained in the known planets had once been distributed around the sun in the form of a disk, the shearing forces of differential rotation would have prevented the condensation of individual planets. Also, the sun possessed less angular momentum than the theory required.

Subsequently, the collision theory gained vogue. For several decades most astronomers thought the planets were formed as a result of a close approach to the sun by another star. Even greater objections were raised against this theory, however, one being that there is no evidence that stars pass so close to one another in galaxies. The nearest star is 60,000 times as far away as Pluto. Thus this theory had to be interred as well.

Modern theories of the origin of the solar system prefer as their starting point a primeval mass of cold gas. There would be considerable turbulence in such a large mass, with currents forming and dying down and reforming. Eventually, this mass would break up into gas clouds or protoplanets. Eventually, the central mass would have become hot enough to radiate, and this radiation would have caused the planets to lose much of their mass into space by evaporation.

But no theory is satisfactory to explain the origin of our solar system. Says the 1974 *Encyclopedia Britannica:*

> It should be emphasized that no theory of the origin of the solar system has as yet won general acceptance. All involve highly improbable assumptions. But the difficulty is in trying to find a theory with any degree of probability at all.[20]

The origin of the planetary system is the oldest problem confronting astronomers, and remains unsolved. A satisfactory theory, yet to be proposed, must account for the fact that all the planetary orbits are almost circular and in the same plane; the planets all move around the sun in the same direction as the sun itself rotates; Venus rotates backwards to the direction of its revolution; planetary moons move in almost circular orbits, mostly in the same plane; moons have masses roughly one-thousandth of the planets, which in turn have masses roughly one thousandth of the sun; the fact that the four inner planets are small and dense, but the giant planets are large, of low density, and are farther from the sun; why the planets are placed at distances from the sun that conform to Bodes' law; and why the sun rotates slowly and has an angular momentum of only one half percent that of the planetary system.

Quite an imposing challenge!

Life in the Universe?

In 1970 amino acids were discovered in certain meteorites from outer space. Since then, Keith Kvenvolden of NASA's Ames Research Center and George U. Yuen of the University of Arizona have detected 17 varieties of fatty acids in two meteorites classed as carbonaceous chondrites.

Carbonaceous chondrites, which fall on earth probably from the asteroid belt between Jupiter and Mars, contain about 1 percent organic matter by mass, far too much to account for by terrestrial contamination. These meteorites suggest that the production of organic molecules occurred with great efficiency in the early history of the solar system.[21]

The compounds apparently formed billions of years ago when the sun and planets condensed from the swirling mass of gas and dust in the solar nebula, scientists conclude. Some of the compounds became incorporated into meteors which bombarded the earth long ago. Says Keith Kvenvolden, "the fatty acids in the tons of meteoric material may have contributed directly to the origin of life on earth."[22]

Is this possible?

Is life, as some say, an "inherent property" of the universe?

Clifford Matthews, professor of chemistry at the University of Illinois, says life is the "inevitable outcome of chemical reactions that are constantly taking place everywhere in the universe–in space and on planets in a process of universal evolution."

Is this true?

Are the basic atoms of life created in the furnaces of stars, and then combined on the planets to form the essential molecules? With hydrogen, oxygen, nitrogen, and carbon existing in the universe, is the chemical formation of proteins inevitable, and are millions of planets covered with proteins that lead to life?

What are the facts? Let's try to isolate facts from theory, and determine what has really been learned about the origin of life in the universe.

Primordial Life

University of Maryland laboratory studies have shown that thunder and violent sea waves pounding on ancient shores of the earth could have produced the organic materials, amino acids, which are the basic building blocks of life. But that is a long shot from producing life itself!

Ancient bacteria, between 10,000 and one million years old, discovered deep below the Antarctic ice cap, have been exposed to air and revived and began to grow. This shows that life has remarkable adaptability and incredible fortitude and strength. Could it have "evolved" by chance?

Granted that under certain conditions, the development of life may be favored by the chemistry of the elements from which life is formed. Granted, also, that chemicals that living cells use to store energy have been made out of simple chemicals thought to have existed in the earth's primitive atmosphere. Granted that the chemical building blocks of life, amino acids, can be synthesized by passing an electric shock through a mixture of methane, ammonia and water vapor, and that bits and pieces of nucleic acid can similarly be formed.

But what do all these fascinating facts really tell us about the origin of life? That it mindlessly, blindly evolved due to inherent residual forces and properties?

Has life evolved on millions of planets similar to the earth throughout the cosmos?

Astronomers have discovered more than two dozen organic molecules in the clouds of interstellar space. They theorize that these molecules could be formed in a solar nebula. According to Gustav Arrhenius of the University of California at San Diego, the earth might have coalesced out of a solar nebula, forming from bits of matter that could have been contaminated by organic substances to begin with.

Rather than illustrate mindless evolution, these discoveries, I believe, reveal a glimpse into the possible methods God, the Creator, used to first create life. It makes sense that God designed the universe to be life supporting. He designed stars to provide the energy that living things need. He designed them to go through a life cycle, as it were, to facilitate the origin and development of life. He designed laws of physics and chemistry to permit the necessary and proper nuclear reactions, and the proper configurations of molecules. As Carl Sagan writes in *The Cosmic Connection*, "We live in a universe remarkably hospitable to life."[23]

God designed the universe so that the initial chemical constituents for life are the most abundant molecules in the universe. As Sagan puts it:

> There is an intimate connection between stars and life. Our planet was formed from the dregs of starstuff. The atoms were cooked in the interiors of red giant stars. These atoms were forced together, to form complex organic molecules, by ultraviolet light and thunder and lightning, all produced by the radiation of our neighboring Sun.[24]

Vital for life, and life processes, are the products of stellar manufacturing plants. Stars don't merely shine brightly, to be enjoyed by man. They are in effect huge manufacturing plants, or assembly lines, as it were–factories that produce the elements ranging from helium to iron, as starstuff is consumed in the star's furnace. Elements heavier than iron are produced in stellar explosions, even as some of these elements are synthesized in nuclear explosions on earth.

Even the death of stars is vital for life. The spectacular death throes of stars slightly more massive than our sun are called supernovaes. In a period of a few weeks to a few months, an exploding star may become brighter than an entire galaxy. During the explosion of a supernova, elements like gold and uranium are generated from iron.

Thus life is inexorably interconnected with the working of fine tuned stars, including our own special sun. From birth to death, stars are servants of life, providing energy and material upon which life depends.

As Kenneth F. Weaver writes in *National Geographic*:

> It may come as a shock to learn that nearly all the atoms in your body and in the earth were once part of a star that exploded and disintegrated.[25]

Our own sun, astronomers believe, was spawned by a gigantic swirling nebula of gas and dust. As the particles were pulled together by gravity, perhaps five billion years ago, they heated up. Within a few million years, temperatures in the interior of the coagulated ball rose to millions of degrees, igniting the nuclear fusion "fire" of the sun. In the fusion process, hydrogen atoms fused to become helium atoms, liberating massive amounts of energy in the process. The sun began to shine. And in this manner, science tells us, "God created light." And that light is necessary for life!

If astronomical theory is correct, then our sun will probably continue burning pretty much as it does now, for another five billion years. Then it will grow larger and become reddish in hue. Eventually it will turn into a "red giant," expanding one hundred times in diameter and filling a quarter of the sky, and increasing a thousand times in brightness. It will very likely melt Mercury and Venus to mere blobs, and bake the earth at temperatures that would melt lead, boiling away the oceans.

But without the past history and present performance of the sun life on earth could not exist.

Was this universe—so remarkably suited for life—a stupendous cosmic accident? Can your mind believe that? I doubt it—and neither can mine!

Yet, many scientists today accept evolution as a logical, rational theory—and dismiss the idea of God.

Why?

The answer in part is giving by Fritz Kahn: "We are today under the spell of the evolutionary thinking begun 150 years ago by Kant and Laplace in astronomy, by Thomas Vuckle and

Herder in history, by Buffon, Lamarck and Darwin in biology."

He added, with astonishing insight, "We the children of those generations automatically think in terms of evolution, assume that everything had a beginning, and that this beginning was 'chaos.' "

This same author then confessed, with honest realism: "The question now arises as to whether astronomical problems can be solved by evolutionary trains of thought"[26]

Many other scientists have reached the same conclusion.

Bigger Than Science

Dr. Jesse L. Greenstein, astrophysicist at the California Institute of Technology, was quoted in an article in the *Los Angeles Times*: "It is a terrible mystery how matter comes out of nothing." He asked, "Could it have been *something outside science?*" And then confessed, "We try to stay out of philosophy and theology, but sometimes we are forced to think in bigger terms, to go back to something outside science."

In a remarkable statement, Harlow Shapley of Harvard said we know something about the structure and operation of the universe, "But when it comes to 'why' we're stuck. All we can say is 'God only knows.' And the information is classified."

He continued, "Science has found the basic hydrogen atom, but *who made the hydrogen atom?* Science comes up against some things which are unanswerable as yet."

Dr. Werner von Braun, one of America's top space and rocketry experts, former director of the National Aeronautics and Space Administration's Marshall Space Flight Center at Huntsville, Alabama, declared:

> In our modern world, many people seem to feel that our rapid advances in the field of science render such things as religious belief untimely or oldfashioned. . . .
>
> The simple answer to this contention is that we are confronted with many more mysteries of nature today than when the age of scientific enlightenment began. For with every new answer unfolded, science has consistently discovered at least three new questions.
>
> Thus there is certainly no scientific reason why God cannot

> retain the same position in our modern world that He held before we *began proving His creation* with telescope and cyclotron.
>
> Religion and science are compatible. The unveiling of more and more of nature's mysteries does not create conflict with our religious recognition of the eternal beauty and order of God's creation.

Dr. Von Braun believes in the existence of a Creator. He asserted: "Anything as well ordered and perfectly created as is our earth and universe must have a Maker, a Master Designer. Anything so orderly, so perfect, so precisely balanced, so majestic as this creation can only be the product of a Divine Idea.

"There must be a Maker; there can be no other way."

Chapter Twenty Five

The Baffling Atom

Simple logic tells us that in order to have matter it is clear that there must be a Creator.

For example, you cannot have a blueprint for the construction of a house or a building unless somebody draws up that blueprint. Generally, the one who draws up such a sketch, or "plans," or a "blueprint" is an *architect.* And the person who builds a new aircraft or automobile is called a manufacturer. But the point is: In order to have a product, you must have an architect, and a builder!

Is the universe itself designed? Does matter exhibit the workmanship of an original "architect"? What are the building blocks of matter?

Let's take a look at matter, and hear its intriguing story.

What Is Matter?

Matter has been commonly defined as that which occupies space and has weight. It has a certain "mass" or substance to it. Gases, like oxygen, are composed of matter. The air itself is composed of matter.

But what is "matter"?

The ancient Greek philosophers Leucippus and Democritus proposed the atomic theory in the 5th century B.C. They speculated that all things can be accounted for by innumerable combinations of hard, small, indivisible particles of various sizes but of the same basic material, called "atoms." The Greek word *atomos* means "undivided," and therefore structureless.

This theory suffered a decline in interest during the Medieval period, but was revived in the 17th Century by such luminaries as Newton, Galileo, Robert Boyle, Robert Hooke and Christian Huygens. In the early 19th Century the English chemist John Dalton postulated that all atoms of a given element are identical, they are different from atoms of any other element and that chemical reactions are merely a rearrangement of atoms.

In 1869 the Russian chemist Dmitry Mendeleyev discovered that if the elements were listed in the order of increasing atomic weight, there was a striking and extensive regularity involving the periodic reoccurrence of similar sequences of elements. Thus the sequence of lithium, beryllium, boron, carbon, nitrogen, oxygen, fluorine runs from the reactive element lithium, which forms positive ions, to the highly active element fluorine which forms negative ions. The next sequence of seven elements–sodium, magnesium, aluminum, silicon, phosphorus, sulfur and chlorine displays the same variation of properties as the first, and each member of it is chemically quite similar to the corresponding member of the preceding seven. By careful observation of this sequence throughout the periodic table of elements, Mendeleyev was able to predict the existence and properties of several elements unknown at that time, including gallium, scandium, and germanium, which were discovered in 1875, 1879 and 1886 respectively.

But what is this "matter"–the "stuff" which comprises a typewriter, a desk, or even a piece of paper–composed of? For thousands of years, no one was able to answer this enigmatic question definitely.

But in the 20th Century science has begun to unravel the answer. Experiments in physics and chemistry revealed that "matter" is composed of little particles called atoms.

But even atoms are composed of infinitesimal particles which are neutral or which have positive or negative electric charge. And scientists today are amazed by the behavior of these sub-atomic particles as they are studied in the high-speed particle accelerators, such as the cyclotron at the University of California's Lawrence Radiation Laboratory.*

The tiny little atom unlocks one of the major evidences of God.

The Baffling Atom

About ninety different atomic elements occur in nature and another twenty have been artificially produced. Atoms are so incredibly small that a teaspoonful of water contains about 500,000,000,000,000,000,000,000 (or 5×10^{23}) atoms. Yet atoms are the very building blocks of the entire universe!

Atomic research has revealed that atoms are, in part, comparable to tiny "solar systems."

About 99.95 percent of an atom's mass is in its nucleus, composed of positively charged protons and perhaps neutral neutrons, orbited by fleeting negatively charged particles called electrons. Loosely bound outer electrons play an essential role in what is called chemical behavior, in the binding together of two or more atoms to form a molecule of a compound.

One typical picture of an atom is the "planetary" or "orbital" model of atomic structure. Other models picture the electrons as clouds rather than orbiting particles. Strangely, if all the properties known about atoms and their components are considered, it is not possible to combine them all into a pictorial representation of the atom. Any pictures we see of atoms are really only approximations or caricatures, overemphasizing some characteristics and suppressing others.

As more information was learned about the atom, it became necessary to consider angular momentum of electrons in their orbits, and further experimentation led to the postulate that electrons also "spin" as they revolve around an atomic nucleus,

---

*What scientists have achieved is remarkable. Using high-energy particle accelerators, they have created matter out of pure energy. Scientists, of course, have also done the reverse—created pure energy out of matter—as illustrated by the awesome power of the atomic and hydrogen bombs. In effect, therefore, matter may be considered as "frozen" energy.

and that electrons tend to orbit in "shells" or groups of orbits all similar in their spatial configurations and not too widely separated in energy.

But further research led the French physicist Louis-Victor de Broglie in 1923 to propose that particles possess wave properties, a bold and imaginative proposal. Meanwhile, Heisenberg and the German physicists Max Born and Pascual Jordan further developed atomic theory, and Heisenberg contributed the "uncertainty principle" named after him. This principle states that it is inherently impossible to determine simultaneously the exact position and momentum of a particle, a matter of great significance on the atomic scale but which plays no role in ordinary experience.[1]

The central part of an atom—the "nucleus"—is so small compared to the size of the atom itself that it would be like a tiny insect flying about in a huge cathedral.

Says author Fritz Kahn: "In contrast to its small size, the nucleus is incredibly heavy. If a drop of dew were made entirely of nuclear mass, it would be 130,000,000,000,000 times heavier than it is now, composed of water molecules. A solid lump of nuclei the size of a lump of sugar would weigh 24,000,000,000 kilograms"—or over 26,000,000 *tons*, equal to five hundred 52,000-ton battleships![2]

The number of electrons revolving around atomic nuclei range from one to over 100. The smallest atom, hydrogen, has a nucleus composed of one proton—a positively charged particle over 1800 times heavier than the electron—which is orbited by one electron.

If atoms, then, are mostly "empty" space, what makes them act as if they were solid? Says Kahn:

> Despite the vastness of the atom, it is extremely difficult to press one atom against another or to compress the orbits of the electrons. Electrons revolve 6×10^{15} times a second (or 6,000,000,000,000,000 times per second) around a nucleus. A system with such a quotient of rotation is harder than steel, no matter how small the mass or how great the distances. An atom behaves like a propeller which makes a million revolutions per second."[3]

Most of an atom then is "empty" space. If you could eliminate all the space inside an atom, it would shrink almost to nothingness. If this were done for all the atoms in the body of a man, he would shrivel up to the size of an infinitesimal piece of *dust*!

Similarly, if all the space in the atoms of the earth were removed, the *entire planet* would shrink to the size of a ball about 6 miles in diameter!

Where did the atom come from? Who or what engineered its fantastic construction? How was it built? Who created the laws that govern it? Who thought it out and *designed* it? What makes the atom appear to be so solid?

Did it all happen by *accident*? Did atoms—all the atoms of the entire universe—just somehow design and make themselves out of nothing?

Inside the Nucleus

The mass of the nucleus of an atom is about 4,000 times that of all the electrons together. The components of a nucleus—protons and neutrons—are called nucleons and are of almost equal masses. The nucleons cling together to form a nucleus because of a strong, attractive force called a nuclear force. There are also strong opposing repulsive forces that arise at extremely close range, caused by the nuclear force and the electrostatic force due to the positive charges of the protons.

Individual nucleons spin on their own axes and circulate vaguely about a common nuclear center in orbits. These orbits (or energies) occur in shells similar to the electron orbits outside the nucleus. The shape of a nucleus can vary from a spheroid, to a lemon-shaped configuration or a tangerine-shaped form. It can vibrate, rotate, or change its shape due to changes in total energy. Nuclei can be converted from one element to another via radioactivity through the process of radioactive disintegration, through nuclear fission, or via nuclear fusion.

The fact that neutrons, protons, and electrons all appear to be spinning like tops and have angular momentum—a term that describes the persistence of rotation of an object—is intriguing.

Many nuclei also have angular momentum due to the spins and orbital motions of the nucleons within them. How was this angular momentum originally installed in these atomic components? What outside force set them spinning?

Neutrons by themselves are unstable. Slightly larger than protons, neutrons in mass are equal to a proton plus 2½ electrons. When a neutron is alone in free space, it lives about 17 minutes and then flies apart, becoming a proton and an electron, emiting an elusive nearly massless particle called a neutrino in the process. Conversely, protons can become neutrons when bound in a nucleus by emitting a positive electron—called a positron—and a neutrino.

For most nuclei, the binding energy is arrived at by multiplying the number of nucleons, A, by 8 million electron volts, 8 MeV, since each nucleon appears to contribute a binding energy of approximately 8 million electron volts to all but the lighter nuclei. The usual unit of nuclear energy is a million electron volts, 1 MeV, or the energy involved in transporting one electron through a potential difference of 1,000,000 volts.

The electrostatic repulsion that one proton exerts on another proton is the best understood part of the total force package acting between nucleons. It is the same as the repulsion force between two electrons, and gives rise to a potential energy inversely proportional to the distance between the two protons.

The specific nuclear interactions that hold a nucleus together, match up almost exactly between neighboring nuclei. The specific nuclear interactions, binding nucleons together, are practically the same for two neutrons, two protons, or a neutron and a proton. These interactions are short-ranged, strong, and attractive. An interesting feature of these binding forces is that one nucleon can interact with only about three other nucleons at a time. If this were not the case, each of the nucleons in a heavy nucleus would be attracted by all the others, and they would all crowd into a small space, within the range of each other's nuclear force, and would have an enormous binding energy, proportional to the atomic mass number squared rather than to the first power.

Nuclear interactions involve other particles known as mesons. In high energy experiments, nucleons have been made to emit mesons, as in beta decay when a neutron emits an electron, but involving higher energies on the order of 10^8 or 10^9 electron volts and much stronger interactions between the nucleon and the emitted particle. Nucleons may, indeed, contain a whole host of mesons associated with them.

The pi meson has no spin; the heavier rho meson and omega meson do have spin. Their participation in nuclear interaction gives a strong spin-orbit coupling to nucleons. Meson exchange between two nucleons also contributes to tensor interaction between nucleons which depends on the direction of spin.[4]

Atomic Nuclei

It is a fact of science that like electrical charges repel—yet the protons in the atomic nucleus are all the same—positive—electrical charge. Since protons repel each other, how were nuclei formed in the first place?

Says Kahn of the protons in the nucleus of an iron atom:

> Since the protons are all equally charged, *they strongly repel each other.* If the twenty-six protons inside the nucleus of the iron atom were liberated from their bonds, they would fly apart with a pressure of 7×10^{18} atmospheres, an 'atmosphere' being the average air pressure at sea level, or about fifteen pounds per square inch. *The released energy corresponds to a temperature of more than 100,000,000°*. Vehemence of action and million-degree heat are the 'nuclear energy' we gain by fissioning the nuclei of atoms, or, as it is generally expressed, nuclear reactions.[5]

All this *energy* was somehow locked within atomic nuclei.* How?

---

*How much energy is locked within the mass of an atom? Einstein's formula "E equals mc^2" tells us. In this equation, *E* stands for energy, *m* for mass (matter) and *c* for the speed of light (186,000 miles per second). This formula shows the tremendous amount of energy stored up in matter. For example, just *one ounce* of matter contains energy equivalent to 750,000,000 kilowatt-hours of electricity, or the explosive power of 625,000 tons of TNT.

Fritz Kahn answers:

> Since energy is liberated when an atom nucleus is split, energy must have been invested in the nucleus. *We do not know how nuclei originated.* To combine 26 positively charged protons into a unit requires an energy of (that is, corresponding to) billions of degrees of heat and a pressure of more than 7×10^{18} atmospheres. Even in its fieriest days the earth could never have furnished such power. *Nor could the sun have endowed the earth with such a heritage.*[6]

What tremendous force compacted the protons of heavier nuclei together? Are they created in the explosions of supernovae? Where did the energy come from to create the particles in the first place? Scientists are not sure.

Could it all have happened by *mere chance*?

Adds this same author: "The nucleus of an atom is the *densest structure in the universe*.... The nucleus has the properties of a drop, but the surface tension of this drop is 10^{18} times stronger than the surface tension of a drop of water. Finally, the binding forces in the nucleus resist every attempt to disperse the closely coherent particles."[7]

From what source did atomic nuclei obtain such binding forces? Could such colossal forces have *accidentally* evolved? Can materialistic evolutionary theory by itself truly account for the existence of atomic nuclei—so tiny and yet so fantastically energetic?

Obviously, nuclei originally had to be designed, and built by an infinitely powerful Super-Intelligence.

Laws of Radioactivity

One of the most important discoveries regarding atomic physics was the discovery of the laws of *radioactivity* by Marie Curie. She began her investigations into the phenomenon of radioactivity in December 1897. Together with her husband Pierre she discovered the radioactive element *radium.*

Certain elements in nature are "radioactive." This means they are unstable—they constantly emit rays or particles of matter. By this radioactive process, these elements gradually disintegrate and eventually become stable.

For example, uranium (U-238) is a radioactive element and has an atomic weight of 238.05. Deposits of uranium are found to give off particles of radiation continually. These natural deposits of uranium are gradually disintegrating through sixteen intermediate stages—including the intermediate elements of thorium, radium, radon, and polonium—finally to become lead (Pb-206). The final product of this disintegration chain—lead—is a stable element and does not decay any further.

The rate of random radioactive decay of uranium to lead behaves as a constant in nature. It is not affected by natural influences such as temperature, wind, rain, or water. Scientists have been able to calculate this random rate of decay. The time required for a given amount of the radioactive element to decay to *one half* of its initial amount is called the "half-life" of the element. The half-life of uranium (U-238) is 4.5×10^9 years, or 4.5 billion years. The half-life of radium, one of the intermediate elements, is 1622 years.

If these uranium deposits have always existed, no radioactive elements would be in existence today. They would have long since decayed to *stable* elements! Therefore, there had to be a time when these radioactive deposits *first began to disintegrate.* At that point of time in the past, these elements must have come into existence.

Scientists have estimated the *age of the earth* on the basis of the radioactive decay of uranium found in natural deposits around the world. The uranium is mixed with other elements in the earth, indicating they all originated at about the same time.

Tests on moon rocks brought back by the Apollo 11 and 12 astronauts also revealed that the rock appears to be from 3.3 to 4.6 billion years old. One highly radioactive lemon-sized rock has an apparent age of 4.6 billion years.[8] The rock was analyzed by Dr. Gerald J. Wasserburg of the California Institute of Technology and ten other scientists from the United States and England.

Meteorites that have fallen onto the earth have also been dated as to origin, based on the relationship between the radioactive uranium they contain and the end products of the disintegrated uranium. Physicists generally agree that no meteorite is less than 3,000,000,000 years old or more than 5,000,000,000 years old. The dating of meteorites indicates an age of more or less 4.6 billion years—the same as the dating of the oldest moon rocks!

On the basis of such information, astronomers have estimated the *age of the solar system* to be about 4.6 billion years!

Is all this mere coincidence?

Whether or not such estimates are precisely correct is not for the moment the crucial question. Rather, their tremendous significance lies in the fact that so many bits of evidence point to a time of creation—*a particular time of origin*—a point in time when meteorites, moon, earth, and the solar system all came into existence! That is significant. It is proof that there was indeed a time of creation of the solar system!

The Subatomic Jungle

Subatomic or elementary particles are the fundamental units of matter and energy known. The accepted view of the nature and properties of these particles has been profoundly altered during the present century. As of the early 1970's, more than 200 such particles has been firmly established and a number of laws governing their interrelationships have been deduced.

The particles observed in nature give rise to four basic forces differing vastly in strength. From weakest to strongest, they are gravitation, weak interaction, electromagnetic interaction, and strong interaction. This classification of forces is associated with a classification of particles into four groups. Those directly acted upon by strong interactions are called hadrons or strongly interacting particles. Those acted on by the three weaker interactions, non-hadrons, are the leptons, the graviton, and the photon.

Hadrons are numerous subatomic particles of varying stability. Among this group is the stable proton, with a mass of 939

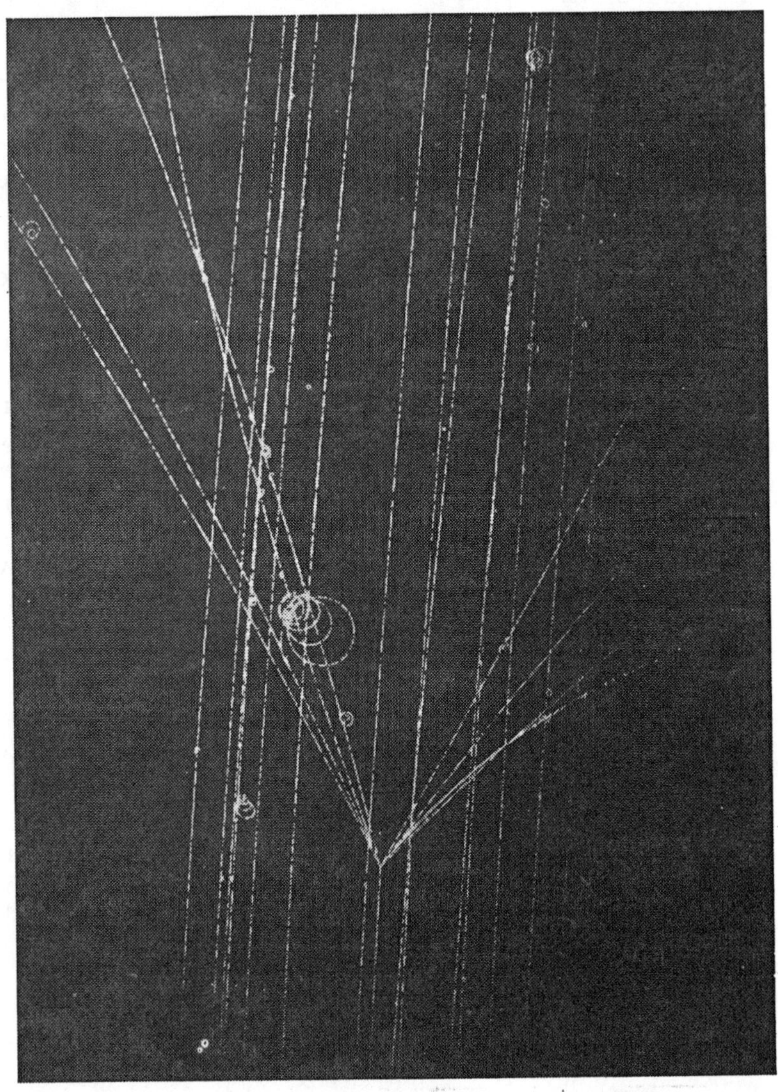

An antiproton collides with an ordinary proton causing the mass of both to be annihilated and converted into mass and kinetic energy of new particles called mesons.—*Courtesy of Brookhaven National Laboratory.*

MeV, and unstable particles of short life such as the omega meson with a mass of 484 MeV and three pions, each of mass 140 MeV.

One way in which hadrons are classified is according to baryon number, B, an integer that is positive, negative, or zero. The particles of baryon number 0 are mesons; that of baryon number 1 are baryons; those of baryon number -1 are antibaryons.

Gravitons, which are the exchanged particles causing the long-range gravitational interaction between two bodies, are massless.

The photon plays the same role for electromagnetic radiation as the graviton does for gravitation and also is massless. Leptons, the next group, include the massless particles known as neutrinos and anti-neutrinos. All known massless particles are electrically neutral and move with the speed of light. Other leptons are the negative electrons, the muon, and their anti-particles, the positive electron and the positive muon.

Particles that are completely stable can be given a precisely determined mass. But particles that decay, lasting only a finite length of time, are characterized by an "average mass."

By 1961 two unstable baryon multiplets had been discovered, the Delta particle, appearing as a quartet: a chargeless particle, a negatively charged particle, a positively charged particle, and a doubly positively charged particle. Another baryon doublet recently discovered is the Sigma particle.

The fact that hadron particles occur in multiplets led Murry Gell-Mann and physicist Yuval Ne'eman of Israel to independently propose in 1961 an "eightfold way" to explain the jumble of hadron multiplets. Starting with the eight stable baryons known at the end of 1960, they plotted them on a chart according to charge, hypercharge, and isospin and a striking hexagonal snowflake pattern emerged.

The seven stable mesons known at the beginning of 1961 were similarly plotted and another hexagon pattern emerged.

Since hadron multiplets seemed to occur in groups, these regular patterns suggested that hadrons must be composed of even more primitive elements fitted together. Physicist Murry

Gell-Mann named these speculative particles "quarks." Thus far, despite many efforts to spot quarks, none have been observed, though they seem to be essential for organizing knowledge.

Three quarks are postulated, and the existence of three antiquarks is implied as well. Mesons can be considered as quark and antiquark pairs bound together by strong interaction, and baryons as bound states of three quarks (*qqq*).

In 1950, if knowledge had ceased to grow from that time, the realm of subatomic particles would have consisted of only the photon, negative electron, positron, proton, neutron, negative pion, neutral pion, positive pion, negative muon, positive muon, neutrino and anti-neutrino.

Fortunately, or unfortunately, depending on one's point of view, years of painstaking study revealed more elementary particles—four "strange" K-mesons with masses between those of the pion and the proton, two neutral and two charged, and seven strange baryons, with masses greater than that of the proton, called Lambda neutral, Sigma minus, neutral, and plus, Xi zero and Xi minus, and Omega minus.

Even as theorists made new predictions, experimenters working with hydrogen bubble chambers discovered new particles. In 1961 the stable meson octet was completed with the discovery of the eta particle. That same year the rho and omega mesons were discovered.

The 1973 particle tables list approximately 26 meson multiplets and 50 baryon multiplets. Quarks, at this time, are well established in concept although no real, free quarks have yet been discovered.

The Fascinating Future

Where will nuclear physics go from here? Wherever it is going, it seems to be well on its way. Each year around the world several hundred millions of dollars are spent in the elusive quest for greater understanding of the fundamental particles of nature.

Physics is at the cross roads. The next undiscovered particle physicists are searching for, the quark, would apparently be the fundamental building block of matter. Adds the *Brittanica*:

> It would be necessary to go to even higher energies and shorter distances to find out whether or not the quarks themselves are in turn complex objects. That this possibility is taken seriously is indicated by the fact that, as each new accelerator comes into operation, a search is made to see if it is producing quarks.[9]

And once quarks are discovered? Well, there is the undiscovered W-meson, often called the intermediate boson. It would complete the analogy between the weak and electromagnetic interactions, and be involved in weak interactions even as photons are involved in electromagnetic interactions.

And then what?

The next undiscovered particle, first postulated by Dirac in 1931, would be the magnetic monopole. This particle, carrying a magnetic charge instead of electric charge, is particularly intriguing to physicists. Much experimental effort has gone into its detection, but so far no success has met the efforts of researchers.

Then again, another hypothetical particle, capable of four states of respective electric and magnetic charge, is Schwinger's "dion."

Gravitons, although no reasonable theory of gravitation would exclude them, have yet to be observed, though evidence for their existence is so compelling that few doubt they must exist.

Also postulated, hypothesized, but as yet undiscovered, is the existence of antimatter in the universe. Antimatter, consisting of atoms in which positrons orbit around nuclei composed of antinucleons, theoretically should exist somewhere, because physicists are convinced that for every particle there must exist an antiparticle. If and when antimatter is discovered, it will be a cause of great celebration among scientists.

Meanwhile, the search for these novel particles goes on relentlessly.

The Supreme Lesson

One lesson physicists have learned from the study of

subatomic particles is that there is still much to be learned. The physics of the subnuclear world is still far from being a closed subject.

Confronted with an array of hundreds of new "particles," which seemed fundamental, physicists are bewildered and really can't designate any of them as truly basic. Even the electron seems to have something inside it.

Recent experiments have made a shambles of the theories physicists have spun to account for all matter, says Cowen. Wolfgang K.H. Panofsky of Stanford University, president of the American Physical Society, sums the situation up best. According to him, physics has been thrown into a state of maximum confusion at its most basic level!

Says Robert C. Cowen in the Christian Science Monitor:

> Physicists who study matter's basic nature feel so perplexed with its conundrums that some of them now wonder if matter has any basic reality at all.[10]

If the universe derives from principles and their operation and not from interaction of elemental particles, this would explain the failure to find any truly basic particles.

Meanwhile the search goes on.

Physicists studying subatomic particles are groping in a fantastic, unbelievable realm. The strange particles, and their bizarre and mysterious behavior, all combine to dumbfound scientists as they discover what seems to be "worlds within worlds."

But the supreme lesson taught by the incredible microcosm of the atom and the basic physics is that they reveal a great intelligence behind their complex fascinating behavior. This fact was stressed by Dr. John H. Martin, associate physicist at Argonne National Laboratory.

Dr. Martin, a highly regarded nuclear scientist, declared that research investigators, peering into the heart of the atom, have discovered a whole new set of awesome forces which eloquently "reaffirm" the existence of a Supreme Being.

Said Dr. Martin:

> But after we got inside the atom and began to investigate the forces which apply to atomic structure, we found that ordinary forces

> governing the attraction of bodies don't work as we expected. The new forces represent a seeming *new order of law*, but it is a law which is orderly even though we cannot comprehend it at this time. . . .
>
> . . . In this new situation we are confronted by forces that are almost beyond comprehension.
>
> Moreover, we are encountering phenomena which *really bewilder* us. . . .

Added Dr. Martin, in conventional nuclear physics the energies binding the major units together inside the atoms are measured to be a few million electron volts. "But we have to pry very much harder when we try to take a neutron or a proton apart. We now find that we have to go to energies of the order of 10 billion electron volts to do this.

"In this realm we are dealing with dimensions and quantities that are *almost meaningless.* To overcome this handicap we are inventing explanatory terminology to serve as *crutches* while we try to learn what is happening.

"The strange new particles knocked from the neutron befuddle us. Where these particles come from, in most instances, hasn't been clearly defined."

Said Dr. Martin:

> We see in the atom, as in the rest of the universe, a system that goes beyond our understanding. It is an infinite system extending into the wholly invisible particles of the atomic nucleus, and far beyond the reach of the most powerful astronomical telescopes.
>
> It is a legal system, too, that was established by a great legalist whom I call God.

What "probability" is there that the matter of the universe evolved by chance? "In terms of a probability figure," asserts Dr. Martin, "the universe is so highly ordered that the probability of its having come into existence by chance is *for all practical purposes zero.*"

The incredible array of matter and energy in the universe clearly points to the existence of the Great Creator—the Great Nuclear Physicist—who devised and designed and developed the entire cosmos.

I do not know what I may appear to the world; but to myself I seem to have been only like a boy playing on the seashore, and diverting myself in now and then finding a smoother pebble or a prettier shell than ordinary, whilst the great ocean of truth lay all undiscovered before me.

Memoirs of Newton (1855).

Chapter Twenty Six

Science Versus Theology?

Life is full of mystery. Whether you plumb the unfathomable mysteries of outer space and the void of the immense cosmos, or you explore the bizarre realm of the atom and the minute points of energy, creation proves to be dazzling and bewildering, strange and marvelous. And no less awesome is the fascinating realm of life—all living creatures, from the lowly paramecium and its odd sex habits, to the ocean-cruising deadly man-of-war.

What is behind this incredible unifying thread of universal mystery? Can it all be explained by the evolutionary perspective—the framework of evolutionary theory? Or is evolutionary belief laughably narrow in its attempt to explain the unexplainable?

Is evolutionary theory a primary concomitant of man's colossal arrogance—his belief that he is the fortuitous end-product of a long chain of evolutionary developments?

Evolutionists often are heard to ridicule any who dispute the general theory of evolution, holding them up as objects of abuse, jokes, remnants of the 18th century, victims of superstition. Under the banner of academic freedom, they attack all who profess belief in a divine creation, whether or not they think such a divine act took place just 6,000 years ago. It seemingly does not matter to them that Darwinism has never been proved either true or useful. They are not overly concerned that part of the theory is based on physical evidence (the age of the earth, the random decay of radioactive elements, the succession of fossils in the geologic strata, minor mutations), and part on pure speculation (all life evolved from a common ancestor, mutations and natural selection cause changes from one species into another ad infinitum, original primordial life arose out of a chance combination of non-living elements, peptide chains and the grouping of amino acids). Regardless of these facts, evolution is generally presented in the form of case-closed fact. When admitted to be a theory, it is always passed off as the "only acceptable theory for educated man."

But is it any wonder that parallel with the rise of Darwinism in the scientific world has been a general casting adrift of the moral anchor of society, and a coinciding lowering of ethics, morals, and respect for tradition, religious faith, and the Judeo-Christian foundation of society?

We live in perilous times. No one fully knows just how much of this modern peril is due, at least in part, to the philosophy enjoined by the teaching of Darwinism, evolution, and anti-supernatural rationalism. Undoubtedly, many of the atheistic, godless dialectics owe their origin in no small measure to the influence of Darwinism and evolutionary theory, subverting religious faith and undermining belief in the existence of a super-powerful Creator God and the veracity of His revealed Word to mankind.

Evolution says that the "hypothesis of God" is unnecessary. But with what are the evolutionists going to replace the "hypothesis of God?" Pure randomness? Chance? Coincidence built on top of unbelievable coincidence, in turn built on top of more series of coincidences? On nothing at all?

If there be no God, then where does evolutionary theory lead us? To a blind end? To an unsure, whimsical, capricious faith in "nothing?" To an unreasoning faith in man himself?

When the evolutionist does away with faith in a Creator God, a faith impelled and empowered and attested to by the marvelous mysteries and miracles of Creation all around us, then the evolutionist leaves mankind without hope, without a sure anchor of the soul, without a tangible, purposeful goal in life, without a purpose for his being.

Are we mere accidents in the aeons of a cosmic universe, an effervescent, evanescent ripple in the ocean of time? Or were we planned, designed, created for a purpose?

Genesis

In a recent article in *Intellectual Digest* entitled "Does Matter Exist?" physicist Allen D. Allen marvels at the problem of finding the basic unit of matter. In fact, he writes: "We have decided that it doesn't exist. After all, every time we think we've found it, it turns out that we haven't."

Allen and his colleagues suggest that perhaps the ultimate reality is not mere *objects*, particles, or matter, but rather fundamental *laws* of physics, such as the law of the conservation of momentum and the law of the conservation of energy. So long as we obey these laws, we can create any matter we have the means to produce. Says Allen:

> This concept, that ultimately the world is constructed from principles rather than from units of matter, is almost theological in character. Yet it is now an established (if competing) theory in the mainstream of theoretical physics.[1]

Allen maintains that it is theoretically possible to disprove that a particle is elemental by simply splitting it into smaller particles. But, says he, it is impossible, even in theory, to disprove the assumption that a particle is not elemental–that it could be split given enough energy and opportunities. All that can be proved is that it cannot be split in such a way that would violate the *laws* of physics. Thus laws, rather than particles, may be the ultimate reality.

This is a novel hypothesis, and is strikingly reminiscent of certain profound statements in the Bible. Declares Allen:

> These laws are far removed from theological or moral laws–nonetheless, theoretical physicists seem well on their way to agreeing with the Gospel of St. John that "in the beginning was the word."[2]

Thus as research continues, it seems that the age old rift between science and theology is gradually being repaired, healed, narrowed, and abolished. Of course, as long as there are errors in either theological thinking, based on false assumptions or inaccurate interpretations, or as long as errors exist in scientific theories, hypotheses, there will continue to be a rift of greater or lesser proportions. But as we all grow in truth, and a correct evaluation of the data, these differences will continue to lessen, until they finally disappear when the grand, ultimate unifying Reality becomes obvious.

Omega

Thus there is no necessary difference between science and theology when it comes to understanding the origin of the cosmos. But what about the fate of the universe?

Presently, the cosmos appears to be expanding in every direction, even as the Bible itself alludes when Isaiah says that God "stretches out the heavens like a curtain, and spreads them like a tent to dwell in" (Isaiah 40:22).

The fate of the cosmos may also be alluded to or vividly described in the Scriptures, when Peter writes:

> But the day of the Lord will come like a thief, and then the heavens will pass away with a loud noise, and the elements will be dissolved with fire, and the earth and the works that are upon it will be burned up.[3]

After describing this fiery holocaust, Peter adds: "But according to his promise we wait for new heavens and a new earth in which righteousness dwells."[4]

This strange prediction also squares with the latest thinking of some cosmologists. Although the universe is presently expanding, a number of astronomers theorize that eventually the expansion will run out of steam, and the universe will contract. At first contracting slowly, it will build up momentum as the gravitational pull draws all the elements of the cosmos together faster and faster, until they once again merge into a giant fireball.

If the universe began expanding roughly 10 billion years ago, John Archibald Wheeler, the Joseph Henry Professor of Physics at Princeton, estimates that maturity will not be reached for another 20 billion years. At that time, further expansion will be arrested, celestial forces of gravitation will overpower the forces of expansion, and the great moment of collapse will set in. The remotest galaxies will at first begin reversing direction almost imperceptibly, and gradually pick up speed until they approach the speed of light itself—or so suggests Wheeler. Fifty billion years from today our universe will "return to the womb."

What would happen then?

That is the enigma of the ages! According to certain assumptions and Einstein's equations, the entire universe could eventually arrive at a condition of infinite compaction in a finite time. But other laws of physics, encompassed in *Quantum principles*, are thought to forbid the conclusions Einstein's general relativity would demand. Thus theoretical science comes to an ultimate paradox.

The quantum uncertainty principle predicts that you can never foretell with complete precision just how a system will change in the future because you can never know simultaneously what a particle is doing right now and how fast it's changing—or if you know the location of a particle at a given moment, you cannot know precisely how fast it is moving.

If the entire universe someday contracts back into virtual infinity, we must comprehend and learn more about what happens at subatomic distances. Wheeler postulates there is a "world" of "things" that makes even subatomic particles look massive by comparison—"things" that are smaller than an electron by 10^{20} power. These "things" are composed of energetic space, "pure fluctuating space."

Is space itself fluctuating, energetic, active? Says Wheeler:

> From an airplane six miles high, the ocean looks smooth. Down at sea level, in a life raft, however, we see that waves are breaking, and the surface is highly irregular; what's more, instead of its being merely irregular, there are droplets breaking loose. Now space, too, looks smooth at the scale of everyday life, smooth at the scale of atomic structure, and smooth at the scale of nuclear structure. But when one gets down to the scale of distances 20 powers of ten smaller than the scale of nuclear structure, then one predicts that space is foamlike.[5]

What would happen to the universe when it is compressed to such tiny dimensions? Where does everything go? All the stars, nebulae, galaxies, atoms, particles, light? This is the crisis of collapse. Nobody knows what would happen.

Do we come to a domain where collapse loses its terror—where it is taking place all the time, and where it is also constantly being undone, or converted into fluctuations in space itself everywhere and all the time?

Will the whole mass expand once again? Will particles, losing their identity in collapse, be "reborn?"

If all the matter is "squeezed through a knothole in space," forced down to a level where fluctuations in space is everything, will new matter re-emerge according to laws of physics not now understood?

But this brings us to an even greater possibility. Is there a greater level of existence than the universe itself? Is the cosmos merely an island in a greater trackless realm? Wheeler says yes. Logically, there must be something larger, some entity beyond.

> The stage on which the space of the universe moves is certainly not space itself. Nobody can be a stage for himself; he has to have a larger arena in which to move. The arena must be a larger object: *superspace.*[6]

Wheeler and other scientists believe the quantum principle demands the existence of "something out there." The history of our universe is merely a "track in superspace." When the universe collapses, and the classical general theory of relativity offers no further explanation of events, the quantum principle tells us the dynamics should continue. A new cycle should be started. Each new cycle, or new universe, would have its own peculiar selection of laws, constants and properties. It would be a new universe, remade, or the old universe, transformed, metamorphosed, "born anew."

The concept of superspace leads to a far reaching, metaphysical conclusion. It reminds one of the Biblical statement that the things which are seen are made of that which is not seen (Hebrews 11:3). "Superspace" could be viewed as the dimension of the spirit. God, you should remember, is Spirit

(John 4:24). Thus His existence transcends the physical universe. He stands apart, supreme, untouched by changes in the physical cosmos. His spirit, which is everywhere is the underlying basis of the existence of all things—the ultimate fundamental reality.

General relativity alone might give the impression that the universe is something that is just here by accident. But the idea that the universe makes many cycles, and that each cycle has its own number of particles, mass of particles, size, length of cycle, etc., suggests, says Wheeler:

> . . . that most cycles of the universe will not permit the development of stars like the sun, of planets like the earth, of the atoms and molecules necessary for life as we know it.
>
> This suggests that there exists a degree of harmony between us and our surroundings that we never realized before. . . . If this new view is correct, our surroundings are very special and tuned to us, like a plant to its flower: this cycle of the universe like the plant, and we like the flower that comes into a brief bloom and then fades away.[7]

Such a concept of the universe suggests very strongly the existence of a Creator who designed the harmony between life and its surroundings—a God who designed the development of stars, planets, atoms and molecules necessary for life as we know it. To believe that such a marvelous blending of complex interdependency, resulted from blind chance in an ancient primordial "explosion" of matter, is a logical absurdity.

The existence of our marvelous universe, and the latest theories as to its origin and fate, all point to the existence of the great Creator, God, who inhabits a dimension of reality which could be called superspace!

Life on Earth

But the God who inhabits superspace, if we call it that, is very concerned about life on earth.

He created the alga *Cyanidium caldarium* which can grow in concentrated solutions of hot sulphuric acid, and procaryotic bacteria which live in pools at Yellowstone National Park at temperatures above 194° Fahrenheit.

He devised organisms which employ organic or inorganic *antifreezes* to lower the freezing point of their internal liquids so they can live at temperatures below zero. Don Juan Pond in Antarctica, which has about one molecule of calcium chloride for every two water molecules and does not freeze until -49° Fahrenheit, contains a microflora that continues to live at temperatures -9° Fahrenheit.

Though water is important to all organisms, God designed some organisms which obtain no water in the liquid state; they entirely depend on water released from chemical bonds through the metabolism of food. Spanish moss lives in environments where it has no contact with groundwater, obtaining water directly from the air.

Bacteria and fungal spores have been discovered as high as 100,000 feet in altitude, and birds have been observed flying at 27,000 feet. Jumping spiders have been found at 22,000 feet on Mt. Everest.

At the opposite extreme, a variety of fish have been found at ocean depths of thousands of feet, where pressures are hundreds of times that at sea level.

Although some micro-organisms can be killed off by just a small amount of solar ultraviolet light, the bacterium *Pseudomolas radiodurans* thrives in the large neutron flux at the cores of swimming pool reactors, to the annoyance of nuclear physicists.

All these amazing forms of life attest the marvelous mind of God. And so does man, himself.

Man

Professor Anthony Ostric, of St. Mary's College, told the ninth International Congress of Anthropological and Ethnological Sciences in the spring of 1974 that there is no evidence man has not remained essentially the same since the first evidence of his appearance. He sharply criticized his colleagues for declaring "as a fact" that man descended from ape-like creatures.

"To say there were pre-human ape ancestors transformed into humans is speculative," he asserted. "Man's unique biophysical and socio-cultural nature appears now to represent an unbridgeable abyss separating him from all other animals, even from his closest 'anthropoid relatives.' "

Ostric continued: "It is not possible to see how biological, social or cultural forces or processes could transform any kind of prehuman anthropoid or 'near-man' into homosapiens."

Ostric pointed out that there is no compelling evidence to support the thesis that man became fully dominant about 10,000 years ago as his brain enlarged to about its present size. He pointed out that Neanderthal's brain was as large as that of the most modern races, but Neanderthalensis became extinct. Furthermore, Ostric added, in weight of brain in proportion to body weight, the marmoset—the dwarf monkey of South America—surpasses man.

In the light of the evidence presented in this book, we must fully agree with Professor Ostric. Man is unique. He is special. That means that *you* are special.

Science and Theology

When all is said and done, we need to realize that there need be no contradiction between true science and theology, between faith and fact. This truth has been acknowledged by many highly principled and recognized authorities in the field of science. Science and religion can be compatible so long as dogmatism and human nature do not prevail.

As if to verify this truth, my family and I were vacationing in Mazatlan, Mexico. We relaxed on the beach at the hotel, the children frolicking in the waves, and playing in the swimming pool. At night, I sat stretched out in a low slung cloth beach chair, and meditated with the sound of the surf in my ears observing an island lit up by lights out in the sea. It was a time of calm, tranquility, relaxation—a time to offer prayerful thanks for God's goodness, and to appreciate in a special, intimate way the wonders of His creation.

A beautiful seashore, soft powdery sand, a continuous

succession of breaking waves crumbling from left to right, shimmering in the light of the moon, held me spellbound, in rapt awe.

Here was great evidence, in a personal way, of the power and majesty of God. My mind was in tune with the universe. I felt a distinct oneness with the fathomless mind that fashioned it all, the God of beauty, the God of order, the God who is concerned for each and every man, woman and child—the God who allowed us to enjoy such a wonderful solitude. I felt almost as if I could catch a few of the resplendent thoughts of God.

Then, further confirming the truth of God's revelation, at the airport at Mazatlan I engaged in a conversation with a professional geologist from Reno, Nevada. Although he was 68 years old, he didn't look a day over 50. His youthfulness and vitality were well preserved. This geologist had been examining the Sierra Madre Mountains in the hinterland for silver. He told me that a lot of silver still remained in those mountains, but there were very few roads. He was checking out the possibility of mining investments in the region for a client back in Reno.

As we talked, for some reason the subject turned to science and philosophy and the Bible. He told me that he didn't find any conflict between religious faith and science. To him there was no contradiction between the Genesis account of creation and the facts of science. To him, the first chapter of Genesis seemed to speak of "days" which were like a thousand years to God—vast aeons of time. There was no contradiction at all.

Another man who sees no contradiction between faith and science is Professor Frank C. Hibben, anthropologist at the University of New Mexico. I interviewed Dr. Hibben in his office at the University a few years ago. He has excavated remains of early man throughout the Southwestern United States, the remains of ancient animals in the Alaskan mucks, and has also done much investigation in Europe and Africa. Hibben is also a world-renown big game hunter, and his den at home is lined with trophies that he bagged from points around the globe.

Hibben is an interesting, colorful person, and a fascinating lecturer. He told me that he has Mormons, Fundamentalists and others in his classes at the University. He added, "And I simply tell them the facts are that life was created—that is where a Creator comes in who built into life several characteristics. One is the fact of being alive. Another thing that's built into life is extinction. Certain forms of life reach a dead end and become extinct. Another thing that's built into life is change. So that as life recreates itself, the offspring is never absolutely identical with the parent. And various factors act upon that kind of life to direct its change."

Frank C. Hibben looks upon all life as a "divine plan." And that, I think, sums up the truth best. All life is indeed part of a divine plan. So this noted authority of science says; and so the Biblical record reveals.

The whole cosmos, from beginning to end, is also a part of that supreme divine plan. Your existence is a part of it, too. The divinity that shapes our lives, and molds us, the one who created us, is God.

Chapter Twenty Seven

Biblical Science or Superstition?

The earth, of course, is the planet that we live on. It is about 8,000 miles in diameter. Although it seems big to us humans, when we fly above it in an airplane, or take a journey across the ocean, it is a small tiny speck in the infinite vastness of space.

This planet earth, which we call home, is a miraculous creation all by itself. It is surrounded by a marvelous atmosphere of air which supports life. If it were not for the oxygen in the air, almost all living creatures would perish, including Man. But also, far above the earth, there is a belt of gas called ozone which filters out harmful rays from the sun. Without that ozone layer life as we know it would be impossible.

The earth is specially designed by God to support life. About three million different species of plants and animals call the earth their home, from tiny amoeba living in swamps, tidal pools, and water droplets, to huge whales cruising the seas. The earth has plenty of water, also very important for all living creatures.

The earth is about 93,000,000 miles from the sun, just the right distance so that it is not too hot or too cold to support life. The tiny planet Mercury is much closer to the sun and is so hot that life there would be impossible. Also, the giant planets of Jupiter and Saturn are too far from the sun to support life—they are intensely cold all the time, with temperatures hundreds of degrees below zero.

The earth spins like a top as it travels around the sun. One complete revolution takes 24 hours and equals one day. One trip around the sun equals one year. If the earth turned much faster on its axis, and the day were only 8 hours, terrific hurricanes would blow constantly, and tornadoes and terrible winds would make life virtually impossible. If the earth only turned on its axis once a year, as it circled the sun, then the same side would always face the sun—and one half the planet would be in eternal darkness, and the other half bathed in eternal light. Life under such conditions would be a nightmare, if possible at all.

But God designed the earth just right to support life.

The Bible tells us a great deal about the earth. It is an amazing book.

While pagans worshipped sticks and stones, the sun, moon, and stars; while entire nations were bowing under a cloud of magic and superstition, ignorant of the truth—at the very same time, a Book of books was being written which contained many astronomical facts generally unknown to most of the nations in the world!

Notice how amazingly scientific the Bible really is!

Many people have erroneously believed that the Bible teaches the earth is flat. The Medieval Catholic Church held to the notion the earth is flat and is the center of the universe. When Galileo presented scientific evidence to the contrary, his facts and theories were branded as "absurd in philosophy, and formally heretical, because expressly contrary to Holy Scripture."

But nowhere does the Bible teach the flat earth theory, or that the earth is a stationary object at the center of the universe.

Galileo's theories were declared heretical in the 17th century. But, amazingly enough, six hundred years before Christ, the prophet Isaiah was inspired by Almighty God to write and speak of the spherical shape of the earth!

In Isaiah 40:22 we read of God, "It is He that sitteth upon the CIRCLE of the earth." Moffatt translates this verse clearer,

"He sits over the ROUND EARTH." The *Critical and Experimental Commentary* states this expression is "applicable to the globular form of the earth." The original Hebrew is *chung* and means a "compass, circle, or *sphere.*"

But how did Isaiah, an ancient Hebrew prophet, know that the earth is round? Other peoples didn't learn this fact for hundreds of years.

How much did the ancient writers of the Bible really know about astronomy? Did they believe the notions of pagan Egyptian contemporaries who believed the earth was carried about on the back of a great tortoise?

The fact that the earth revolves around the sun once every year was not generally understood until the days of Copernicus in the 16th century—just a little more than 400 years ago. He taught that the sun is the center of the solar system.

However, thousands of years before Copernicus lived, in the days of the patriarch Moses, the Bible indicates, the revolution of the earth around the sun once a year was probably *known* to ancient Biblical astronomers! In Exodus 34:22 we read, in the King James Version, the innocent phrase, "And thou shalt observe the feast of weeks, of the firstfruits of wheat harvest, and the feast of gathering at the *year's end.*" According to the original Hebrew, however, this should be translated "at the *revolution of the year.*" The original Hebrew word is *tequwphah* and means "*to move in a circle,*" "circuit," "*to go around,*" "*orbit of the sun,*" "revolution of time."

Also in II Chronicles 24:23 the words "end of the year" in the original Hebrew really mean "in the *revolution of the year.*"

These verses suggest the fact that the ancient Hebrews knew the earth revolves around the sun, and completes one *revolution*—one turning—each year.

But this is not all. Notice Job 38:12-14—"Hast thou commanded the morning since thy days; and caused the dayspring to know his place; that it might take hold of the ends of the earth . . . IT IS TURNED *as clay to the seal . . .*"

What does this mean? God is talking to Job about the morning—the rising of the sun. How is it that the sun appears to rise in the morning? The earth itself *turns,* or "rotates"—from west to east, causing the sun to rise in the morning, in the eastern sky.

The original Hebrew in this verse says, of the earth, "it turns itself." What could be a more apt expression? The allusion of the clay and the seal refers to the rolling cylinder seal, one to three inches long, such as was used in ancient Babylon, which left its plastic impression on the clay *as it turned about* or rolled around. What more apt figure of speech could be used to represent the rotation of the earth itself, causing day and night?

The laws of gravity were not understood until Sir Isaac Newton discovered them in the 18th century. The laws of motion were discovered by the same genius.

However, amazing as it may sound, thousands of years ago the Bible alluded to the laws of centrifugal force, centripetal force, gravity and motion.

How else do you explain the enigmatic statement in the book of Job, speaking of the earth—"*He . . . hangeth the earth* UPON NOTHING?" (Job 26:7).

The pagans believe a tortoise carried the earth about; but God revealed to His people the truth—that the earth hangs suspended in space by powerful laws of force and motion!

Also in the book of Job we read a remarkable statement. One who claims to be God says to Job, "Can you bind the chains of [the cluster of stars called] Pleiades, or loose the cords of [the constellation] Orion?" (Job 38:31, *Amplified Version*).

And in the next verse, we read: ". . . Or can you guide [the stars of] the Bear with her young?"

The One speaking to Job apparently knew that the Pleiades, the stars of Orion, and the Bear (Ursa Major or the Big Dipper) travel together. In particular, since the "*chains* of Pleiades" and the "*cords* of Orion" are mentioned, the One speaking was stressing the fact that these particular groups of stars are more than just constellations in the sky—they are actually *local groups* of stars in space!

The King James Version hides the real meaning of verse 31, calling the "chains" of the Pleiades "sweet influences." However, the original Hebrew word is *ma'adannah* and literally means "*to lace fast,*" bind or tie.

The "cords" or "bands" of Orion, in the original Hebrew are called *mowshekah,* meaning something "drawing," from *mashak,* "to draw."

The *Larousse Encyclopedia of Astronomy* says:

> Usually it is found that the motions of the different stars of a constellation figure are oriented quite at random—confirming our conclusion that their apparent mutual proximity is simply an effect of perspective. But there are *certain exceptions* to this rule:
>
> Occasionally, velocities of the same order of magnitude, and oriented in more or less parallel directions, are observed. Such stars, without being 'near' to one another in the ordinary sense, nevertheless form a PHYSICALLY CONNECTED UNIT AND ARE VOYAGING THROUGH SPACE TOGETHER. They are said to belong to the same star stream, or to form a MOVING CLUSTER.
>
> Five of the principal stars of the *Great Bear* form such a moving cluster. The same thing is encountered among the *stars of Orion,* and with the two clusters of stars in Taurus known as the Hyades and the *Pleiades* (p. 308).

The One who spoke to Job talks as if He knew these particular star groups, or constellations, are bound or "yoked" together—that the stars within each group are joined and move as a unit through space!

These words are written about 2,000 B.C. Modern astronomers only discovered these facts about Orion, the Bear, and the Pleiades, through the use of modern, sophisticated equipment—huge telescopes. *How did the One speaking to Job know 4,000 years ago what modern astronomy has only discovered in this century?* The answer is simplicity itself: He created them!

The ancient patriarchs had a great deal of knowledge of astronomy. The Creator GOD taught them amazing facts about the earth and universe which modern science has only just begun to verify.

God asked Job, "Where wast thou when I laid the foundations of the earth? . . . Whereupon are the foundations [sockets] thereof fastened [made to sink]?" (Job 38:4, 6). It is interesting that science has discovered that the earth's axis is pointed in the direction of the North Pole Star, allowing for the wobble and precession, and the north and south poles are the points where the earth's axis of rotation meets the surface of the earth. *God* is the One who planned it all out; set the earth to spinning on its axis; and pointed the north pole toward the star Polaris!

The science of weather and understanding the earth's atmosphere is of relatively recent origin. It, too, has developed greatly during the last two hundred years. Chemistry and physics play a vital role in this science. Before the nature of matter and air were understood, weather science was in total chaos.

The key to understanding weather is the hydrological cycle. Today it is well known that water evaporates from the surface of the oceans, rivers, lakes and all bodies of water; that it rises into the atmosphere; and that later it returns to the earth as rain, snow, sleet, or hail. The evaporation-condensation-precipitation cycle was not generally known, however, before the nature of water, water vapor, and the chemistry of matter was understood.

The Bible reveals this basic cycle *was* understood, however, thousands of years ago!

Notice Jeremiah 10:13—"When he uttereth his voice, there is a multitude of *waters* in the heavens, and he causeth the vapours to ascend from the ends of the earth."

Jeremiah knew about the evaporation of water into water vapor, condensation of water vapor as rain droplets, and the precipitation cycle.

Jeremiah was not the only Biblical meteorologist, however. Solomon knew the weather cycle. Wrote Solomon about one thousand years before Christ, "The wind goes to the south, and circles about continually, and on its circlings the wind returns again. All the rivers run into the sea, yet the sea is not full; unto the place from which the rivers come, to there and from there they return again" (Eccl. 1:6-7, *Amplified Version*).

Solomon understood the circuits of the wind—and of water.

Consider, for a moment, how amazing Solomon's knowledge was. It was not until the 1800's that William Ferrell, An American meteorologist, formulated "Ferrell's law" which explains the prevailing directions of the winds over the earth, based on the earth's rotation.

Said Matthew Fontaine Maury, an American hydrographer who lived in the late 1800's, "The direction in which a wind blows is so constantly changing that we often speak of the winds as fickle, inconstant, and uncertain. There is, however, order in the movements of the atmosphere. The fickle winds are obedient to laws."

Amazing facts about the seas are also revealed in Scripture.

In Job 38:16, God asked, "Have you explored the *springs of the sea?* Or have you walked in the *recesses* of the deep?" (*Amplified Version*).

How could the writer of the book of Job have known that beneath the oceans of the world are *springs* or fountains of fresh water?

An article in the *Saturday Review* (July 1, 1967) said, "Although they usually remain undetected, submarine springs of fresh water are often more common along certain types of shoreline than are rivers and other surface streams."

Along some shorelines, as much as 20 million gallons of fresh water a day flows into the sea for every mile of shoreline.

In fact, one major submarine spring in the Persian Gulf flows with enough volume to create a large area of fresh water in the midst of the sea, because of favorable limestone geology in Iran and Saudi Arabia. In Greece, an estimated 100 million cubic feet of fresh water goes into the sea through submarine springs.

But about *four thousand years ago,* God asked Job if he knew about the springs in the sea!

What about the "recesses of the deep?" There are deep trenches of the oceans—such as the Marianas Trench in the Pacific, 36,198 feet deep, discovered in September, 1959 by the Soviet ship Vityaz. The same ship discovered a depth of 35,702 feet in the Tonga Trench; there are four other deep trenches in the North Pacific. The greatest depth in the Atlantic Ocean is north of Puerto Rico—the Puerto Rico Trench, 27,498 feet deep.

The dark world of the bottom of the ocean is now being explored by scientists in bathyscaphes, and special cameras, mounted with strobe lamps, have been lowered miles into the depths.

New instruments have revealed that the ocean bottom is surprisingly rugged. Depths of valleys and canyons running underwater when averaged out are five times greater than heights reached on continents. The undersea world is cut, and sliced, by huge canyons bigger than the Grand Canyon. One such canyon is the Hudson Canyon off New York. Sixty miles off shore, this mammoth canyon knifes downward to 8000 feet, and then slopes on down to 16,500 feet.

The sea floor is called the abyssal plains. At their edge are sometimes found tremendous chasms or trenches, averaging 20 miles wide at the top and hundreds of miles long. The deepest such trench discovered is the Challenger Deep in the Marianas Trench, almost seven miles down.

Thousands of years ago, God asked Job what he knew about these "recesses" deep under the ocean! In the original Hebrew, the word for "explore" is *cheger* and means to "search out, examine; secret, inmost part." The word for "deep" is *tehown* and means "confusion"—or "the abyss, *the great* deep."

What an amazing book!

Matthew Fontaine Maury, when reading the Bible, was struck by the words of Psalm 8:8—"The fowl of the air, and the fish of the sea, and whatsoever passeth through *the paths of the seas.*" His curiosity aroused, he set out to map the currents of the oceans of the world and became the foremost hydrographer of his day (1806-1873). He discovered the ocean routes which would make best use of prevailing ocean currents and winds. His research enabled ship owners to cut many days from the time required to make their voyages and helped them save many thousands of dollars. He was called the "Pathfinder of the Sea." The *Bible* was his source of inspiration!

But how did King David, the author of the Psalm, who lived about one thousand years before Christ, know about these paths of the seas and the great currents in the oceans?

In 1855 Matthew Fontaine Maury, pioneer oceanographer, wrote, "There is a river in the ocean. In the severest droughts it never fails, and in the mightiest floods it never overflows.

Its banks and its bottom are of cold water, while its current is of warm. The Gulf of Mexico is its fountain, and its mouth is in the Arctic Seas. It is the Gulf Stream" (*The Physical Geography of the Sea, 1855*).

Truly a river in the middle of the sea, the Gulf Stream flows for the most part through the Caribbean into the Gulf of Mexico and leaves through the Straits of Florida, from where it flows out into the broad Atlantic across to Northwestern Europe.

Seaward of New England, the Gulf Stream can be 100 miles wide and 16,400 feet deep, and have a surface velocity of six miles an hour. There it carries past a given point about 150,000,000 tons of water every second; the equal of 700 Amazons or 8,800 Mississippis!

If the Gulf Stream were emptied upon the United States, it would flood the entire nation to a depth of over four feet in just one day!

This mighty river is truly a PATHWAY in the sea. The larvae of a snail (*Cymatium Parthenopeum*) found from Brazil to the west coast of Africa ride the Gulf Stream, perhaps taking 300 days to cover 2,640 miles from the Bahamas to the Azores. Although the "odds" against a successful passage for the snails may be 2 million to 1, it is commonly done!

The Gulf Stream is just one of many mighty ocean currents, such as the cold Humboldt Current, pushed by antarctic winds up the west coast of South America. Then there is the Japan Current, or Kuroshio, in the Pacific.

The earth's great wind systems push before them the great sea currents, and have enormous impact on world weather. The westerlies drive the Gulf Stream and Japan Current; the polar easterlies drive before them the Humboldt Current and Brazil Current, and others. The Labrador Current, in the North Atlantic flows down from the north polar region, pushed along by polar easterlies.

All these mighty currents are virtual rivers or paths in the seas. But—how did David, one thousand years before Christ, know such mighty paths in the seas existed? How indeed, unless navigation was far more advanced in his day than skeptics like to admit?

Clearly, the Bible is far more scientific than most people would suppose!

Even in the days of David, facts about bird migration and fish migration were understood!

You are probably familiar with the fact that air has weight. At sea level air pressure is 14.7 pounds per square inch. As you go up in altitude, air pressure is less and less. A mountain climber ascending Mount Everest finds the air so thin that he has to take oxygen along to breathe.

When did science discover that air has weight? Any textbook on Physics reveals that the laws of pressure, temperature and volume of gases were not discovered until the last few hundred years. It was not known, previously that the invisible air actually had weight.

But notice what God wrote in His Word over three thousand years ago:

"God . . . looks to the ends of the earth; beneath the whole heavens he sees. When he made a *weight* for the wind, and meted out the waters by measure [rainfall on the United States averages 29 inches every year!]; when he made a LAW for the rain, and a way for the thunderbolt" (Job 28:23-26).

The *Amplified Bible* makes it even more specific: "When He gave to the wind *weight or pressure* . . . ."

Here is another remarkable instance of science in the Bible—thousands of years before modern science discovered these same laws of nature and principles of physics!

These verses indicate that Job knew the relationship between barometric pressure of the atmosphere and the weather *three thousand years* before Torricelli, an Italian physicist (1608-1647) proved the same relationship with his barometer!

In Job 28:26 we read, "When he [God] made a decree for the rain, and a WAY *for the lightning of the thunder.*"

Lightning kills more people yearly than any other natural disaster—about 400. It destroys $37 million worth of property annually, plus the losses due to 8,000 annual forest fires started by lightning.

How are lightning bolts formed? The story is fascinating. Inside enormous thunderclouds are so-called chimney currents—a column of air rising upward with gale force. Within this turbulence near the top small hailstones become positively charged, while raindrops in the lower portion are charged negatively. Below on the earth there is another positive charge buildup, following the drifting cloud.

Tremendous differences of electric potential are created between the top and bottom of the thundercloud, and the earth's surface.

At this point, a gaseous arc reaches down from the cloud for perhaps fifty feet, hanging there, building up, growing. Meanwhile, positive particles on the earth below streak upward as high as fifty feet, called "St. Elmo's fire." When one of these earth "streamers" meets one of the cloud's dangling gaseous arcs, called "leaders," suddenly A PATH IS FORMED BETWEEN THE THUNDERCLOUD AND THE EARTH!

This is where the darting, flickering BOLT OF LIGHTNING hurtles through the air, starting at the point of contact between negative and positive charges of electricity, ripping up to the cloud along the gaseous arc path already formed. The lightning actually travels *upward,* and the fact that it *appears* to travel downward is an optical illusion.

The point of this fascinating story is—HOW DID JOB KNOW? *Yes, how could he* have ever known that there is "A WAY for the lightning of the thunder?"

Science did not discover the secret of this phenomenon until very recent times. But God Almighty, the Creator of heaven and earth, revealed it to Job and inspired him to write of it over 3,700 years ago!

Imagine that!

What about the earth science of geology? Does the Bible have anything to say about it?

Again, the book of Job contains the answers. We read of the process of erosion in Job 14:19—"The waters *wear* the stones: thou washest away the things which grow out of the dust of the earth . . . ."

Notice, also, Job 28:10–"He cutteth out rivers among the rocks." Ever stop and notice the majesty of the Grand Canyon? Geologists say that enormous canyon was formed by cutting action of the Colorado River, gouging out a pathway through the rock.

The whole lesson of the science recorded in the Bible is given in the book of Job. Here is revealed the SUPREME LESSON that science itself teaches, if men only have the wit to see it!

"But ask now the beasts and they shall *teach* thee; and the fowls of the air, and they shall tell thee: or speak to the EARTH, and *it shall teach thee:* and the fishes of the sea shall declare unto thee. Who knoweth not *in all these* that the HAND OF THE LORD HATH WROUGHT THIS?" (Job 12:7-9).

GOD is the Creator! This is the supreme lesson and teaching of ALL true science, and the science of the Bible!

Stop and think, for a moment. The pagans worshipped the heavenly bodies. Christians worship the Almighty One who put them there!

Pagans believed in astrology and worshipped the sun, moon and stars. But, in the pages of the Bible, God tells us the purpose of the creation of the heavenly bodies: "And God said, Let there be lights in the firmament of the heaven to divide the day from the night; and let them be for signs, and for SEASONS, and for *days* and YEARS" (Gen. 1:14).

Did you know that *time* is based on the motion of the heavenly bodies? The earth rotates at a constant speed, giving us day and night; it revolves around the sun at a constant speed, taking one year per revolution. The moon revolves around the earth, giving us the lunar month. Every watch and clock is kept accurate by timing them with the most precise Clock ever invented–the solar system and the stars!

Time is kept accurate by basing time calculations and computations on the precise movements of the stars and the positions of the fixed stars. The master clock in the United States is at the Naval Observatory, Washington, D.C. By measuring time by the stars, the Naval Observatory keeps track of time to the tiniest fraction of a second.

By knowing the exact movements of the heavenly bodies, solar and lunar eclipses can be PREDICTED *thousands of years* in advance!

God inspired David to write, "He made the moon for *fixed times;* the sun knows its time of setting" (Psalm 104:19, *Godspeed*). Or, as the *Amplified* has it, "the sun knows the EXACT TIME of its setting."

Take a look at a watch—a manmade instrument for telling time. You know that a watchmaker made a watch. It didn't just somehow decide to put itself together! Great painstaking workmanship went into it, most likely, and its delicate parts were made with great precision.

The universe is a Great Master Clock. It has been running smoothly, accurately, for millions—if not billions—of years. It is still accurate—in fine working order. Its parts still move with age-old, timeless precision!

You know your own watch didn't accidentally "evolve." What about the Great Master Clock in the skies—so much more perfect than your watch, so grander in its execution and operation?

You keep your watch running by winding it up. Who keeps the Great Clock of the universe operating?

TRUE SCIENCE admits the existence of the original "Clock Maker"—Almighty God. True science admits GOD made the heavens and the earth.

A little philosophy inclineth
man's mind to atheism; but depth
in philosophy bringeth man's
mind about to religion.

Bacon—*Essays*

Chapter Twenty Eight

Twilight of Evolution

This is the age of the knowledge explosion. Every ten years the sum total of human knowledge doubles. It has been estimated that ninety per cent of all the scientists who ever lived are alive right now. And this proliferation of knowledge shatters the illusions of previous concepts, ideas, interpretations, theories and hypotheses. Even Sir Isaac Newton's famous "law of gravity" has been subjected to modifications and clarifications due to Einstein's general theory of relativity. And someday it, too, may seem to be but a crude exposition of the truth.

From a theological point of view, the discoveries in the field of anthropology and geology might be categorized as what Charles Fort used to call "the damned facts"—that is, the facts that do not fit in, that cannot be reconciled with the 19th century concepts of man and his world.

But if we have learned one thing from this book, it should be that we reject no knowledge, no matter how obstinate, how contradictory, how inexplicable, it may appear to be. We should keep our minds open, inquisitive, eager for new knowledge which will help us to better understand mankind and the meaning of Biblical revelation.

Man's science is incomplete. Man's understanding of God and theology is, also, incomplete. As the apostle Paul wrote centuries ago in I Corinthians, chapter 13: "Love never ends; as for prophecies, they will pass away; as for tongues, they will cease; as for knowledge, it will pass away. For our knowledge is imperfect and our prophecy is imperfect; but when the perfect comes, the imperfect will pass away."

Paul went on:

> When I was a child, I spoke like a child, I thought like a child, I reasoned like a child; when I became a man, I gave up childish ways. For now we see in a mirror dimly, but then face to face. Now I know in part; then I shall understand fully, even as I have been fully understood. So faith, hope, love abide, these three; but the greatest of these is love.

The Science Messiah?

Does our age worship science? Has science become, in the eyes of many, the great deliverer, the great savior, the great "god" of progress?

Said Dr. R. Hooykass, Professor of the History of Science at the Free University in Amsterdam: "Science and technology are the *real gods of our age*, and to a large extent the real priest of the modern world... is the scientist." Lamented Robert Sinsheiner, professor of biophysics at the California Institute of Technology, "The scientist has now in effect become Nature with a capital N and God with a capital G."[1]

Richard Bube, Professor of Material Science and Electrical Engineering, Stanford University went so far as to assert: "Today scientific advances have placed the control of the world so completely in the hands of men that the *hypothesis of God* is hardly relevant any longer."

Despite the awe felt by many laymen in the presence of science, however, attitudes are changing. Science is strictly *limited*. Science and technology have not brought the answers to the basic questions of life: who are we, what are we, why do we exist, where are we going?

Science by definition is accumulated systematized knowledge that is formulated with reference to the discovery of general truth and the operation of general laws. Science means simply "knowledge." But it is knowledge gained via the "scientific method."

The scientific method involves skillful handling of the material being studied, careful observations, controlled experiments, close attention to detail, clear thinking in drawing conclusions, and modifications of conclusions when necessary.

Science has produced the marvels of our modern technological world. It has also produced pollution, nuclear weapons, and computerized crime. Science has landed men on the moon. But it has limitations. It has not solved the problem of pollution.

This is not to condemn science. Used constructively, science has been a great tool and a boon to mankind.

But—we must admit—science alone does not have all the answers to the big questions in life. It cannot replace theology.

Where, then, do we stand, today?

Imperfect Knowledge

In both the realms of science and theology, we must confess to an unknown amount of ignorance. God has not revealed all things to us. He intends for us to use our human faculties, and "grow in grace and knowledge."

Since none of us is perfect in knowledge, we should learn to be tolerant of others whose opinions differ from ours. We should not assume a position of authority, intolerance, and dogmatism. And it is particularly dangerous to be dogmatic in a field where we are not an expert. Let's not accuse others, who don't see eye to eye with us, of being blind, myopic, or astigmatic, when it may be that we, ourselves, are also in ignorance.

The principle of tolerance is part of the paradox of knowledge. No matter how much progress we make in peering into nature's secrets, with our microscopes and telescopes, it seems that nature seems to elude us. We never come to final answers. At one time it was thought that the atom was the building block of all matter. But then it was discovered that the atom could be split, and that it consists of many parts.

At one time it seemed as if the photon, or particle of light, was the smallest particle as it had zero rest mass. But now physicists talk about theoretical particles called "quarks."

No matter how precise our observations of the stars, there is always a little uncertainty, so we take several readings. But the position we arrive at is still merely an average of the positions which we noted.

There is always the problem too, that we ourselves affect that which we observe and thus we never see an "electron" in its natural state. It is affected by the beam of light from the electron microscope.

For mankind, therefore, we must humbly confess as did Sir Isaac Newton, that we are like little boys standing on the seashore of the vast ocean of truth. We cannot claim absolute knowledge about the world around us or about God, the Creator. We observe, we generalize, we grow in knowledge; but our observations are but an approximation of the truth. The more we learn, the more we realize there is left to be learned.

Tolerance

Probability, the Principle of Tolerance. The law first became apparent in the study of nuclear physics. Man learned in the early 20th century to split the atom. He invented the electron microscope, to look into the core of atoms. But the smallest object he could see was a single atom of thorium. But even the hardest electrons within it do not give a hard outline. They still seem "fuzzy."

It is part of the paradox of knowledge: No matter how much progress we make in devising new instruments with which to peer into nature, either the macrocosmos or the microcosmos, nature seems to elude us. It is like chasing a goat across a precipitous landscape. It always seems to keep in front of us, no matter how fast we run. The object of our scientific quest always seems to lurch away from us at the last frail moment. Eroding into infinity.

If we know the precise position of an electron, then we cannot know its speed. If we know its speed, then we cannot fathom its position.

It seems that no matter how hard we try, the errors cannot

be completely extracted from our observations. There is always a little uncertainty. So we take several observations, or readings, in order to pin down our elusive object. But the position we arrive at is still an average of the positions which we noted. Thus, errors are bound up in what we call human knowledge. Human knowledge, by its very nature, cannot be perfect.

Thus everything in life involves a measure of chance–risk–an element of faith. The questions all ultimately involve faith.

The Principle of Uncertainty. In essence, it states that you cannot know all there is to know about anything–whether electrons, or atoms, or the stars. You cannot know all there is to know about yourself. Therefore, we must all walk within certain parameters of faith.

In 1927 Werner Heisenberg said the electron is a particle, but yields only limited information. You can specify where it is at this instant, but you cannot impose on it a specific speed and direction. Or, if you insist that you are going to fire it at a certain speed in a particular direction, then you cannot, obtusely, know precisely where it is, what its starting point is, where it will stop.

This principle of physics led to the development of Quantum Theory and Quantum Mechanics.

The principle should teach us that any form of human thought that becomes dogma is a major tragedy. Dogmatism, whether in theology or science, is a fool's game that only fools play at. When any faith, belief, creed, or theory, becomes encrusted as scientific dogma, truth has perished and error has been enshrined.

Only despots believe they have absolute knowledge. Only tyrants profess to have complete certainty. No room for doubt. No capacity for re-evaluation, re-analysis, rethinking old concepts.

Not long ago I stood at the foot of the Jefferson Memorial in Washington, D.C., and watched the boats cruising up and down the Potomac River, as two army helicopters clattered through the air. One of them was obviously carrying the President of the United States to some destimation that only the President, the secret service, and a few of the top men in government knew.

After I climbed to the top of the Memorial, I paused to look at the serene sculpture of Jefferson, and to read his immortal words: *"I have sworn upon the altar of God, eternal hostility against every form of tyranny over the mind of man."*

Those words, originally written in a letter to Dr. Benjamin Rush, September 23, 1800, were Jefferson's credo. Capturing the spirit of the man himself, they were inscribed in the marble walls of the Jefferson Memorial for all generations to read and contemplate.

Somehow, the words of Jefferson seem curiously meaningful today. Because today the tyranny of dogma enslaves millions!

The Need for Courage

Whatever the nature of dogma, whether it be religious or scientific, all the innovative thinkers of old had the courage to challenge prevailing dogma. Galileo, Copernicus, Kepler, Newton, all challenged the prevailing notions of their time. They were called heretics, they were ridiculed as buffoons, they were held up to obloquy and calumny, but they advanced the cause of truth, despite the consequences to themselves. They challenged the religious hierarchy of their times, and suffered for it. Bruno died at the stake for it. But the chains of Medieval dogma were eventually cast off and scientific knowledge, based on empirical observation, was advanced.

So it must be today. We must cast off the dogmas of science, falsely so called, and scientific theories which are based on an illusion of faith, and reject as well theological dogma which flies in the face of proven fact. We must impress deeply within our consciousness the words of Oliver Cromwell who said: "I beseech you, in the bowels of Christ, think it possible you may be mistaken."

History is replete with the bones of those who scoffed at new ideas. One hundred years ago the Commissioner of Patents in the United States sent his letter of resignation to President Lincoln. He felt that everything worth inventing had been invented and he wanted to take up a new occupation!

Today we might smile at the people of Lancaster,

Pennsylvania of 1832. They refused the use of their schoolhouse for a discussion about railroads. Their reasoning went this way: "Railroads are impossible and a great infidelity. If God had intended that his intelligent creatures should travel at the frightful speed of 17 miles an hour by steam he would have foretold it in the Holy Prophets. Such things as railroads are devices of Satan to lead immortal souls down to hell."

We must never allow our minds to be closed to new truth, in whatever guise it comes, or from whatever source. No matter how challenging it may appear, if we close our minds to it, we become a mossback—a theological or scientific reactionary, resistant to change, impervious to new truth, living in a world of self-imposed error.

From time to time all of us need to be reminded of the words of William Shakespeare who wrote in *Hamlet*:

> There are more things in heaven and earth,
> Horatio,
> Than are dreamt of in your philosophy.

Any religious faith that exhorts followers to embrace an absurd or impossible dogma, thus humiliating the mind and suppressing the soul, has sown the seeds of its own demise. Likewise, any scientific creed that is impervious to change, will eventually be thrown out by bright young minds seeking for truth.

At all costs, we must overcome the desperate human impulse to claim greater certainty than we can have. To naively tout the untrue, and the irrational, to allow one's intellect to become servile and obsequious, is to destroy character, nobility and honor.

The Scientific Method

Hopefully, this book has provided a new insight into the facts of science and meaning of revelation. Hopefully, too, we have come to see that neither science nor theology is merely a matter of inductive reasoning—i.e., observing either nature or Scripture objectively and then putting the facts in sensible order.

The study of both science and theology is more than that. This conception of the scientist or theologian's role makes them separated by a huge gulf from people like artists, poets, writers and others who work through the imagination. It makes the scientist or theologian, each in his respective field, to be "rude mechanicals," as Sir Peter Medawar, biologist, put it.

Sir Karl Popper, an Austrian intellectual, believes all basic discoveries of science originate in a hypothesis—an imaginative preconception of what the truth might be. The scientific hypothesis should forecast what future observations or experiments will show. It must be put in such a way as to be testable, or falsifiable, or refutable, if untrue.

In the same way, an opinion as to the meaning of a verse in the Bible, must be testable, falsifiable. If future observations militate against a particular explanation of a verse, then the former interpretation has been disproved and should be cast aside; if future observations confirm the explanation of the verse, then that understanding should be regarded as having passed a test successfully, though the theory or explanation still may not be "proved."

Ironically, both science and theology must bear witness that both fields have a history of superseded theories and dogmas. Both have grown by repenting of previous erroneous opinions, based on insufficient data or erroneous interpretations.

A particular interpretation of Scripture, like a theory of science, is alive and valuable only as it lives dangerously. "In science," said Hermann Bondi, theoretical astronomer at London University, "it isn't a question of who is right and who is wrong: it is much more a question of who is useful, who is stimulating, who has helped things forward." He adds, "I like scientists who are quite passionate about their ideas. But they must always realize that the value of their ideas lies in how disprovable they are, in what tests they attract and in what discussions they stimulate."

In the same light, it is my own hope that this book, setting forth a new case for Creation, and the evidences of science, and theology, will serve a similar purpose, will stimulate discussion, be useful to theologians and scientists alike, provoke further research into many areas, challenge prosaic thinking and be a spur to the development of knowledge.

Some of the facts put forward in this book may seem surprising to many. Life is always surprising. We should learn to expect surprises and to enjoy them and to rejoice in truth, regardless of how shattering it may be, temporarily.

This book challenges deeply held assumptions of both evolutionist and the traditional Creationist. I believe that I have stated the case for the existence of a Creator comprehensively and abundantly. The evidence is overwhelming. But so is the evidence that life on earth and the universe are very old.

What about you? What are you going to do with this awesome and incredible evidence?

The Creator Revealed

The Bible itself says that the testimony of two or three corroborating witnesses is sufficient to prove a case under normal circumstances. But in this book, we have innumerable independent witnesses, all testifying to the antiquity of the earth and the existence of God.

We possess the evidence of uranium-thorium dating, potassium argon dating, carbon 14, thermoluminescence, recemization, as well as geological evidence, algal reefs, coal deposits, salt domes, cross-bedding and erosion, dendrochronology, the evidence of the rate of expansion of the universe, all indicating an old age for the universe and the earth, and life. What shall we do with this evidence?

The majority of creationists, for reasons of their own, would have us throw it all out because it contradicts their theory and interpretation of the Bible. But does it make sense that we should reject the united witnesses of various scientific disciplines in order to hold on to traditional beliefs? Does it not limit the glory and grandeur of God to try to squeeze all the marvels of the universe into a short 6,000 year span of time? Does not the revelation of the antiquity of the universe add immeasurable glory to the Creator, who designed it aeons ago and like a master builder first laid the foundation, then added the superstructure, then built the various rooms or ecological niches, and designed the inhabitants for each?

Which makes more sense? Is God like a supreme Builder who does all things logically, step by step, in order? A builder first plans his construction, bulldozes the land, then lays the foundations of the buildings, raises the walls, puts down the floor joists, nails down the rafters, adds the roof, puts in the windows, doors, and wiring, plumbing, heating ducts, furnace, and finally, paints the edifice. When God created the universe "in the beginning," did He merely wave His hand, say the magic words, and presto! the great cosmic Magician caused the earth to appear? Is God a sleight of hand artist? If He is a Creator, then does it not follow that He is continually creating?

Too often I think we try to pigeonhole the work of God. We say that at one point in the dim past God created; ever since then He has merely been maintaining what He originally created. But that concept limits God; it describes Him as merely a cosmological maintenance man, or a divine janitor. It doesn't make sense. If God is a Creator, as the Bible describes Him, then it logically follows that creativity is an inherent part of His nature and character and that He is always in the process of creating new wonders.

In essence, therefore, the amazing discoveries of science have pushed back the recesses of time and revealed in greater glory and majesty the eternal glory of the Creator God. We learn from observation of the handiwork of God that the creation of the universe evidently began some 10-20 billion years ago, and that the earth and elements were created some six to ten billion years in the past, and that the first beginning of the creation of physical life on earth may have occurred roughly one billion years ago, during the Precambrian period, and that at various stages since that time there were periods of vast new creativity, such as at the Cambrian-Precambrian boundary, during the Cretaceous, Tertiary, and Pleistocene.

This sharply focused picture of creation helps us understand what God, an eternal, everlasting being, has been doing for aeons of time. It shows us what God is like. But if God merely snapped His fingers 6,000 years ago, and the entire fullblown universe appeared and all the intricate life forms, we are left with two problems: first, such a concept hardly does justice to the Biblical revelation of God as a master potter and builder, who designed the earth in His wisdom, as the Psalmist of Israel said (Psalm 104:24). Secondly, such a concept leaves a complete blank for aeons of time prior to 6,000 years ago. It leaves us wondering, what did God do *before* 6,000 years ago when suddenly He created everything at one burst of creative energy? What was God doing 10,000 years ago? 50,000 years ago? 1,000,000 years ago? One billion years ago? Before that?

If we are willing to admit that the amazing discoveries of science are true, then we can glimpse what God has been doing for aeons of time, and we can appreciate His tremendous interest in the earth and His concern for all its living creatures. Especially Man. Man, with a mind like that of his Creator. Man, fashioned in the image of God. Man, put here on this earth to experience life, build righteous character, learn lessons of humility, and to become one with His divine Parent and Creator–God.

Footnotes

Chapter Two

1. Tax, Sol, *Issues in Evolution*, p. 41.
2. Tax, Sol, etc., *Issues in Evolution*, vol. III, p. 252.
3. Huxley, *Religion Without Revelation*, p. 62.
4. Simpson, George Gaylord, *This View of Life*, p. 214.
5. Gorney, Robert, *The Human Agenda*, p. 27.
6. *Ibid*, p. 28.
7. *Ibid*, p. 53.
8. *Ibid.*
9. Stokes, *Essentials of Earth History*, p. 32.
10. Prosser, C.L., *American Scientist*, "The *Origin* after a Century: Prospects for the Future," vol. 47, Dec. 1959, p. 536.
11. Morgenthau, Hans, *Politics Among Nations*, p. 92.
12. Darlington, C.D., "The Origin of Darwinism," *Sci. American*, May 1959, p. 60,66.
13. Munitz, *Theories of the Universe, From Babylonian Myth to Modern Science*, pp. 115-116.
14. Kerkut, G.A., *Implications of Evolution*, p. 3.
15. *Ibid*, p. 5.
16. Krutch, Joseph Wood, *The Great Chain of Life*, New York, Pyramid Books, 1966, p. 163.

Chapter Three

1. Pfeiffer, John, *The Cell*, p. 90.
2. *Ibid.*, p. 83.
3. Wald, George, "The Origin of Life," *The Molecular Basis of Life*, published by *Sci. American.*
4. *Ibid.*, p. 339.

5. *Ibid.*, p. 341.
6. Asimov, Isaac, *The Chemicals of Life*, p. 21.
7. Shklovskil, I.S., Sagan, C., 1966, *Intelligent Life in the Universe*, Dell Pub. Co., pp. 196, 228.
8. Orgel, L.E., *The Origin of Life*, 1973, John Wiley and Sons, New York, pp. 154.
9. Mora, Peter T., 1965, "The Folly of Probability," on *The Origins of Prebiological Systems*, edited by S.W. Fox, Academic Press, New York, p. 45.
10. *Ibid.*
11. Bernal, J.D., 1967, *The Origin of Life*, The World Pub. Co., Cleveland, pp. 140-141.
12. *Encyclopedia Britannica*, 1970, "Life" by Carl Sagen, p. 10.
13. *Ibid.*

Chapter Four

1. Pfeiffer, John, *The Cell*, p. 68.
2. *Ibid* p. 70.
3. *Biological Science: Molecules to Man*, 2nd ed., Biological Sciences Curriculum Study, 1968, p. 101.
4. Monsma, *Behind the Dim Unknown*, 1966, p. 43.
5. *Ibid*, p. 125.
6. Stokes, William, *Essentials of Earth History.*
7. *Ibid.*
8. *Ibid.*
9. *Ibid.*

Chapter Five

1. *Encyclopedia Britannica*, 1974 edition, "Sex and Sexuality," vol. 16, p. 586.
2. Simpson, G.G., *The Major Features of Evolution*, p. 115.
3. Simpson, G.G., *This View of Life*, p. 77.
4. Stokes, *Essentials of Earth History*, p. 391.
5. *Encyclopedia Britannica*, op. cit.
6. *Ibid.*

Chapter Six

1. Von Frisch, Karl, *Animal Architecture*, New York and London:

Harcourt Brace Jovanovich, 1974, p. 140-141.
2. *Ibid.*, p. 144.
3. *Ibid.*, p. 147.
4. *Ibid.*, p. 149.
5. *Ibid.*, p. 150.
6. *Ibid.*, p. 278.
7. Froman, Robert, "Putting the Beaver Back To Work," *Reader's Digest, Our Amazing World of Nature Its Marvels and Mysteries*, p. 86-89.

Chapter Seven

1. *Encyclopedia Britannica*, 1974, "Adaptation."
2. Quoted in *Darwin Retired*, Macbeth, Gambot Inc., Boston, 1971.
3. *Encyclopedia Britannica*, 1974, "Seals."
4. *Ibid*, "Salmonidae."
5. Quoted in *Reader's Digest's Our Amazing World of Nature Its Marvels and Mysteries.*
6. Simpson, *This View of Life*, p. 21.
7. Quoted in Simpson, *This Way of Life.*
8. Simpson, *This View of Life.*
9. *Ibid.*
10. *Ibid*, p. 200.

Chapter Eight

1. Milne, Loras and Morgery, *The Balance of Nature*, 1969, p. 4.
2. Taylor, Gordon Rattray, *The Doomsday Book*, 1970, p. 72.
3. Buchsbaum, Ralph and Mildred, *Basic Ecology*, 1969, p. 79.
4. Farb, *Living Earth*, 1966, p. 147.
5. *"The Biosphere," Scientific American*, Sept. 1970, p. 51.
6. Taylor, *op cit*, p. 94.
7. Stover, John, *The Web of Life*, 1963, p. 41.
8. Introduction to *The Web of Life* by John H. Stover, p. V.
9. Stover, *Ibid.*, p. 45.
10. Farb, Peter, *op cit*, p. 140.
11. *Ibid.*, p. 143.
12. *Ibid.*, p. 144.
13. *Ibid.*, p. 141.
14. *Ibid.*, p. 103.
15. Faulkner, Douglas, in *National Geographic*, "Finned Doctor of the

Deep," December 1965, pp. 872-873.
16. Krutch, Joseph, *The Great Chain of Life*, 1966, p. 177.

Chapter Ten

1. Sol Tax, *Issues in Evolution*, p. 44.
2. Darwin, Charles, *Origin of Species*, p. 523.
3. Nelson, *After Its Kind.*
4. *Science Digest*, "Should We Burn Darwin," Jan. 1961, p. 61.
5. Nelson, *op cit.*
6. Villee, Claude, *Biology*, p. 538, 1967.
7. *Ibid.*, p. 611.
8. McVay, J.R., *Cancer*, July 1964.
9. *A Textbook of Histology*, 1957, p. 324.
10. *Chemical and Engineering News*, May 1, 1967.
11. Villee, *op cit*, p. 610.
12. *Ibid.*, p. 611.
13. *Ibid.*, p. 615.
14. Urey, Harold C., newspaper article.
15. Simpson, G.G., *This View of Life*, pp. 190-191.
16. *Ibid*, p. 202.

Chapter Eleven

1. Waddington, C.H., *The Nature of Life*, p. 98.
2. Caullery, Maurice, *Genetics and Heredity*, p. 10.
3. Dobzhansky, Theodoseus, *Heredity and the Nature of Man*, p. 126.
4. Carson, Hampton L., *Heredity and Human Life*, p. 40.
5. Simpson and Beck, *Life: An Introduction to Biology*, p. 258.
6. *Concepts of Zoology*, pp. 317-318.
7. *Ibid.*, p. 318.
8. Simpson, G.G., *This View of Life*, p. 203.
9. *Concepts of Zoology*, p. 319.
10. *Ibid.*, p. 320.

Chapter Twelve

1. Dunbar, Carl, *Historical Geology*, p. 73.
2. Villee, Claude, *Biology*, p. 516.
3. Romer, A.S., in *Genetics, Paleontology and Evolution*, p. 114.
4. Stokes, William, *Essentials of Earth History*, First edition, p. 90.

5. Darwin, Charles, *The Origin of Species*, p. 319.
6. Kitts, David B., "Paleontology and Evolutionary Theory," *Evolution International Journal of Organic Evolution,* vol. 28, September 1974, no. 3, p. 467.
7. *Genetics, Paleontology and Evolution*, 1949, p. 74.
8. Moment, Gairdner B., *General Biology*, p. 611.
9. Buschbaum, *Animals without Backbones*, p. 324.
10. 1961, p. 359, *The Larouse Encyclopedia of the Earth.*
11. Glassner, Martin F., 1969, Trace Fossils from the Pre-Cambrian and Basal Cambrian, Lethia, *2*, pp. 369-393.
12. Simpson, *The Major Features of Evolution*, p. 360.
13. Ladd, Charles H.S., *Treatise on Marine Ecology and Paleontology*, vol. II, Geological Society of America Memoir 67, 1957, p. 7.
14. Cloud, Preston E. Jr., 1968, Pre Metazoan Evolution and the Origins of the Metazoa, from *Evolution and Environment*, E.T. Drake, Editor, Yale University Press.
15. Hutchins, Ross E., *Insects*, pp. 3-4.
16. Romer, *Vertebrate Paleontology*, p. 15.
17. *Ibid.*, p. 53.
18. Cromie, William J., *The Living World of the Sea*, pp. 268-269.
19. Stokes, *op. cit.*, p. 420.
20. Colbert, *The Age of Reptiles*, p. 122.
21. Seinton, *Fossil Birds* p. 2.
22. Marshal, A.J., *Biology and Comparative Physiology of Birds*, p. 1.
23. Romer, *op. cit.*, p. 134.
24. Colbert, *op. cit.*, p. 156.
25. Romer, *op. cit.*
26. *Ibid*, p. 337.
27. Millot, Jacques, "The Coelacanth," *Scientific American*, December 1955, p. 37.
28. *Scientific American*, November 1951, p. 60.
29. Hutchins, *op. cit.*, p. 6.
30. Stokes, *op. cit.*, p. 431.

Chapter Thirteen

1. Newell, Norman D., "Evolution Under Attack," *Natural History*, June, 1974, pp. 32-39.
2. Stokes, William, *Essengials of Earth History*, pp. 32-33.
3. *Ibid.*, p. 79-80.
4. *Ibid.* p. 80.

5. Whitcomb, John C., and Morris, Henry M., *The Genesis Flood, The Biblical Record and Its Scientific Implications*, Philadelphia, The Presbyterian and Reformed Publishing Company, 1969, p. 123-124.
6. *Ibid.*, p. 137.
7. *Ibid.*
8. Marsh, Frank Lewis, *Life, Man and Time*, Escondido: Outdoor Pictures, 1967, pp. 67-68.
9. Stokes, *op. cit.*, p. 6.
10. *Ibid.*, p. 34.
11. O.D. von Engeln and Kenneth E. Caster, *Geology*, p. 417.
12. Carl Dunbar, *Historical Geology*, pp. 35-36.
13. "Evaluation of Scientific Ages," excepted from a science faculties meeting of Ambassador College, Jan. 22, 1971.
14. *Encyclopedia Britannica*, 1956, "Geology," vol. 10, p. 168.
15. "Evaluation of Scientific Ages," *op. cit.*
16. *Ibid.*
17 *Ibid.*
18. Robert C. Macdonald, "Geology," an unpublished thesis, p. 30, Feb. 22, 1973.
19. Curt Teichert, 1958, "Some Biostratigraphical Concepts," Bulletin Geological Society America, V. 69, p. 99-120.
20. Macdonald, "Geology," op. cit., p. 15. See also Murchison and Westall, 1968, *Coal and Coal Bearing Strata*, American Elsevier Publishing Co., Inc., p. 33.
21. Genesis 17:4-6.
22. II Peter 3:8, RSV.
23. Dobzhansky, Theodosius, "Nothing in Biology Makes Sense, Except in the light of Evolution," a paper presented at the NABT convention in San Francisco, Oct. 26, 1972.
24. Russell, Bertrand, *An Outline of Philosophy*, 1927, p. 7.
25. Proverbs 24:2-3, RSV.
26. Compare Dobzhansky, *op. cit.*

Chapter Fourteen

1. Newell, Norman D., *Scientific American*, Feb. 1963, p. 77.
2. *The Earth*, p. 138.
3. *Ibid.*
4. Newell, N.D., "Adequacy of the Fossil Record," May 1959, *Journal of Paleontology*, p. 492.
5. "Ecology, Paleontology and Stratigraphy, *Science*, Jan. 9, 1959, p. 72.

6. Matthew, W.D., *Dinosaurs*, pp. 136-138.
7. Dunbar, *Historical Geology*, p. 426.
8. Cohen, "The Great Dinosaur Disaster," *Science Digest*, March 1969, pp. 45-57.
9. Charles Darwin, *The Origin of Species*, New York: Collier, 1962, p. 341.
10. Darwin, *Journal of Researches into the Natural History and Geology of the Countries Visited During the Voyage of H.M.S. Beagle Round the World*, citation under date of January 9, 1834.
11. Stokes, *Essentials of Earth History*, Second edition, p. 282.
12. *Ibid.*, p. 258.
13. *Ibid.*
14. *Ibid.*, p. 248.
15. Arkell, W.J., 1957, Introduction to Mesozoic Ammonoidea, p. 81-129, in Moore, R.C., Editor, Treatise on Invertebrate Paleontology, Geol. Scientific American and University of Kansas Press.
16. Stokes, *op. cit.*, p. 437.
17. *Ibid.*, p. 441.
18. Dunbar, *op. cit.*, p. 348.
19. Ager, *The Nature of the Stratigraphic Record*, London: Macmillan, 1973, pp. 20-21.
20. *Ibid.*, p. 25.
21. *Ibid.* p. 26.

Chapter Fifteen

1. Bergier, *Extraterrestrial Visitations from Prehistoric Times to the Present*, pp.1-2.
2. *Ibid.*, p.4.
3. *Ibid.*, p.14.
4. *Ibid.*, p.4.
5. Bergamini, *The Universe*, p.80.
6. *The Long Day of Joshua and Six Other Catastrophes*, pp.88-89.
7. Jonathan Swift, *Gulliver's Travels*, p.134.
8. Immanuel Velikovsky, *Worlds in Collision*, pp.363-364.
9. Payne-Gaposhkin, *Introduction to Astronomy*, p.222.
10. *The Universe*, p.67.
11. *Ibid.*, p.69.

Chapter Sixteen

1. *Diodorus of Sicily*, Book 1, 8.
2. *Ibid.*
3. *Fossil Men*, Boule and Vallois, p. 512.
4. *Ibid.*
5. Stokes, *Essentials of Earth History*, p. 361.
6. *The Missing Link*, by Maitland A. Edey, and the Editors of Time-Life Books, p. 129.
7. *Ibid*, pp. 131-136.
8. Pfeiffer, John B. *The Emergence of Man*, pp. 54-55.
9. *Ibid.*, p. 136.
10. Richard E. Leakey and Bob Campbell, "Skull 1470–New Clue to Earliest Man?", *National Geographic*, June 1973, p. 819.
11. *Reader's Digest*, "Border Cave," by Ronald Schiller, reprinted from *Tuesday*, Aug. 12, 1973.
12. *Ibid.*

Chapter Seventeen

1. Brothwell, Don, and Higgs, Eric, *Science in Archaeology: A Comprehensive Survey of Progress and Research.*
2. C.W. Ceram, *The First American*, New York: Harcourt Bace, Inc., 1971, p. 134.
3. Stokes, *Essence of Earth History*, p. 23.
4. Pfeiffer, *The Emergence of Man*, p. 159.
5. Constable, *The Neanderthals*, p. 124.
6. *Ibid.*, p. 127.
7. *Ibid.*, p. 130.
8. Pfeiffer, *Emergence of Man*, p. 242.
9. Hamblin, Dora Jane, *The First Cities*, p. 9.
10. *Ibid*, p. 10.

Chapter Eighteen

1. Sanderson, Ivan T., "The Riddle of the Quick-Frozen Mammoths," *Reader's Digest, Marvels and Mysteries of the World Around Us*, 1972, pp. 34-37.
2. *Ibid.*
3. Frank C. Hibben, *The Lost Americas*, p. 118.
4. *Ibid.*, p. 121.
5. *Ibid.*, p. 122.

6. *Ibid.*
7. Charles Hapgood, *The Paths of the Pole*, p. 150.
8. *Ibid.*, italics his.
9. *Ibid.*, pp. 152-153.
10. Stokes, *Essentials*, p. 328.
11. *Ibid.*, p. 336.
12. Edward Seuss, *The Face of the Earth*, 398:I, 17, 18.
13. Hapgood, *op. cit.*, p. 236.
14. Ceram, *The First American*, p. 278.
15. Hibben, *op. cit.*, pp. 77-78.
16. *Ibid.*, p. 81.
17. *Ibid.*, p. 157.
18. *Ibid.*, p. 158.
19. *Ibid.*, p. 162.
20. *Ibid.*, pp. 163-164.

Chapter Nineteen

1. Alfred Metraus, *The History of the Incas*, New York: Random House, Translated from the French by George Dridich, p. 45.
2. Nelson, Byron C., *The Deluge Story in Stone*, Minneapolis: Augsburg Publishing House, 1962, p. 186.
3. *Ibid.*, p. 182.
4. Fornander, Abraham, *An Account of the Polynesian Race Its Origin and Migrations*, p. 98-99.
5. Nelson, *op. cit.*, pp. 176-177.
6. Finegan, Jack, *Light from the Ancient Past.*
7. Flavius Josephus, *Antiquities of the Jews*, I:3:5-6.
8. *The Toledo Blade*, September 3, 1962.
9. Rehwinkel, *The Flood.*
10. Toronto *Daily Star*, July 31, 1965.
11. *Everybody's*, November 10, 1956.

Chapter Twenty

1. Ferguson, Marilyn, *The Brain Revolution*, New York, Taplinger Pub. Co., 1973, p. 17.
2. *Ibid.*, p. 18.
3. Maya Pines, *The Brain Changers*, New York: Harcourt Brace Jovanovich, Inc. 1973, p. 4.
4. Ferguson, *op cit.*, p. 280.
5. Pines, *op. cit.*, p. 184.

6. *Man and Memory: Breakthroughs in the Science of the Human Mind*, N.Y. Harper and Row, 1970, p. 4.
7. *Encyclopedia Britannica*, 1974, "Brain," p. 228.
8. Halacy, *Computers, The Machines We Think With*, p. 125.
9. *Ibid.*, p. 126.
10. Asimov, "The Thinking Machine," *Science Digest*, December 1967, p. 73.
11. Philip Bard, *Medical Physiology*, p. 1291.
12. *Ibid.*, p. 1309.
13. *Evolution of Man*, ed. by Louise B. Young, 1970, p. 253.
14. Loren Eiseley, *The Immense Journey*, 1957, p. 79.
15. Symposia of the Society for Experimental Biology, XII, *Evolution*, p. 395.
16. Eiseley, *op. cit.*, p. 87.
17. Moore, *Man, Time and Fossils*, p. 415.
18. Eiseley, *op. cit.*, pp. 93-94.
19. Halacy, *Man and Memory*, *op. cit.*, p. 47.
20. Ferguson, *op. cit.*, p. 279.
21. *Ibid.*, p. 309.
22. *Ibid.*

Chapter Twenty-One

1. Marilyn Ferguson, *The Brain Revolution.*
2. *Ibid.*, p. 344.
3. *Ibid.*, p. 235.
4. *Encyclopedia Britannica*, "Mind, Philosophy of," vol. 12, p. 224.
5. Maya Pines, *The Brain Changers*, pp. 16-17.
6. *Evolution of Man*, ed. by Louise B. Young, 1970, p. 316.
7. *The Human Mind*, p. 79.
8. *Science News*, "Thinking about how we think," McBroom, Dec. 2, 1967, p. 544.
9. *Ibid.*
10. *The Human Mind*, pp. 7-8.
11. *The Uniqueness of Man*, p. 56.
12. *Ibid.*
13. *The Human Mind*, p. 9.
14. *Ibid.* p. 24.
15. *Ibid.*, pp. 25-26.
16. Ferguson, *op. cit.*, p. 313.

Chapter Twenty-Two

1. *Encyclopedia Britannica*, 1974, vol. 11, p. 518, "Mars," vol. 10, p. 908, "Life."
2. *U.S. News and World Report*, April 15, 1974, p. 44.

3. *Encyclopedia Britannica, op. cit.*, vol. 19, p. 79, "Venus."
4. *Ibid.*, p. 82.
5. *Time* magazine, April 1, 1974, p. 61.
6. Pasadena *Star-News*, January 28, 1974.
7. *U.S. News and World Report*, Dec. 17, 1973, p. 40.
8. *Science News*, vol. 104, December 8, 1973.
9. *Encyclopedia Britannica*, 1974, vol. 10, "Life."
10. Theo Loebsack, in *Marvels and Mysteries of the World Around Us, Reader's Digest*, p. 238.
11. Lewis Thomas, M.D., "The Miraculous Membrane," *New England Science* of Medicine, September 13, 1973.
12. Storer and Usinger, *General Zoology*, p. 211.
13. New York *Science-America*, June 11, 1961.
14. *Ibid.*

Chapter Twenty-Three

1. Fritz Kahn, *Design of the Universe*, p. 215.
2. *Ibid.* p. 163.
3. Kenneth Weaver, *National Geographic*, p. 618.
4. *Ibid.*
5. *The Cosmic Connection: An Extraterrestrial Perspective*, 1973, Doubleday and Co., Inc.
6. *Newsweek*, April 22, 1974.
7. Weaver, *op. cit.*, p. 608.
8. *Ibid.*, p. 620.

Chapter Twenty-Four

1. *Reader's Digest*, Feb. 1966.
2. *Quasars*, p. 1.
3. *Encyclopedia Britannica*, "Universe, Origin and Evolution of," p. 1009.
4. *Ibid.*
5. Rothman, *The Laws of Physics*, p. 144.
6. *Ibid.*
7. Lincoln Barnett, *The Universe and Dr. Einstein*, p. 104-106.
8. *The Johnson Drillers Journal*, May-June, 1966.
9. Simpson, *This View of Life*, p. 21.
10. Fred Hoyle, *Frontiers of Astronomy*, p. 342.
11. *View from a Distant Star*, p. 47.
12. *Ibid.*
13. Hoyle, *Harper's Magazine*, February 1951, p. 68.

14. *National Geographic*, p. 625. Weaver.
15. Bergamini, Time-Life Books, *The Universe*, p. 180.
16. Fritz Kahn, *Design of the Universe*, p. 171.
17. Payne-Gaposchkin, *Introduction to Astronomy*, p. 469.
18. *Ibid.* p. 93.
19. Kahn, *op. cit.*, p. 192.
20. *Encyclopedia Britannica*, "Solar System," vol. 16, p. 1030-32.
21. *Ibid*, "Life," vol. 10:907.
22. *Science News*, Feb. 2, 1974.
23. *The Cosmic Connection*, Sagan, p. 973.
24. *Ibid.*
25. Weaver, *op. cit.*, p. 609.
26. Kahn, *op. cit.*, p. 202.

Chapter Twenty-Five

1. *Encyclopedia Britannica*, 1974, "Atomic Structure," vol. 2, pp. 330-343.
2. Kahn, *Design of the Universe*, p. 87.
3. *Ibid.*, p. 59-60.
4. *Encyclopedia Britannica*, 1974, "Nuclear Structure and Properties," vol. 13, p. 334.
5. Kahn, *op. cit.*, p. 91.
6. *Ibid.*, p. 96.
7. *Ibid.*, p. 102.
8. *Reader's Digest*, August 1970.
9. *Encyclopedia Britannica*, "Particles, Subatomic," vol. 13:1035.
10. *Christian Science Monitor*, June 4, 1974.

Chapter Twenty-Six

1. Allen, "Does Matter Exist?" *Intellectual Digest*, Spring 1974.
2. *Ibid.*
3. II Peter 3:10.
4. II Peter 3:11.
5. Wheeler, John A., "The Black Hole of the Universe," *University, A Princeton Quarterly*, Summer 1972.
6. *Ibid.*
7. *Ibid.*

Chapter Twenty-Eight

1. *Saturday Review*, January 20, 1968, p. 43.

Bibliography

Asimov, Isaac, *The Genetic Code*. New York, The Orion Press, 1962.

Asimov, Isaac, *Life and Energy*. Garden City, New York, Doubleday and Company, Inc., 1962.

Barnett, Lincoln, *The Universe and Dr. Einstein*. New York Mentor Books, William Sloane Associates, Inc., 1952.

Barnett, S.A., *Century of Darwin*. Cambridge, Harvard University Press, 1958.

Beiser, Arthur, *Basic Concepts of Physics*. Department of Physics, New York University, Reading, Mass., and London, Addison-Wesley Publishing Co., Inc., 1961.

Beiser, Arthur, and the Editors of LIFE, *The Earth*. New York, Time Inc., 1962.

Bennett, Clarence E., *Physics Without Mathematics*. New York, Barnes and Noble, Inc., 1949. Reprinted, 1965.

Bergamini and The Editors of LIFE, *The Universe*. New York, Life Nature Library, Time Inc.

Biological Science: Molecules to Man. 2nd ed., Biological Sciences Curriculum Study, American Biological Society, New York, Chicago, Houghton-Mifflin, 1968.

Brumbaugh, Robert S., *Six Trials*. New York, Thomas Y. Crowell Co., 1969.

Bube, Richard, ed., *The Encounter Between Christianity and Science*. Grand Rapids, Eerdman, 1968.

Buchsbaum, Ralph and Mildred, *Basic Ecology*. Pittsburgh, The Boxwood Press, 1969.

Busher, Herbert Henry, *The Amazing Human Mind*. New York, Frederick Fell, Inc., 1965.

Carson, Hampton L., *Heredity and Human Life*. New York and London, Columbia University Press, 1963.

Caullery, Maurice, *Genetics and Heredity*. New York, Walker and Company, 1964.

Caullery, Maurice, *A History of Biology.* New York, Walker and Company, 1966.

Colbert, Edwin H., *The Age of Reptiles.* New York, W.W. Norton & Co., Inc., 1965.

Coleman, James A., *Modern Theories of the Universe.* New York, The New American Library of World Literature, Inc., 1963.

Conger, G.P., *New Views of Evolution.* New York, The MacMillan Company, 1929.

Cutten, George Barton, *Mind: Its Origin and Goal.* New Haven, Yale University Press, 1925.

Dana, James D., *Mineralogy.* New York, John Wiley and Sons, Inc., 1966.

Darrah, William C., *Principles of Paleobotany.* New York, The Ronald Press Co., 1960.

Darwin, Charles, *The Origin of Species.* New York, Collier, 1909, 1962.

Davis, Kenneth S. and Leopold, Luna B., *Water.* Life Science Library, New York, Time, Inc. 1966.

Dewar, Douglas, *Difficulties of the Evolution Theory.* London, Edward Arnold & Co., 1931.

Dickler, Gerald, *Man on Trial.* Garden City, New York, Doubleday and Co., Inc., 1962.

Dobzhansky, Theodosius, *Heredity and the Nature of Man.* New York, and Toronto, The New American Library, 1966.

Dunbar, Carl O., *Historical Geology.* New York–London, John Wiley & Sons, Inc., 1960.

Eiseley, Loren, *The Immense Journey.* New York, Alfred A. Knopf, Inc. & Random House, Inc., 1957.

Elliott, H. Chandler, *The Shape of Intelligence.* New York, Charles Scribner's Sons, 1969.

Elton, Charles, *Animal Ecology.* London, Methuen & Co., Ltd., 1968.

Farb, Peter, and The Editors of Life, *Ecology.* New York, Time Incorporated, 1967.

Frings, Hubert, and Frings, Mable, *Concepts of Zoology.* New York, Toronto, The MacMillan Company, 1970.

Fuchs, Walter R., *Physics for the Modern Mind.* New York, The MacMillan Co., 1967.

Gamow, George, *The Creation of the Universe.* New York, The Viking Press, 1952.

Gamow, George, *One Two Three ... Infinity.* New York, The Viking Press, 1961.

Gerking, Shelby, *Biological Systems.* Philadelphia, London, Toronto, W.B. Saunders Company, 1969.

Hibben, Frank C., *The Lost Americans.* New York, Thomas Y. Croswell Co., 1946 (Apollo Edition 1961).

Highet, Gilbert, *Man's Unconquerable Mind.* New York, Columbia University Press, 1954.

Holden, Alan & Singer, Phylis, *Crystals & Crystal Growing.* Garden City, Anchor Books, 1960.

Hoyle, Fred, *Frontiers of Astronomy.* New York, The New American Library, 1955.

Hutchins, Ross, *Insects.* Englewood Cliffs, N.Y. Prentice-Hall, 1966.

Huxley, Julian, *Evolution in Action.* New York, Harper & Row, 1953.

Huxley, Julian, *Religion Without Revelation.* London, New York, Ernest Benn, Random House, Reprint 1969.

Kahn, Fritz, *Design of the Universe.* New York, Crown Publishers, Inc., 1954, 1955.

Karplus, Robert, *Introductory Physics–A Model Approach.* New York and Amsterdam, W.A. Benjamin, Inc., 1969.

Krutch, Jsoeph Wood, *The Great Chain of Life.* New York, Pyramid Books, 1966.

Lapp, Ralph E., and the Editors of LIFE, *Matter.* Life Science Library, New York, Time, Inc., 1965.

Larousse Encyclopedia of the Earth. New York, Prometheus Press, 1961.

Lasker, Gabriel Ward, *The Evolution of Man.* New York, Holt, Rinehart and Winston, Inc. 1961.

Locke, David M., *Enzymes–The Agents of Life.* New York, Crown Publishers, Inc., 1969.

Lovell, Sir Bernard, *Our Present Knowledge of the Universe.* Cambridge, Mass., Harvard University Press, 1967.

Meldau, Fred John, *Why We Believe in Creation Not in Evolution.* Denver, Colorado, Christian Victory Publishing Co., 1959.

Miller, Benjamin F. and Goode, Ruth, *Man and His Body.* New York, Random House, 1960.

Milne, Lorus J. and Margery, *The Balance of Nature.* New York, Alfred A. Knopf, 1969.

The Molecular Basis of Life, An Introduction to Molecular Biology. Readings from the Scientific American, Haynes, Haynes, R.H., and Hanawalt, P.C., editors, San Francisco, and London, W.H. Freeman and Company, 1968.

Moment, Gairdner B., *General Biology.* New York, Appleton-Century-Crofts, Inc., second edition.

Moore, Ruth, *Evolution.* LIFE Science Series, New York, Time Inc., 1964.

Moore, Ruth, *Man, Time, & Fossils.* New York, Alfred A. Knopf, 1953.

Morris, Henry M., *The Twilight of Evolution.* Grand Rapids, Mich., Baker Book House, 1963.

Nelson, Byron C., *After Its Kind.* Minneapolis, Minn., Augsbury Publishing Co., 1952.

Odum, Eugene P., *Ecology.* New York, Holt, Rinehart and Winston, Inc., 1966.

Oparin, Alexander I., *The Origin of Life.* New York, Dover Publication, Inc., 1953.

Osborn, Henry, *From Greeks to Darwin.* New York, The MacMillan Co., 1896.

Papazian, Haig P., *Modern Genetics.* New York, W.W. Norton and Company, Inc., 1967.

Payne-Gaposchkin, Cecilia, *Introduction to Astronomy.* Englewood Cliffs, N.Y., Prentice-Hall, Inc., 1954.

Pfeiffer, John, *The Cell,* LIFE Science Library, New York, Time, Inc., 1964.

Pfeiffer, John E., *The Emergence of Man.* New York, Evanston, and London, Harper & Row, 1969.

Pollard, Ernest C. and Huston, Douglas C., *Physics, an Introduction.* New York, London, and Toronto, Oxford University Press, 1969.

Roddam, John, *The Changing Mind.* Boston, Toronto, Little, Brown and Company, 1966.

Romer, Alfred Sherwood, *Vertebrate Paleontology.* Third edition, Chicago and London, The University of Chicago Press, 1966.

Roslansky, John, Ed., *The Human Mind.* New York, Fleet Academic Editions, Inc., 1969.

Roslansky, John, Ed., *The Uniqueness of Man.* New York, Fleet Academic Editions, Inc., 1969.

Ross, Herbert, *Understanding Evolution.* Englewood Cliffs, N.J., Prentice-Hall, 1966.

Rothman, Milton, *The Laws of Physics.* New York, Basic Books, 1963.

Rousseau, Pierre, *The Limits of Science.* London, Phoenix House, 1963.

Sagan, Carl, Leonard, Jonathan Norton, and the Editors of LIFE, *Planets.* New York, Time Inc., 1966.

Scher, Jordan M., *Theories of the Mind.* New York, The Free Press of Glencoe, 1962.

Scopes, John T., *Center of the Storm.* New York, Chicago, San Francisco, Holt Rinehart and Winston, 1967.

Simpson, George Gaylord, and Beck, W.S., *Life—An Introduction to Biology.* New York, Harcourt, Brace and World, 1957, 1969.

Simpson, George Gaylord, *The Geography of Evolution.* New York,

Capricorn Books, A Division of Chilton Company, 1967.

Simpson, George Gaylord, *This View of Life.* New York, Harcourt, Brace and World, 1964, 1966.

Sisler, Harry H., *Electronic Structure, Properties, and the Periodic Law.* New York and London, Reinhold Publishing Corp., 1963.

Stokes, William Lee, *Essentials of Earth History, An Introduction to Historical Geology.* Englewood Cliffs, N.J., Prentice Hall Inc., first and second editions, 1960, 1966.

Storer, John H. *The Web of Life*, New York, Signet Science Library Books, 1963.

Storer, Tracy I. and Usinger, R.L., *General Zoology.* 4th edition, Q, New York, McGraw-Hill, 1965.

Sturtevant, A.H., *A History of Genetics.* New York, Harper and Row, 1965.

Tax, Soland Charles Callender, editor, *Issues in Evolution.* London, Paternoster Press, 1958.

Villee, Claude A., *Biology.* Philadelphia, London, W. B. Saunders Company, 1968.

Wilson, John Rowan, and the Editors of TIME-LIFE Books, *The Mind.* New York, Time-Life Books, Time, Inc., 1970.

Wilson, Mitchell, and the Editors of Life, *Energy.* Life Science Library, Time Inc., 1963.

Young, Louise B., *Evolution of Man.* New York, Oxford University Press, 1970.